LOCATION Toucans live in tropical forests in South America.

BEAKS The male toco toucan's beak can grow to be 8 inches in length.

SKIN COLOR The toco toucan has blue skin, which you can see around its eyes and on its feet.

IDENTITY The colorful patterns on a toucan's face and beak help the birds recognize each other.

FLORIDA EDITION

Science

Toucan

Harcourt
SCHOOL PUBLISHERS

Orlando Austin New York San Diego Toronto London

Visit *The Learning Site!*
www.harcourtschool.com

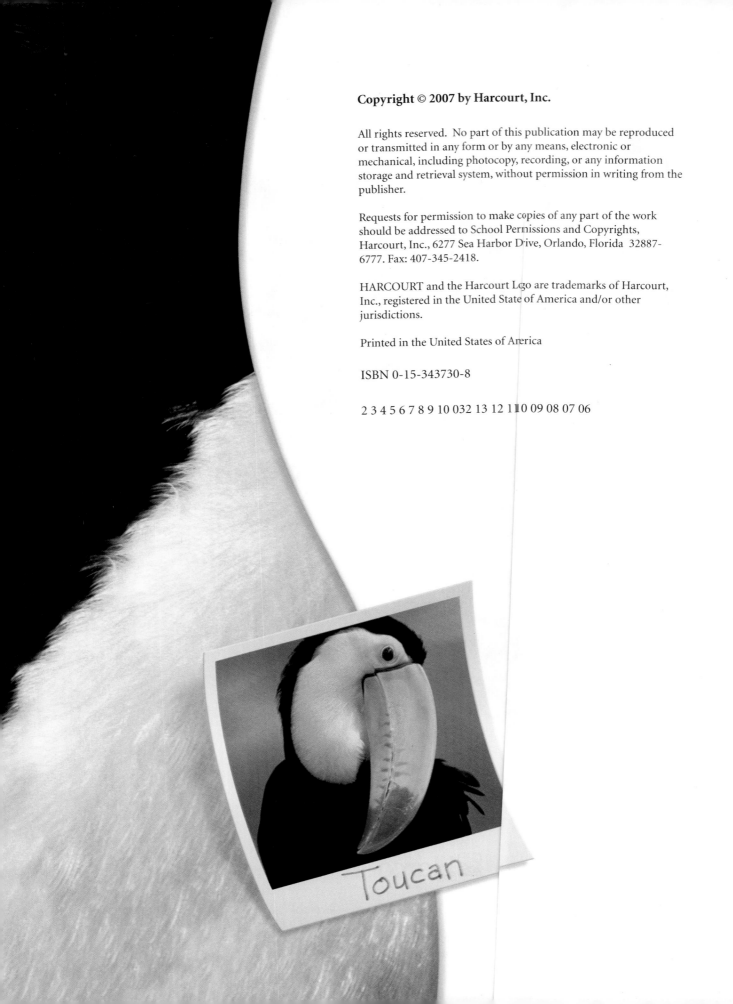

ISBN 0-15-343730-8

2 3 4 5 6 7 8 9 10 032 13 12 11 10 09 08 07 06

Toucan

Consulting Authors

Michael J. Bell
Assistant Professor of Early Childhood Education
College of Education
West Chester University of Pennsylvania

Michael A. DiSpezio
Curriculum Architect
JASON Academy
Cape Cod, Massachusetts

Marjorie Frank
Former Adjunct, Science Education
Hunter College
New York, New York

Gerald H. Krockover
Professor of Earth and Atmospheric Science Education
Purdue University
West Lafayette, Indiana

Joyce C. McLeod
Adjunct Professor
Rollins College
Winter Park, Florida

Barbara ten Brink
Science Specialist
Austin Independent School District
Austin, Texas

Carol J. Valenta
Senior Vice President
St. Louis Science Center
St. Louis, Missouri

Barry A. Van Deman
President and CEO
Museum of Life and Science
Durham, North Carolina

Senior Editorial Advisors

Napoleon Adebola Bryant, Jr.
Professor Emeritus of Education
Xavier University
Cincinnati, Ohio

Robert M. Jones
Professor of Educational Foundations
University of Houston-Clear Lake
Houston, Texas

Mozell P. Lang
Former Science Consultant
Michigan Department of Education
Science Consultant, Highland Park Schools
Highland Park, Michigan

PHYSICAL SCIENCE

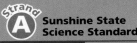

The Nature of Matter

Strand A Sunshine State Science Standard

Science Spin Weekly Reader

Technology
Better Than Nature Can Make?, **56**

People
The Father of the Barometer, **58**

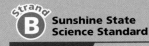

Energy

Strand B Sunshine State Science Standard

Science Spin Weekly Reader

Technology
Batteries Included, **86**

People
A Handy Idea, **88**

Strand C Sunshine State Science Standard

Forces and Motion

EARTH SCIENCE

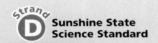

Strand D Sunshine State Science Standard

Processes That Shape the Earth

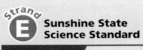
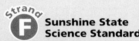

How Living Things Interact with Their Environment

Getting Ready for Science

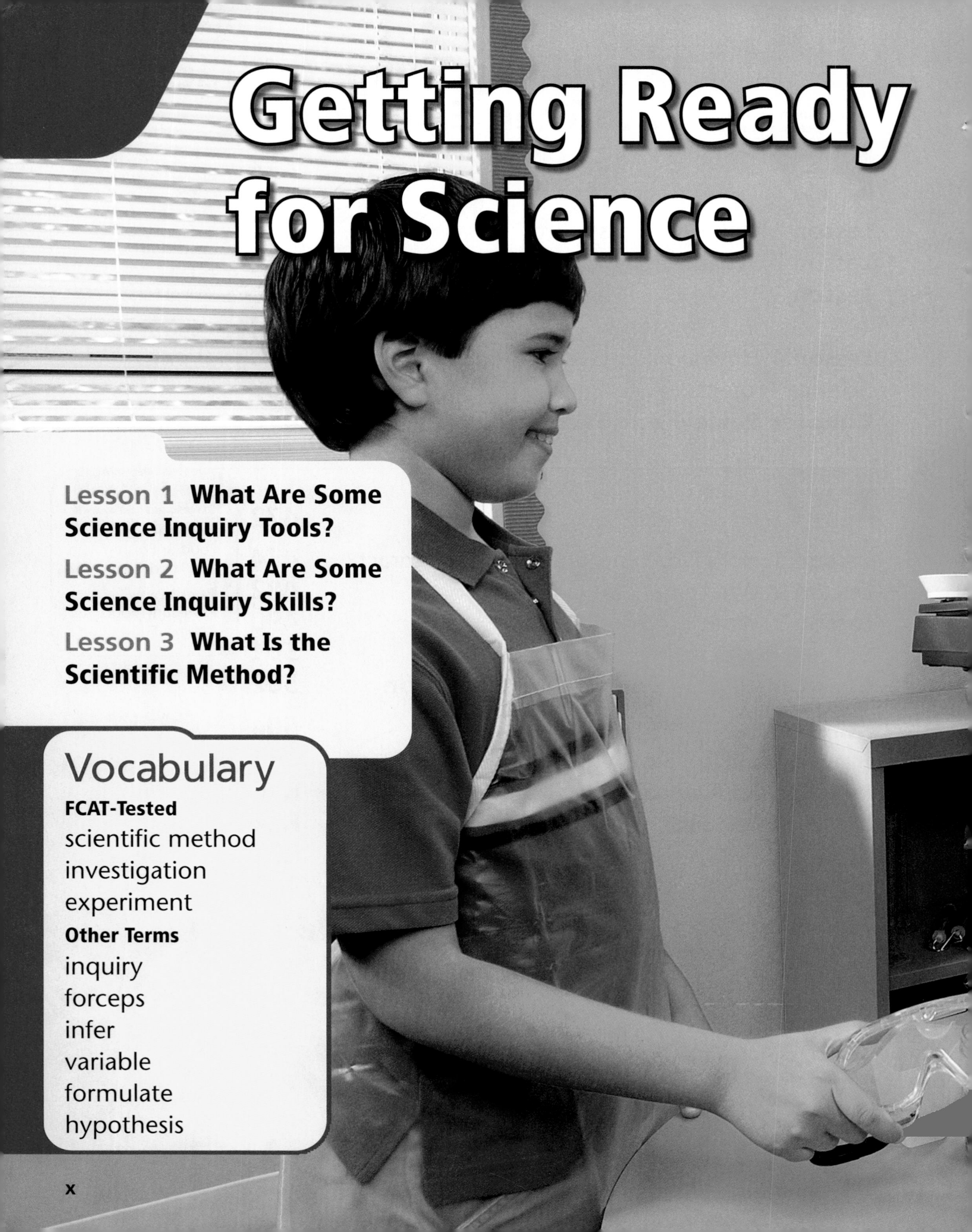

Lesson 1 What Are Some Science Inquiry Tools?

Lesson 2 What Are Some Science Inquiry Skills?

Lesson 3 What Is the Scientific Method?

Vocabulary

FCAT-Tested

scientific method
investigation
experiment

Other Terms

inquiry
forceps
infer
variable
formulate
hypothesis

What do YOU wonder?

Do you ever wonder why plants are green or what causes the seasons? If so, you are already thinking like a scientist! Scientists ask questions. How are these students getting ready for science?

What Are Some Science Inquiry Tools?

Measuring Up The first tools used by people to measure things were not rulers and measuring cups, but body parts! In fact, the foot measurement was based on the length of a person's foot. In the Investigate, you will learn more about measurement.

Making Bubbles

Materials
- safety goggles
- large container
- straw
- metric measuring cup
- dishwashing soap
- small containers
- water
- stirring stick
- hand lens

Procedure

1. CAUTION: **Put on safety goggles.**
   Use the measuring cup to **measure**
   1 L (1,000 mL) of water. Pour the
   water into a large container.

2. Then **measure** 50 mL of
   dishwashing soap. Add the soap to
   the container of water, and then stir.

3. Pour some of the soap-and-water
   solution into small containers.
   Use the straw to blow air into the
   solution. Be careful not to blow too
   hard or to spill some of the solution.
   Bubbles should form. **Observe** the
   bubbles with a hand lens. **Record**
   your **observations**.

Step 1

Draw Conclusions

1. What did you **observe** about the
   bubbles?

2. **Inquiry Skill** Scientists use many
   different tools to **measure** things.
   In this Investigate, you used a
   measuring cup to **measure** both
   water and soap. What kind of
   measuring tool could you use to
   measure the size of the bubbles you
   made? Explain your answer.

Step 3

Investigate Further

Add 60 mL of glycerine and 8 mL
of sugar to the solution. Blow
bubbles. **Compare** these bubbles
to the first bubbles.

Reading in Science

SC.A.1.2.1.3.1 measurement, tools, **SC.A.2.2.1.3.1** tools to see details, **SC.H.1.2.2.3.2** using scientific instruments, **LA.A.2.2.1** main idea and details

VOCABULARY

inquiry p. 4

forceps p. 5

SCIENCE CONCEPTS

▶ what some measurement tools are

▶ how measurement tools are used

READING FOCUS SKILL

MAIN IDEA AND DETAILS Look for details about tools used for measuring things.

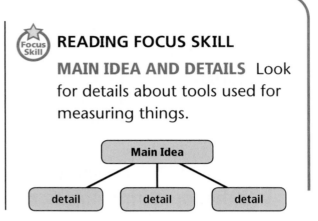

Tools Used for Inquiry

Have you ever asked questions about something? If so, you made an inquiry. An **inquiry** happens when someone asks a question or studies something closely. In almost every science inquiry, tools must be used to observe, measure, and compare the objects that are being studied.

Hand Lens

What It Is: A hand lens is a tool used to magnify, or enlarge, an object's features.

How to Use It: Hold a hand lens up to an object that you want to observe closely. Look through the clear part of the hand lens. You can move the hand lens closer to or farther from the object to make the object clearer.

Safety: Some hand lenses have a glass lens. Be careful not to drop a hand lens. If a hand lens breaks, do not try to clean up the broken pieces. Ask an adult for help.

4

Forceps

What They Are: Forceps are used to pick up and hold on to objects. They are similar to tongs and tweezers.

How to Use Them: Place the tips of the forceps around the object you want to pick up. Apply pressure to the forceps' handles, and lift the object.

Safety: The tips of the forceps can be sharp. Keep forceps away from your face. Always clean forceps after you use them.

Magnifying Box

What It Is: Like a hand lens, a magnifying box is a tool used to magnify, or enlarge, an object's features.

How to Use It: Place the magnifying box on top of a flat surface. Look through the clear part of the box.

Safety: Some magnifying boxes have a glass lens. Be careful not to drop the box. Do not use a magnifying box that has a cracked or damaged lens.

Dropper

What It Is: A dropper is a tool that can be used to pick up and release small amounts of liquid. Some droppers have marks on them that can be used to measure the liquid.

How to Use It: Squeeze the dropper's bulb. Place the end of the dropper in a liquid and release the bulb. Some of the liquid will move up into the dropper. To release the liquid, squeeze the bulb again.

Safety: Droppers should be cleaned after each use.

Use a Magnifying Box
Place a magnifying box on your textbook. Use it to look at the letters on this page. What do you observe? Now look at other objects, such as a leaf.

Thermometer

What It Is: A thermometer is a tool that measures temperature, or how hot or cold something is.

How to Use It: Put the thermometer in the place where you would like to measure the temperature. Wait about five minutes. Then see where the liquid in the thermometer's tube is. Use the markings along the side of the tube to read the temperature.

Safety: If a thermometer breaks, do not touch it. Ask an adult for help.

Ruler

What It Is: A ruler is a tool used to measure length, width, height, or depth.

How to Use It: Place the ruler against the object you would like to measure. Use the markings on the ruler to see how long, wide, high, or deep the object is.

Safety: Many rulers are made of plastic or wood. Do not use rulers to measure warm objects. This may cause the plastic to melt or the wood to catch on fire.

Measuring Tape

What It Is: Like a ruler, a measuring tape is used to measure length, width, height, or depth. A measuring tape is useful for measuring a curved object.

How to Use It: Place the measuring tape along the object you would like to measure. Use the markings on the measuring tape to see how long, wide, high, or deep the object is.

Safety: Measuring tapes are often made of plastic. Do not use measuring tapes to measure warm objects.

What It Is: A measuring cup measures volume, or the amount of space that something takes up. Measuring cups are usually used for liquids and loose solids such as powders.

How to Use It: Pour the substance you need to measure into the measuring cup. Use the marks on the outside of the cup to see how much of the substance is in the cup.

Safety: Some measuring cups are made of glass. Be careful not to drop the cup, or it could break.

Spring Scale

What It Is: A spring scale is a tool that measures an object's weight.

How to Use It: Attach the object you want to weigh to the hook at the bottom of the spring scale. Allow the object to hang as you hold the spring scale up. The weight of the object will be displayed on the scale's readout.

Safety: Only weigh objects on a spring scale when told to do so by your teacher.

Forceps, rulers, spring scales, and more can all be used during science inquiry. Each of these tools is used for different things. Part of learning about science is learning how to choose which of these tools you can use to help you answer your questions.

 MAIN IDEA AND DETAILS What are two tools used to observe an object closely?

Some Other Tools Used in Science

Many science tools have similar uses. For example, a measuring cup, measuring spoons, and graduated cylinders can all be used to measure how much space something takes up. You choose which of these three tools to use by finding out how much you have to measure.

Microscopes are used to magnify an object. They are helpful to see things that you can't see with your eyes alone.

Balances are used to measure the mass of objects. By placing the object in one pan and weights in the other pan, you are able to "balance" out the object's mass.

 MAIN IDEA AND DETAILS **When might you use a microscope?**

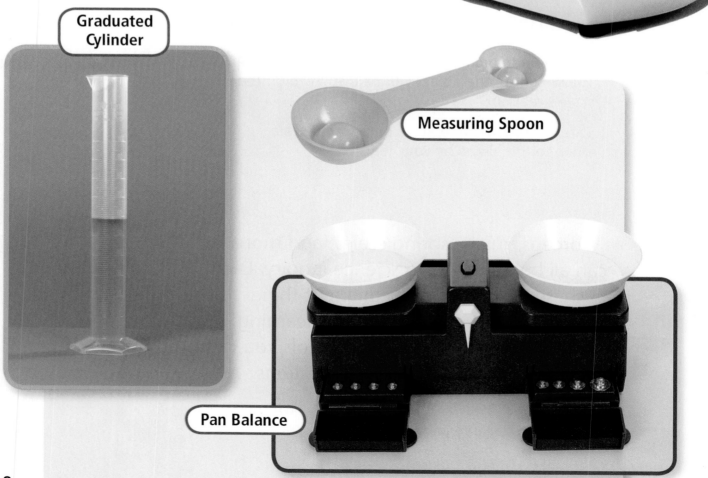

Microscope

Graduated Cylinder

Measuring Spoon

Pan Balance

1. MAIN IDEA AND DETAILS Draw and complete this graphic organizer.

Main Idea: There are many tools that can be used in science inquiry.

Tools that magnify objects
Ⓐ _____
Ⓑ _____
Ⓒ _____

Tools that measure length
Ⓓ _____
Ⓔ _____

Tools that measure how much space an object takes up
Ⓕ _____
Ⓖ _____
Ⓗ _____

2. SUMMARIZE Make a table listing all the tools you learned about in this lesson, along with their uses.

3. DRAW CONCLUSIONS You need to look closely at a soil sample. Which tool would you use? Explain your choice.

4. VOCABULARY Write a sentence describing how you can use forceps during a science inquiry.

FCAT Prep

5. Which tool should you use to add two drops of food coloring to a bowl of water?
- **A.** dropper
- **B.** forceps
- **C.** measuring cup
- **D.** measuring spoons

Links

Writing

Expository
A ruler and a measuring tape can both be used to measure length. Write an **explanation** of when it is best to use each of these tools.

Math

Measure Elapsed Time
Timers and stopwatches can be used to measure how much time passes. Use one of these two tools to measure how long it takes five of your classmates to each run 50 meters. Record the results in a table.

 For more links and activities, go to www.hspscience.com

What Are Some Science Inquiry Skills?

Fast Fact

Blowing Bubbles The longest bubble ever blown and measured was about 32 m (105 ft) long! What shape do you think this huge bubble was? Do the Investigate to find out the different shapes that bubbles can take.

Shapes of Bubbles

Materials • safety goggles • wire hangers • plastic flying disc • bubble solution

Procedure

1. **CAUTION: Put on safety goggles.** Use wire hangers to make bubble wands of different shapes. For example, you could make a round, a square, and a triangular wand.

2. Predict the shape of the bubbles that will be made by each wand.

3. Turn the flying disc upside down. Pour some of the bubble solution into it. Dip one of your wands into the solution. Use the wand to make bubbles. Observe the bubbles' shapes. Repeat this activity with all of the wands that you made.

Step 1

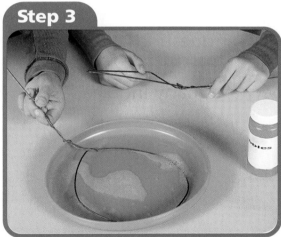

Step 3

Draw Conclusions

1. What did you predict about the shape of the bubbles? Were your predictions correct?

2. **Inquiry Skill** Scientists use observations of the natural world to make predictions. Use your observations to predict the shape of a bubble blown with a heart-shaped wand.

Investigate Further

What wand shape would make the biggest bubble? Blow bubbles with different wands. Measure and compare the bubbles' sizes.

SC.H.1.2.2.3.1 following experimental design, SC.H.2.2.1.3.1 makes predictions

11

Reading in Science

SC.H.1.2.1.3.1 keeping accurate records, SC.H.1.2.5.3.1 uses models, SC.H.2.2.1.3.1 makes predictions, SC.H.3.2.2.3.1 collects data, SC.H.3.2.2.3.2 presents scientific information, LA.A.2.2.1 main idea and details

VOCABULARY

infer p. 13

variable p. 15

formulate p. 16

SCIENCE CONCEPTS

▶ what some inquiry skills are

▶ how inquiry skills are used

READING FOCUS SKILL

MAIN IDEA AND DETAILS

Look for details about skills for science inquiry.

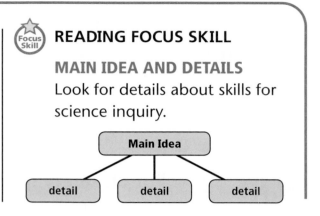

Skills Used for Inquiry

When scientists try to find an answer to a question, they use thinking tools called inquiry skills. You have already used many of these skills while doing the Investigates. You have measured, observed, compared, and made predictions. All of these are inquiry skills.

Think about how you used inquiry skills to answer questions about bubbles. You used some of the skills at the same time. That's because many inquiry skills work well together.

These students are setting up an investigation. They will need to use inquiry skills to complete the investigation.

Use Numbers
Scientists use numbers when they collect and display their data. Understanding numbers and using them to show the results of investigations are important skills.

Measure
You use numbers when you measure something. To make measurements, you can use tools such as thermometers, timers, rulers, measuring tapes, spring scales, and measuring cups.

Gather, Record, Display, or Interpret Data
When you make measurements, you are gathering data. Data are pieces of information. Data can be displayed in charts, tables, graphs, and so on. Recording data can help you interpret, or understand, what the data are telling you.

Infer
When you **infer**, you draw conclusions about something by using gathered data or previous knowledge. Often you must make inferences to interpret data.

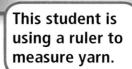

This student is using a ruler to measure yarn.

⭐ **MAIN IDEA AND DETAILS** List two inquiry skills and
(Focus Skill) state how they are connected.

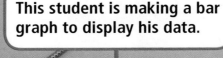

This student is making a bar graph to display his data.

13

More Skills Used for Inquiry

You will use more than one inquiry skill in every science inquiry you do. You have already learned how some inquiry skills are used together. On the next few pages, you will read about more skills that can be used during an inquiry.

This student is classifying different writing items. What characteristics is the student using to classify the items? ▼

Compare
When you compare, you identify characteristics of things or events to find out how they are alike or different.

Predict
When you predict something, you use what you know to tell what may happen in the future.

Classify/Order
To classify something, you group or organize it into categories based on specific characteristics. To order things, you place them in the correct sequence.

This student is using a stopwatch to time a process. Timing something involves using a time/space relationship. ▼

Use Time/Space Relationships
Where were you at noon yesterday? By answering this question, you are using a time/space relationship. In fact, whenever you notice where something is at a certain time, you classify that object according to the time and space that it is in.

Identify and Control Variables
Suppose you want to know what color of flower bees like best. To find out, you could plant roses of different colors in a garden and count how many bees visit each rose. In this inquiry, only one thing is different—the color of the roses. The flowers' color is a variable. A **variable** is the one thing in a science inquiry that is different. You also need to make sure that all the other parts of the inquiry stay the same.

Other inquiry skills include observing, communicating, planning, and more. Throughout this book, you will get the chance to practice each of these skills.

 MAIN IDEA AND DETAILS What inquiry skills would you use to place events in the correct order on a time line?

Make a Model
Use modeling clay to make a model of a plant or an animal that you are interested in. How does your model compare to the real plant or animal?

Formulate or Use Models
Formulate means to come up with a plan. Formulating plans can help you stay organized and on track. Models are often used in science to study things that are too big or too small to see easily in real life.

These students are building a model of a volcano.

16

1. MAIN IDEA AND DETAILS Draw and complete this graphic organizer.

> **Main Idea: There are many skills that can be used in science inquiry.**

A _____ seeing how two things are alike and different

B _____ deciding what might happen in the future

C _____ using data to draw conclusions

2. SUMMARIZE List five inquiry skills and explain how they might be used.

3. DRAW CONCLUSIONS Can two objects be in the same space at the same time? Explain your answer, and relate it to time/space relationships.

4. VOCABULARY Choose one vocabulary word from this lesson, and explain its meaning.

FCAT Prep

5. Read/Inquire/Explain You need to find out how the heights of third graders differ from the heights of second graders. What inquiry skills should you use?

Links

Writing

Persuasive
What do you think the three most useful inquiry skills are? Write a paragraph listing the three skills that in your **opinion** are the most useful.

Language Arts

Solving a Mystery
Inquiry skills are not only useful for scientists—they are also useful for detectives. Write a short story about a detective who uses inquiry skills to solve a mystery.

For more links and activities, go to **www.hspscience.com**

What Is the Scientific Method?

Bubble Art These students added tempera paint to bubble solution to make art. But paint doesn't need to be added to bubbles for them to be colorful. Do the Investigate to find out why.

Bubble Colors

Materials
- safety goggles
- clear tape
- clear plastic lid
- flashlight
- cotton ball
- bubble solution
- spoon
- straw

Procedure

1 CAUTION: **Put on safety goggles.** Tape the plastic lid over the part of the flashlight that light shines from.

2 Hold the flashlight so the light will shine straight up. Dip a cotton ball in the bubble solution. Wipe the cotton ball over the whole top of the lid. Then put a spoonful of the solution on the lid.

3 Use a straw to blow one big bubble. Turn off the lights, and hold the flashlight so that the attached lid is about even with your eyebrows.

4 Observe the bubble. Dip the end of the straw in bubble solution, and put the straw inside the big bubble. Blow very gently. Observe what happens.

Step 1

Step 4

Draw Conclusions

1. Communicate your observations by drawing what happened.

2. Inquiry Skill Use your observations to compare the colors in the bubble when you first watched it to the colors you saw right before the bubble popped.

Investigate Further

Predict how adding some tempera paint to bubbles will change the Investigate. Plan and conduct a simple experiment to test your predictions.

SC.H.1.2.2.3.1 following experimental design, **SC.H.1.2.4.3.1** comparing/contrasting, **SC.H.3.2.2.3.2** presents scientific information

19

Reading in Science

SC.H.1.2.1.3.1 keeping accurate records, SC.H.1.2.2.3.1 following experimental design, SC.H.3.2.2.3.1 collects data, SC.H.3.2.2.3.2 presents scientific information, SC.H.3.2.4.3.1 solving problems/new ideas, LA.A.2.2.1 main idea and details

VOCABULARY

scientific method p. 20

investigation p. 20

hypothesis p. 21

experiment p. 21

SCIENCE CONCEPTS
► what the scientific method is
► how to use the scientific method

READING FOCUS SKILL

MAIN IDEA AND DETAILS Look for details about how to use the scientific method.

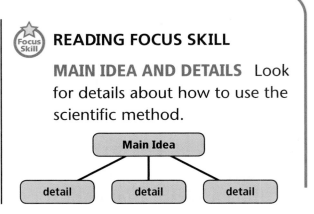

Scientific Method

How do scientists answer a question or solve a problem? They use an organized plan called the **scientific method** to conduct a study. The study that a scientist does is called an **investigation**. In this lesson, you will learn how the scientific method can be used to plan an investigation to study bubbles.

MAIN IDEA AND DETAILS What do scientists use to help them answer questions?

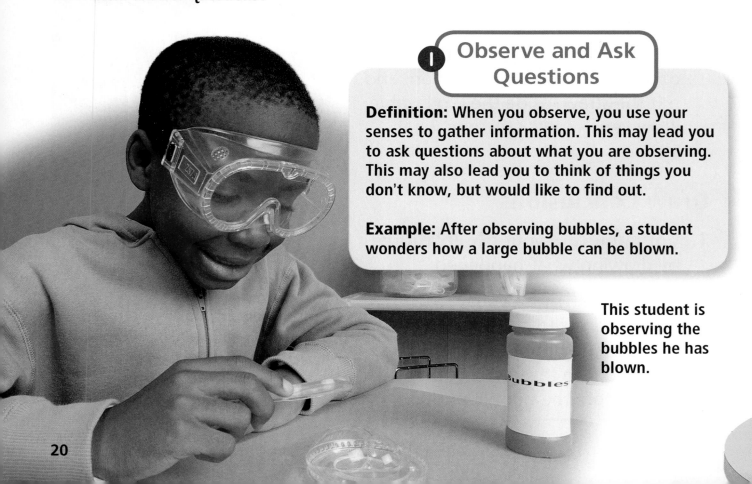

1 Observe and Ask Questions

Definition: When you observe, you use your senses to gather information. This may lead you to ask questions about what you are observing. This may also lead you to think of things you don't know, but would like to find out.

Example: After observing bubbles, a student wonders how a large bubble can be blown.

This student is observing the bubbles he has blown.

This student is writing his hypothesis in a complete sentence.

② Form a Hypothesis

Definition: Write a possible answer to your question. A possible answer to a question is a **hypothesis**. A hypothesis can be tested to see if it is correct.

Example: The student thinks that the best way to make a big bubble is to use a wand that is flexible instead of a wand that is rigid.

③ Plan an Experiment

Definition: An **experiment** is a test done to find out if a hypothesis is correct or not. When you plan an experiment, you need to describe the steps, identify the variables, list the equipment you will need, and decide how you will gather and record your data.

Example: The student will test his ideas about bubbles by making a *rigid* bubble wand out of chenille sticks and a *flexible* bubble wand out of string.

Safety: Consider your safety when planning an experiment. Study the steps of the experiment and include any safety equipment needed.

This student is planning an experiment to study bubble size.

④ Conduct an Experiment

Definition: Follow the steps of the experiment you planned. Observe and measure carefully. Record everything that happened. Organize your data so you can study it more easily.

Example: The student makes two different wands of the same size and blows bubbles with both. He has a ruler to measure each bubble.

Safety: Follow all of the safety instructions in the experiment's plans.

This student is using a flexible wand to try to make large bubbles.

5 Draw Conclusions and Communicate Results

Definition: Analyze the data you gathered. Make charts, tables, or graphs to show your data. Write a conclusion. Describe the evidence you used to determine whether your test supported your hypothesis. Decide whether your hypothesis was supported. Communicate your results.

Example: The student looks at the data he collected and realizes that the biggest bubbles were blown by the more flexible wand.

This student is analyzing the data he collected.

Often the observations you make during an experiment will lead you to ask new questions and form a new hypothesis. Remember, you can learn something even if your hypothesis is not supported.

 MAIN IDEA AND DETAILS What part of the scientific method is often done after a scientist asks a question?

Investigate Further

Definition: If your hypothesis was supported, you may want to ask another question about your topic that you can test. If your hypothesis was not supported, you may want to form another hypothesis and do a test of a different variable.

Example: The student decides to test how different movements of his flexible wand affect bubble size.

Safety: Make sure your new investigation will keep you and others safe.

Insta-Lab

Blow a Super Bubble!
Thread a 90-cm string through two straws. Tie the ends of the string together to make a wand. Hold the straws so that the string is tight. Dip the wand in bubble solution and make bubbles. What did your bubbles look like?

1. MAIN IDEA AND DETAILS Draw and complete this graphic organizer.

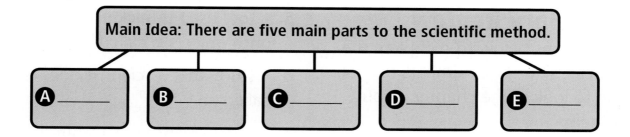

Main Idea: There are five main parts to the scientific method.

A _____ **B** _____ **C** _____ **D** _____ **E** _____

2. SUMMARIZE Draw a graphic organizer to show the parts of the scientific method and how they relate to each other.

3. DRAW CONCLUSIONS A scientist hypothesizes that cats prefer eating fish to eating chicken. He does an experiment and finds that his hypothesis is not supported. Did the scientist learn anything? Explain your answer.

4. VOCABULARY Explain how the terms *hypothesis* and *experiment* are related.

FCAT Prep

5. Tina did an experiment and drew conclusions. What should she do next?

A. ask a question
B. communicate her results
C. plan an experiment
D. form a hypothesis

Links

Writing

Expository
Write a **how-to** booklet about the scientific method. You may want to include illustrations and examples in your booklet.

Math

Construct a Bar Graph
Graphs are often used to communicate data. Go through this lesson and count the number of times the words *hypothesis* and *experiment* appear. Make a bar graph to show your results.

 For more links and activities, go to www.hspscience.com

23

Review and FCAT Preparation

Vocabulary Review

Use the terms below to complete the sentences. The page numbers tell you where to look in the chapter if you need help.

inquiry p. 4

forceps p. 5

infer p. 13

variable p. 15

formulate p. 16

scientific method p. 20

investigation p. 20

experiment p. 21

hypothesis p. 21

1. Steps that are called the _____ are used to plan and conduct a scientific study.

2. When you _____, you draw conclusions about something by using gathered data or previous knowledge.

3. When someone asks a question or closely studies something, an _____ is done.

4. The one thing in a science inquiry that is different is a _____.

5. A tool used to pick up and hold onto objects is called _____.

6. A study that a scientist does is called an _____.

7. A possible answer to a question is a _____.

8. A test done to find out if a hypothesis is correct or not is an _____.

Check Understanding

Write the letter of the best choice.

9. **MAIN IDEA AND DETAILS** Which of the following tools would you use to measure the height of a book?
   A. measuring cups
   B. balance
   C. ruler
   D. spring scale

10. Identify the tool in the picture.
   F. forceps
   G. hand lens
   H. magnifying box
   I. microscope

11. Which of the following tools is **not** used for measurement?
  A. graduated cylinder
  B. hand lens
  C. ruler
  D. thermometer

12. Which inquiry skill would most likely require you to use this tool?

  F. formulate models
  G. infer
  H. interpret data
  I. use time/space relationships

13. MAIN IDEA AND DETAILS Which inquiry skill do you use when you identify how things are alike or different?
  A. compare
  B. formulate models
  C. control variables
  D. predict

14. When you measure, which other inquiry skill would you most likely use?
  F. classify   **H.** predict
  G. infer   **I.** use numbers

15. Which of the following is an example of a good hypothesis?
  A. Plants grow best in sunlight.
  B. Some apples are red.
  C. What is inside the sun?
  D. Why are bubbles round?

16. During which scientific method step do you observe and make measurements?
  F. Conduct an experiment.
  G. Draw conclusions.
  H. Form a hypothesis.
  I. Plan an experiment.

Inquiry Skills

17. Infer why it is important for scientists to communicate their experiments' results with one another.

18. Form a hypothesis and plan a simple experiment that could test the hypothesis.

Read/Inquire/Explain

19. What inquiry skills are necessary for forming a hypothesis?

20. What tools would be best to use to measure the milk and book? Explain your answers.

The Nature of Matter

 The chapters in this unit address these Grade Level Expectations from the Florida Sunshine State Standards.

Chapter 1 Properties of Matter

SC.A.1.2.1.3.1 determines the physical properties of matter using metric measurements that incorporate tools such as rulers, thermometers, balances.

SC.A.1.2.2.3.1 understands that physical changes in the states of matter can be produced by heating and cooling.

SC.A.1.2.3.3.1 knows that the weight of an object is equal to the sum of the weights of its parts.

SC.A.2.2.1.3.1 uses a tool to observe and study minute details of objects (for example, hand lens).

The investigations and experiences in this unit also address many of the Grade Level Expectations in Strand H, The Nature of Science.

PHYSICAL SCIENCE

Science in Florida

Miami

Dear Trisha,

Today we went to the beach in Miami. We saw a huge sand sculpture! It must have taken all day to make. There was a breeze, so my brother and I flew a kite.

The lifeguard told us that no matter where you are in Florida, the beach is no more than 60 miles away. With 1,800 miles of coastline, Florida has a lot of beaches.

See you soon,

Matt

The Sunshine State

USA

FCAT Writing

Writing Situation
Think about the beach. Explain how sand and water are alike and different.

Experiment!

Mold Sand Florida is well-known for its sandy beaches. Turning a pile of sand into a sand sculpture isn't easy. What can you mix with sand to make it easier to mold into different shapes? For example, what is the best amount of water to add to sand to make it keep its shape? Plan and conduct an experiment to find out.

Chapter 1

Properties of Matter

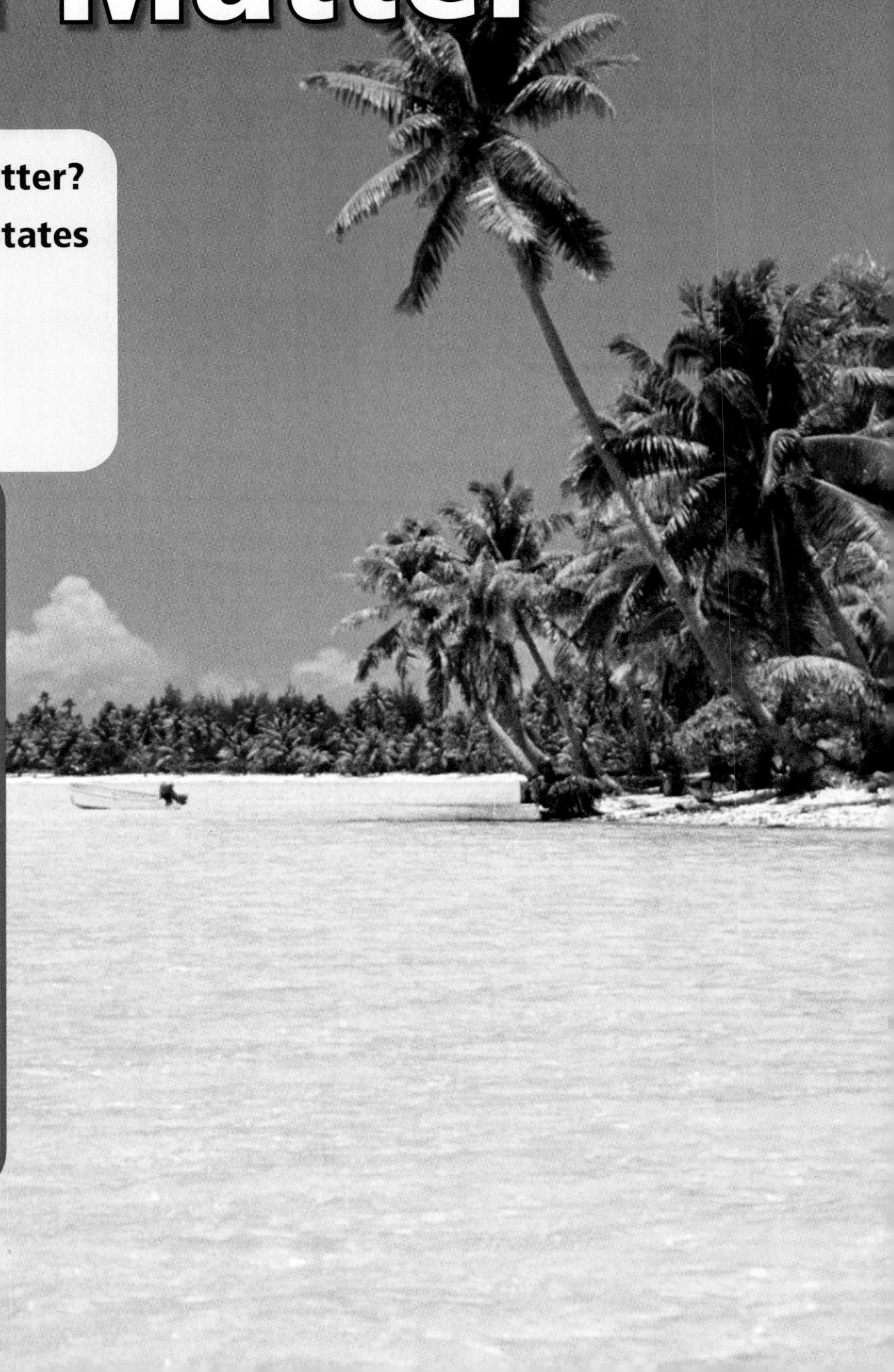

Vocabulary

FCAT-Tested

matter
mass
volume
density
solid
liquid
gas
evaporation
condensation
mixture
solution

Other Terms

physical property

What do YOU wonder?

Matter is anything that takes up space. What matter can you see in this picture? Is there any matter you can't see?

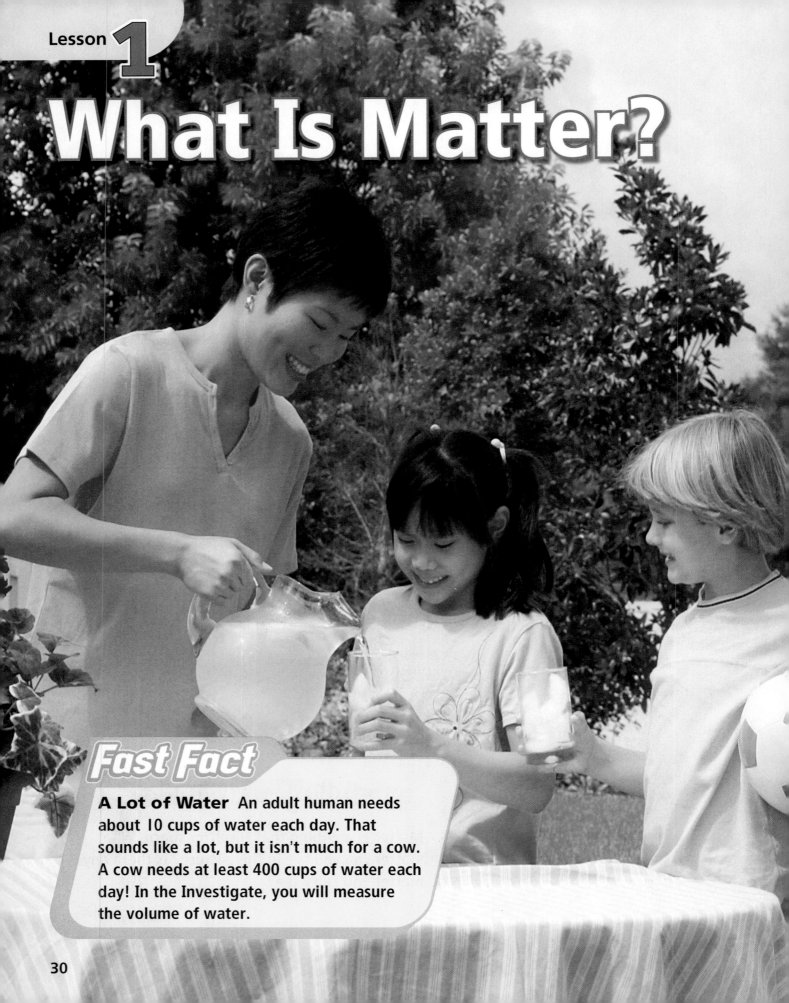

What Is Matter?

Fast Fact

A Lot of Water An adult human needs about 10 cups of water each day. That sounds like a lot, but it isn't much for a cow. A cow needs at least 400 cups of water each day! In the Investigate, you will measure the volume of water.

Measuring Volume

Materials
- metric measuring cup
- water
- masking tape
- 3 clear containers of different shapes

Procedure

1. **Measure** 100 mL of water.

2. Pour the water into a clear container.

3. Use a piece of masking tape to mark the level of the water in the container. Put the bottom edge of the tape at the water line.

4. Repeat Steps 1–3 until all three containers have 100 mL of water in them and all three levels are marked.

Step 2

Step 3

Draw Conclusions

1. How much water is in each container?

2. Describe the height of the water in each container. Explain why the height of the water looks different in each container.

3. **Inquiry Skill** Scientists **use data** and **observations** to **predict** what will happen. What do you **predict** will happen if you pour the water from each container back into the measuring cup?

Investigate Further

Fill three containers of different shapes with water. **Predict** how much water you will find in each container. **Measure** the water in each container. How close were your predictions?

SC.H.1.2.1.3.1 keeping accurate records, **SC.H.1.2.2.3.1** following experimental design, **SC.H.1.2.2.3.2** using scientific instruments, **SC.H.2.2.1.3.1** makes predictions, **SC.H.3.2.2.3.1** collects data

VOCABULARY

matter p. 32

physical property
    p. 34

mass p. 36

volume p. 37

density p. 37

SCIENCE CONCEPTS

▶ what matter is

▶ how to measure
    some physical
    properties of matter

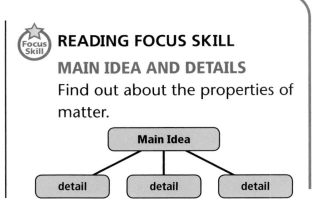

READING FOCUS SKILL

MAIN IDEA AND DETAILS

Find out about the properties of matter.

```
                    Main Idea

    detail          detail          detail
```

Matter

Ice-skating can be fun. Skaters glide over the ice. They feel the breeze against their faces.

Everything that the skaters see and feel is matter. **Matter** is anything that takes up space. Ice, water, and clouds are matter. The air the skaters breathe is matter. Skaters are matter, too.

What examples of matter do you see in this picture? ▼

▲ Is there any matter in this picture that you can't see?

Look around you. What matter can you see? Your desk and books and the other objects in the classroom are matter. Your teacher and your classmates are matter. You know they are matter because they take up space.

Now, look outside. Is it raining? Is it sunny? Is it snowing? Rain, snow, and the sun are all types of matter. Is the wind blowing? Air is matter that you can't see. How do you know that air is matter? Air takes up space. You can see air move leaves on trees. You can feel air on your skin.

 MAIN IDEA AND DETAILS What is matter?

Physical Properties of Matter

Anything you can observe about matter by using one or more of your senses is a **physical property**. Here are some things you observe with your senses.

Sight—Young ducks are small and yellow. You observe their size and color.

Hearing—Bells ring. Rain pings on a metal roof. Wind rustles leaves.

Touch—Ice feels cold and hard. Blankets feel soft. Sandpaper feels rough.

Smell— Baking bread smells delicious. Rotting garbage doesn't.

Taste— One physical property of a food is its flavor. Flavors can be sweet, salty, sour, or bitter.

▲ This pineapple feels rough on the outside. The inside tastes sweet.

Your sense of smell tells you that there is popcorn in the container. ▼

Your sense of touch tells you that the cat is fluffy. ▼

Color, size, shape, and texture are physical properties matter can have. Some matter, such as rubber, can bounce and stretch. Other matter, such as salt, mixes with water. Some metals bend easily. Others, such as steel, do not. These are just a few examples of the many physical properties of matter. Think of the different physical properties of matter that you can find in your classroom.

MAIN IDEA AND DETAILS List two physical properties of a pineapple.

The cymbals are shiny. They also make a different sound than a drum makes. ▼

Color is a property you observe with your eyes. What are other physical properties of this glass? ▼

Measuring Matter

Another property of matter is mass. **Mass** is the amount of matter in something. You can measure mass by using a balance. Mass is often measured in grams (g) or kilograms (kg). One kilogram equals 1,000 grams.

Suppose you have some apple slices. You know their mass. You also have some orange slices. You know their mass, too. You mix them together to make a fruit salad. How can you find the mass of the salad without using a balance? If you said, "Add the two known masses," you were right! The mass of two or more things together is the sum of their masses.

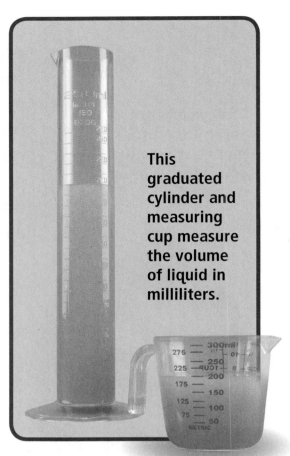

This graduated cylinder and measuring cup measure the volume of liquid in milliliters.

Science Up Close

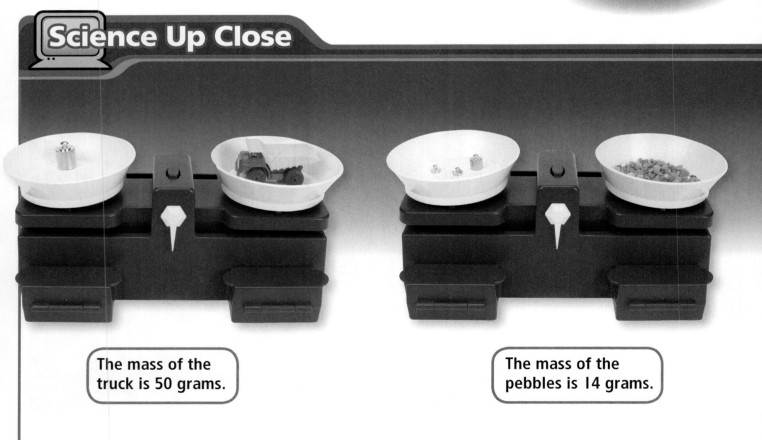

The mass of the truck is 50 grams.

The mass of the pebbles is 14 grams.

Another physical property of matter is volume. **Volume** is the amount of space matter takes up. In the Investigate, you measured 100 mL of water. The volume of the water was 100 mL.

Density is another property of matter. **Density** is the mass of matter compared to its volume. Think about two identical boxes. You fill one box with feathers. You fill the other box with rocks. The boxes have the same volume, but the box of rocks has much more mass. Rocks have greater density than feathers.

 **MAIN IDEA AND DETAILS**
What is density?

Insta-Lab

Compare Densities
Fill one sandwich bag with marbles. Fill another with cotton balls. Seal the bags. Measure the mass of each bag. How do their volumes compare? How do their densities compare? Which matter is denser—cotton or marbles?

The mass of the truck and the pebbles is 64 grams. That is the sum of the two masses added together.

Sink and Float

How well an object floats is a physical property, too. Steel bars sink. Steel boats float. Why?

Density is the reason. Matter that is less dense than water floats. Matter that is denser than water sinks.

How could you make a steel bar float? You would have to change its shape to increase its volume. Changing a steel bar into a boat shape changes the volume of the steel. The same steel in a boat's shape takes up more space. Yet its mass doesn't change. The same mass that has a greater volume is less dense. If the volume of the steel boat is great enough, the boat floats.

MAIN IDEA AND DETAILS What is the difference between an object that sinks and one that floats?

Which balls in this picture are less dense than water? Which are denser? How do you know? ▼

1. MAIN IDEA AND DETAILS Draw and complete this graphic organizer.

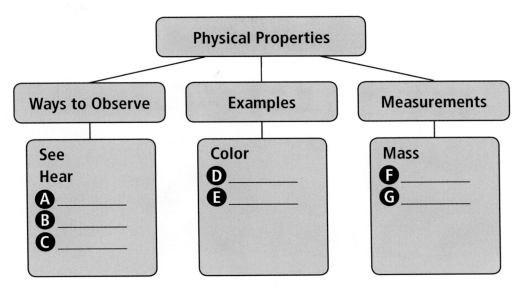

Physical Properties

Ways to Observe

See
Hear
Ⓐ _____
Ⓑ _____
Ⓒ _____

Examples

Color
Ⓓ _____
Ⓔ _____

Measurements

Mass
Ⓕ _____
Ⓖ _____

2. SUMMARIZE Use the completed graphic organizer to write a lesson summary.

3. DRAW CONCLUSIONS You have two equal masses of feathers and rocks. Which has the greater volume?

4. VOCABULARY How is volume different from mass?

FCAT Prep

5. A boat loaded with too much cargo sank. Why?

   A. It became less dense than water.

   B. Its volume became too great.

   C. Its density increased.

   D. All heavy things sink.

Writing

Expository

Gather five classroom objects. Write a **description** of each object's physical properties. Then ask a classmate to identify the objects by using only the properties you described.

Music

Physical Properties Symphony

Use the sounds that different kinds of matter make to perform an original physical properties symphony. Perform your symphony for the class.

 For more links and activities, go to www.hspscience.com

What Are States of Matter?

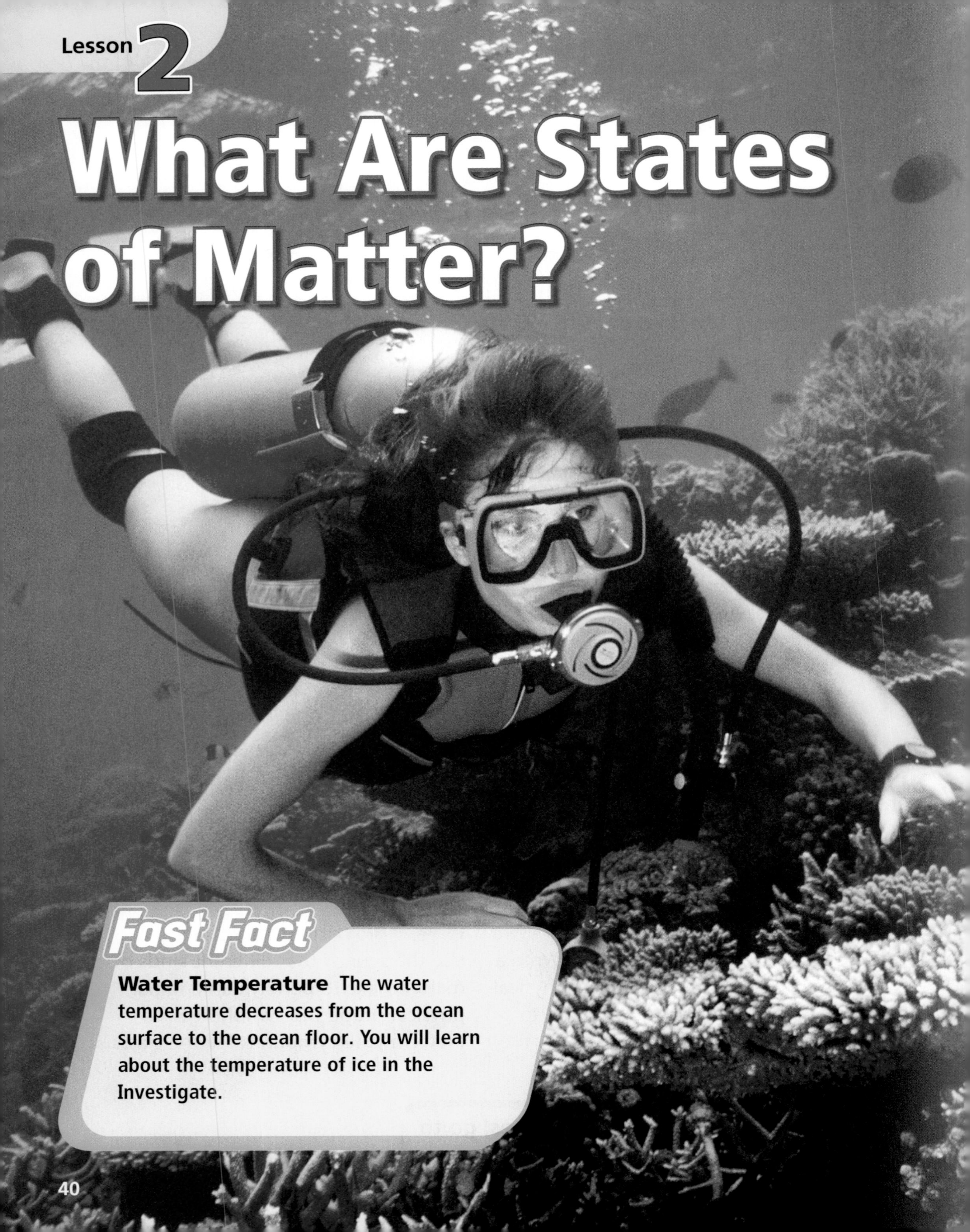

Fast Fact

Water Temperature The water temperature decreases from the ocean surface to the ocean floor. You will learn about the temperature of ice in the Investigate.

Temperature and Matter

Materials
- metric measuring cup
- thermometer
- hot water
- 3 ice cubes
- plastic jar or beaker
- plastic spoon

Procedure

1. **Measure** 200 mL of hot water from the tap in the measuring cup. Pour the water into the jar or beaker.

2. **Measure** the temperature of the water with the thermometer. **Record** the data.

3. Add an ice cube to the water. Stir with the plastic spoon. **Record** what you **observe**.

4. **Measure** the temperature of the water again. **Record** the data.

5. Repeat Steps 3 and 4 twice.

Draw Conclusions

1. What happened to the ice cubes in the water?

2. What happened to the temperature of the water each time you added an ice cube?

3. **Inquiry Skill** One way scientists can **communicate data** is in a bar graph. Make a bar graph to **communicate** what happened to the temperature of the water in this activity.

Step 2

Step 3

Investigate Further

Put 100 mL of water in a freezer. **Measure** its temperature every 10 minutes. **Communicate** the data in a bar graph. **Interpret the data.**

SC.H.1.2.1.3.1 keeping accurate records, **SC.H.1.2.2.3.1** following experimental design, **SC.H.1.2.2.3.2** using scientific instruments, **SC.H.2.2.1.3.2** uses graphs, **SC.H.3.2.2.3.1** collects data, **SC.H.3.2.2.3.2** presents scientific information

VOCABULARY

solid p. 43
liquid p. 44
gas p. 45
evaporation p. 46
condensation p. 46

SCIENCE CONCEPTS

▶ what three states of matter are
▶ how temperature affects states of matter

 READING FOCUS SKILL

COMPARE AND CONTRAST
Find out how states of matter are alike and different.

alike ——— different

States of Matter

You have read that matter takes up space. Matter also has different forms called states. Three states of matter are solid, liquid, and gas.

In the Investigate, you watched an ice cube change states. If you had boiled the water, it would also have changed to another state.

The wax of a candle can also change states. To make a candle, wax is melted and poured into a mold. When the wax has cooled and hardened, it has changed states.

 COMPARE AND CONTRAST
How are ice and the wax of a candle alike?

What are some solids and liquids in this picture? ▶

Name the solids you see in these pictures.

Solids

Think about what an ice cube is like. An ice cube is a solid. A **solid** is matter with a volume and a shape that stay the same.

Solids stay solids unless something, such as heat, changes them. When ice is heated, it melts and becomes a liquid. When you heat matter, the motion of its small particles, or pieces, speeds up.

The opposite happens, too. If you remove enough heat from water, it freezes. When matter cools, the motion of its small particles slows down.

 COMPARE AND CONTRAST How are all solids alike?

Insta-Lab

Is It Solid?

Take a frozen pat of butter and place it on a dish. Record your observations about the butter. Then place the dish and butter under a lamp. Turn the lamp on and record what happens to the butter every minute. Write a description of how the butter changed.

Liquids

Think about a glass of water. The water in the glass is a liquid. A **liquid** is matter that has a volume that stays the same but a shape that can change.

Like a solid, a liquid has a volume that doesn't change. However, a liquid's shape can change. A liquid takes the shape of whatever container holds it. The volume of water can look large in a tall, slim container. In a short, wide container, it can look small.

You know that water is a liquid. Paint, juice, and shampoo are liquids, too. What are some liquids you see or use every day?

▲ This soap is a liquid.

COMPARE AND CONTRAST How are liquids and solids different?

Vinegar and oil are liquids that make salads tasty.

Water changes shape as it falls.

Fizzy drinks have carbon dioxide gas in them. The bubbles you see are bubbles of gas.

Gases

The helium inside this balloon is a gas. A **gas** has no definite shape or volume. A gas takes up all the space in a container. If you blow up a balloon, you can see that the air spreads out to fill the space inside the balloon.

The air that you breathe is a mixture of gases. Some stoves cook with natural gas. You can't see natural gas, but when it burns, you can see a blue flame.

 COMPARE AND CONTRAST How are gases different from solids and liquids?

A gas called helium fills this balloon.

Changes of State

In the Investigate, heat changed solid ice to liquid water. Heat can also change a liquid to a gas. If you leave a cup of water in a warm place, after a day or two, the cup will be empty. The liquid changes into a gas, but it's still water. Water moves into the air in the process of **evaporation**. Boiling also makes water evaporate, but it happens more quickly.

When a gas cools, it changes back to a liquid. The change of a gas to a liquid is **condensation**. You have seen this happen. When the water in air, a gas, changes to a liquid, it rains.

 COMPARE AND CONTRAST How are evaporation and condensation the same? How are they different?

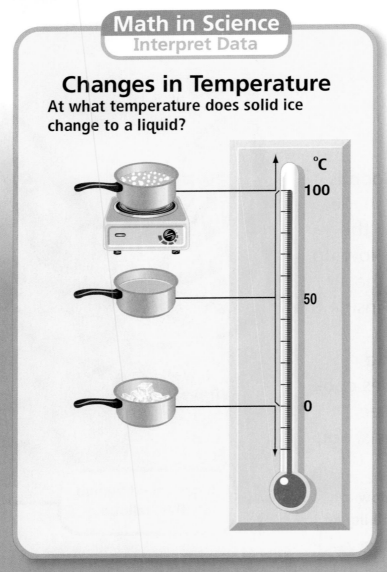

Math in Science
Interpret Data

Changes in Temperature
At what temperature does solid ice change to a liquid?

°C
100

50

0

1. COMPARE AND CONTRAST Copy and complete this graphic organizer.

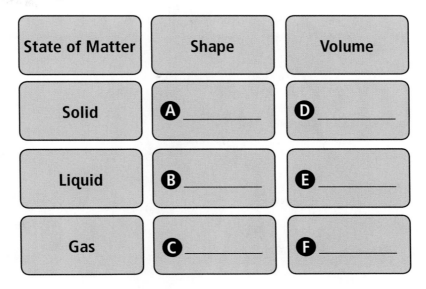

State of Matter	Shape	Volume
Solid	Ⓐ _____	Ⓓ _____
Liquid	Ⓑ _____	Ⓔ _____
Gas	Ⓒ _____	Ⓕ _____

2. SUMMARIZE Use the completed graphic organizer to write a lesson summary.

3. DRAW CONCLUSIONS If matter has a definite volume but no definite shape, in what state is it?

4. VOCABULARY Write a sentence to explain how evaporation relates to a change of state.

FCAT Prep

5. Read/Inquire/Explain A solid object melts to become a liquid. Was heat added or was it removed to cause the change? Explain.

Writing

Narrative
Write a **story** about an ice cube as temperature changes cause it to change into different states of matter.

Math

Solve a Problem
Maria took a frozen pop out of the freezer at 3:23 P.M. and placed it in a dish. At 3:35 P.M., the pop was a puddle of liquid. How long did it take the frozen pop to melt?

 For more links and activities, go to www.hspscience.com

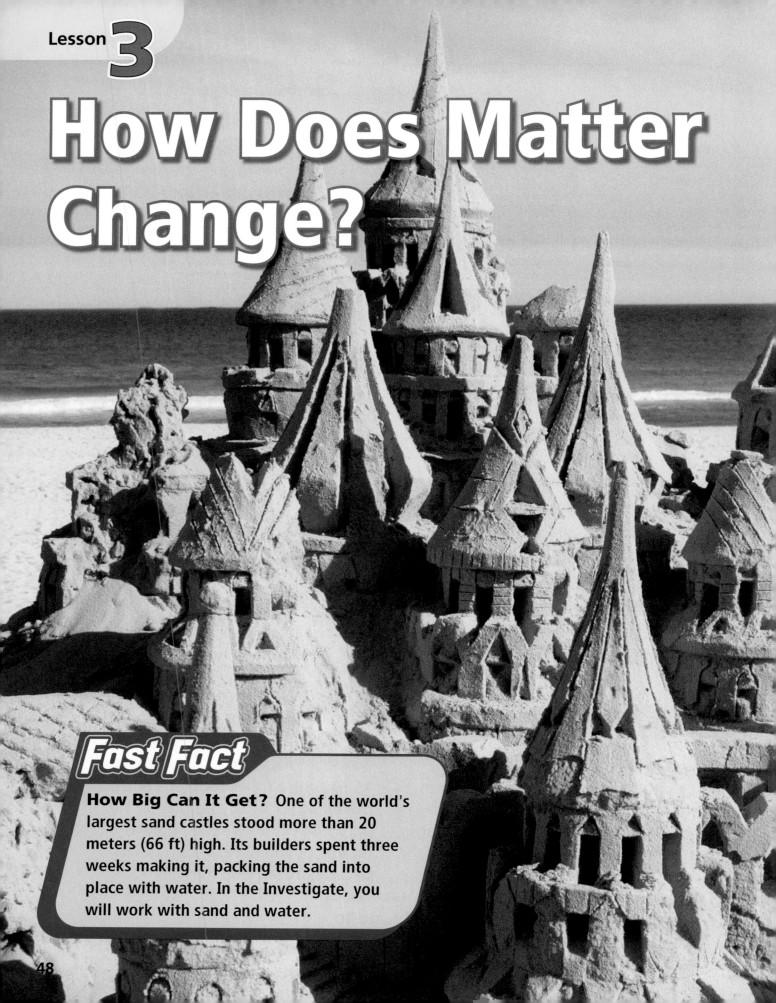

3

How Does Matter Change?

Fast Fact

How Big Can It Get? One of the world's largest sand castles stood more than 20 meters (66 ft) high. Its builders spent three weeks making it, packing the sand into place with water. In the Investigate, you will work with sand and water.

48

Will It Mix?

Materials • water • metric measuring cup • 2 clear plastic jars
• measuring spoon ($\frac{1}{4}$ teaspoon) • sand • plastic spoon • hand lens • salt

Procedure

Step 2

① **Measure** 200 mL of water. Pour the water into one of the jars.

② Add $\frac{1}{4}$ teaspoon of sand to the water and stir. Use a hand lens to **observe** the jar's contents. **Record** what you **observe**.

③ Repeat Step 1, using the other jar.

④ Add $\frac{1}{4}$ teaspoon of salt to the water and stir. Use a hand lens to observe the jar's contents. **Record** what you **observe**.

Step 4

⑤ Repeat Step 4 until you see salt collect on the bottom of the jar after you stir. **Record** the number of teaspoons of salt you used in all.

Draw Conclusions

1. What did you **observe** when you stirred in the sand? The salt?

2. **Inquiry Skill** Scientists sometimes use drawings to **communicate**. Make two drawings that will **communicate** what happened to the sand and the salt when they were stirred into the water.

Investigate Further

What do you **predict** will happen if you leave the jar of salt water in a warm place? Try it. Was your **prediction** correct?

SC.A.2.2.1.3.1 tools to see details, **SC.H.1.2.1.3.1** keeping accurate records, **SC.H.1.2.2.3.1** following experimental design, **SC.H.1.2.2.3.2** using scientific instruments, **SC.H.2.2.1.3.1** makes predictions, **SC.H.3.2.2.3.1** collects data, **SC.H.3.2.2.3.2** presents scientific information

49

SC.A.1.2.4 mixtures and solutions, **SC.A.1.2.5** chemical changes, **LA.A.2.2.1** main idea and details

VOCABULARY

mixture p. 52
solution p. 53

SCIENCE CONCEPTS

▶ what physical and chemical changes are
▶ what mixtures and solutions are

READING FOCUS SKILL

(Focus Skill)

MAIN IDEA AND DETAILS Find out how physical and chemical changes happen.

```
        Main Idea
       /    |    \
 detail   detail   detail
```

Physical Changes

What can change and still be the same? The answer is matter. Changes in matter that don't form new kinds of matter are physical changes.

An example of a physical change is cutting. Cutting makes a piece of paper smaller, but the paper is still paper. Its size changes, but the paper pieces are still the same kind of matter.

Yarn is packaged and sold.

Sheep grow a thick coat of wool.

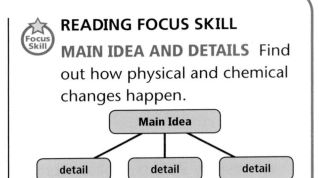

▲ A machine spins sheep's wool into yarn.

Knitting a wool cap is another example of a physical change. The thick wool is cut from sheep in spring. This doesn't hurt them, and they grow a new coat before winter. The wool is combed into soft strands, which are pulled into threads and twisted to make yarn. A knitter then knits the wool yarn into a cap. In the cap, the wool looks different from the way it looked on the sheep, but it is still wool. It is the same kind of matter.

MAIN IDEA AND DETAILS What happens to matter when there is a physical change?

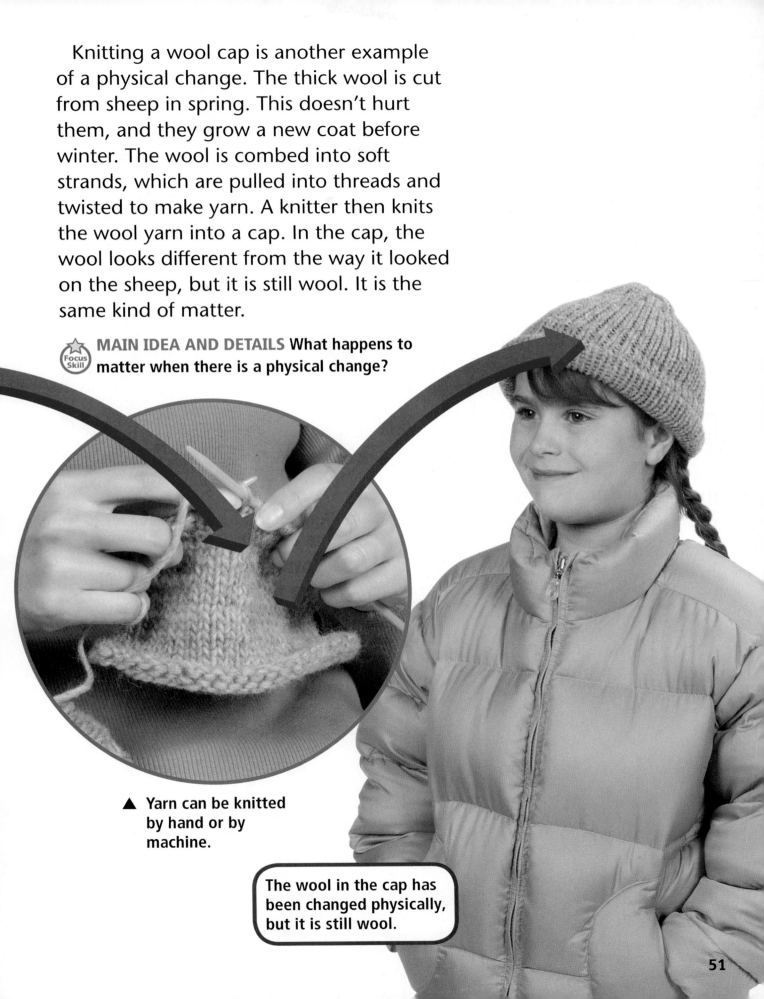

▲ Yarn can be knitted by hand or by machine.

The wool in the cap has been changed physically, but it is still wool.

Mixtures

In the Investigate, you made two mixtures—one of sand and water, and one of salt and water. A **mixture** is a substance that is made up of two or more kinds of matter. Making a mixture is a physical change. You put different types of matter together, but no new types of matter are formed.

Separating the parts of a mixture is a physical change, too. You can separate sand and water by pouring the mixture through filter paper. The water runs through, leaving the sand behind. You can separate salt and water by leaving the mixture in a warm place. The water evaporates, leaving the salt.

▲ This girl has a mixture of beads.

MAIN IDEA AND DETAILS What is a mixture?

This bowl holds a mixture of cereal, strawberries, and bananas.

A solution of drink mix and water is a tasty treat.

▲ A solution of detergent and water gets dishes clean.

Solutions

In the Investigate, when you first stirred salt into water, you could not see the salt. The salt dissolved, or mixed with the water. You made a solution. A **solution** is a mixture in which different kinds of matter mix evenly. Your mixture of salt and water was a solution. Since the sand didn't dissolve in the water, that mixture wasn't a solution.

Focus Skill **MAIN IDEA AND DETAILS** Why is a solution a kind of mixture?

Chemical Changes

Changes that form different kinds of matter are chemical changes. Cooking causes chemical changes. Suppose you stir flour, sugar, eggs, milk, and butter together to make a cake. After you bake the cake, it has properties that are completely different from the properties of the ingredients.

Burning is also a chemical change. When wood burns, it combines with oxygen in the air. Ashes and smoke form. Those are different kinds of matter than the wood. You can't get the wood back.

MAIN IDEA AND DETAILS Name at least four examples of chemical changes.

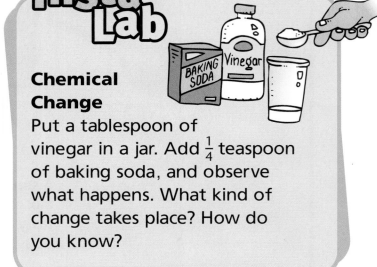

Insta-Lab

Chemical Change

Put a tablespoon of vinegar in a jar. Add $\frac{1}{4}$ teaspoon of baking soda, and observe what happens. What kind of change takes place? How do you know?

Rotting is a chemical change.

Rusting is a chemical change. It happens when oxygen in the air combines with iron in metal.

Focus Skill

1. MAIN IDEA AND DETAILS Copy and complete this graphic organizer.

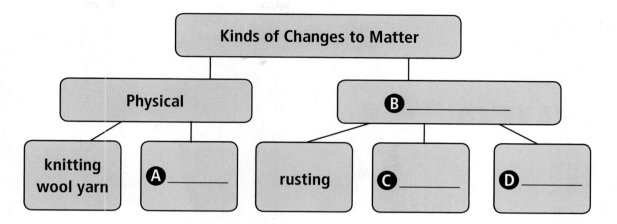

Kinds of Changes to Matter

Physical

B _____

knitting wool yarn

A _____

rusting

C _____

D _____

2. SUMMARIZE Use the completed graphic organizer to write a lesson summary.

3. DRAW CONCLUSIONS Mr. Gonzalez put up a wall made of bricks and mortar. Was the change physical or chemical? Explain.

4. VOCABULARY Explain why all solutions are mixtures but not all mixtures are solutions.

FCAT Prep

5. Which of these is a chemical change?
- **A.** burning gasoline in a car
- **B.** putting on fingernail polish
- **C.** making a chain from strips of paper
- **D.** grinding wheat to make flour

Links

Writing

Expository
Write a **paragraph** or two in which you compare and contrast mixtures and solutions. Make illustrations to help with the explanation.

Math

Solve a Problem
A mixture contains two times as many red beads as white beads. There are six white beads. How many red beads are in the mixture? On paper, show how you solved the problem.

 For more links and activities, go to **www.hspscience.com**

SC.H.3.2.3.3.1
Scientific discoveries
impact humans

Better Than Nature Can Make?

Replacing Nature

For thousands of years, clothes have been made using natural materials, such as cotton, wool, and silk. These materials are all found in nature. For example, cotton comes from a plant, wool is made from a sheep's fur, and silk is spun by worms.

The first synthetic materials were produced less than 100 years ago. These materials, such as rayon, nylon, spandex, and polyester, were all first made in laboratories. Today, synthetic materials have replaced natural fabrics for many purposes.

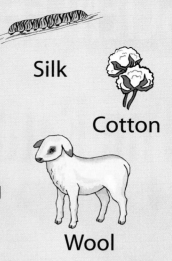

Silk

Cotton

Wool

Many times, scientists come up with new ideas by looking at nature. For example, swimsuit makers made a fabric for Olympic athletes after studying the skin of sharks.

Recently, scientists in Turkey, a country in Europe, also turned to nature for ideas. Scientists there came up with an idea for a new fabric by looking at water lilies. Water lilies are plants that grow in ponds and have big leaves that float on the surface.

Looking at Lilies

The scientists were inspired by how waterproof a water lily's leaves are. They wanted to make a material that shed water similar to the way the plant's leaves shed water.

The scientists then began working with different materials, such as plastic, to form a new kind of material. Like the plant, when this new material gets wet, the water does not soak in but stays on the surface and rolls off.

The new material is synthetic. Synthetic is another way of saying something that is made by people. The new waterproof material will be useful for many people, especially firefighters, who need to keep dry while they work.

Think About It

1. Why do you think people started making synthetic materials?
2. Do you think synthetic materials should replace natural materials? Why or why not?

Find out more! Log on to
www.hspscience.com

SC.H.3.2.1.3.1 history of science, SC.H.3.2.3.3.1 scientific discoveries impact humans

People

The Father of the Barometer

EVANGELISTA TORRICELLI

Modern Barometer ▶

Evangelista Torricelli was a scientist who lived about 360 years ago. He is best known for an invention that helps to predict the weather. That invention is the barometer.

Most people before Torricelli did not know that air has weight. This idea is known as "air pressure." A barometer is used to measure air pressure.

Torricelli's barometer was a glass tube filled with a liquid metal called mercury. When air pressure was high, during good weather, the mercury moved up the tube. When air pressure was low, usually on stormy days, the mercury was lower in the tube.

Career Materials Scientist

How long do think the rubber soles of your new sneakers will last? Chances are, a materials scientist knows the answer. These scientists study how different materials react to changes. They study how rubber might react to cold or how long before it wears out.

Find out more! Log on to
www.hspscience.com

Quick and Easy Project

Sink or Float?

Procedure

1. Predict whether each object will sink or float. Record your predictions in a data table.

2. Test each object. Record the results in the data table. Were your predictions correct?

Materials
- water
- plastic pan
- small objects

Draw Conclusions
From your data, which objects do you infer are less dense than water? Circle the names of these objects in your data table.

Design Your Own Investigation

Measuring Volume

Set a measuring cup in an empty pan. Carefully fill the cup to the brim with water. Put a small but heavy object into the cup. Some water will spill over into the pan. Pour this water into another measuring cup. The amount of water equals the volume of the object. Use this procedure to measure and compare the volumes of three small objects. Make a bar graph to share your findings.

Review and FCAT Preparation

Vocabulary Review

Match the terms to the definitions below. The page numbers tell where to look in the chapter if you need help.

matter p. 32
mass p. 36
volume p. 37
density p. 37
solid p. 43
liquid p. 44
gas p. 45
evaporation p. 46
mixture p. 52
solution p. 53

1. A mixture in which all the parts mix evenly

2. A state of matter with no definite shape or volume

3. The amount of matter in something

4. The process during which water moves into the air

5. The amount of space matter takes up

6. The state of matter in which volume stays the same but the matter takes the shape of its container

7. The mass of something compared with its volume

8. Anything that takes up space

9. A state of matter with a shape and a volume that don't change

10. A substance with two or more different kinds of matter

Check Understanding

Write the letter of the best choice.

11. **MAIN IDEA AND DETAILS** Which of the following is true of these two jars and their contents?

A. They have the same mass.
B. They have the same volume.
C. They have the same density.
D. They have the same matter.

12. COMPARE AND CONTRAST Which states of matter have a volume that doesn't change?

F. solid and liquid

G. liquid and gas

H. solid and gas

I. solid, liquid, and gas

13. Sarah notices that a metal fence rail feels cold and hard. What is Sarah observing?

A. chemical changes

B. densities

C. physical properties

D. states of matter

14. Which of these is a solution?

F. peanut butter and jelly

G. salt and water

H. cereal and milk

I. celery and carrot sticks

15. Which of the following is a chemical change?

A. dissolving soap in water

B. filling a balloon with air

C. grating cheese

D. burning wood

16. A ball of modeling clay sinks in a pan of water. What change could make the clay float?

F. Remove some of the water.

G. Increase the clay's density.

H. Change its shape.

I. Add more water to the pan.

Inquiry Skills

17. How could you measure which of two objects has greater mass?

18. There are two identical boxes. One box is filled to the top with books. The other box is filled to the top with foam pillows. Which box would you predict has greater mass? Explain your answer.

Read/Inquire/Explain

19. You can put sand into a container, and it takes the shape of the container. Why is sand still considered a solid?

20. You have a mixture of two kinds of buttons. Some are large. Some are small.

Part A How can you separate the mixture without picking out the buttons one at a time?

Part B Is the button mixture a solution? Tell why or why not.

Energy

PHYSICAL SCIENCE

 The chapters in this unit address these Grade Level Expectations from the Florida Sunshine State Standards.

Chapter 2 Energy

SC.B.1.2.2.3.2	knows different forms of energy.
SC.B.1.2.3.3.1	knows that the sun provides energy for the Earth in the form of heat and light.
SC.B.1.2.5.3.1	uses a variety of tools to measure the gain or loss of energy.
SC.B.2.2.1.3.1	knows that some source of energy is needed for organisms to stay alive and grow.
SC.B.2.2.2.3.1	knows ways natural resources are important.
SC.B.2.2.2.3.2	classifies resources as renewable or nonrenewable.
SC.B.2.2.3.3.1	knows that alternate energy sources are being explored using natural and mechanical processes.

Chapter 3 Heat

SC.B.1.2.2.3.1	knows objects that emit heat and light.
SC.B.1.2.2.3.2	knows different forms of energy.
SC.B.1.2.3.3.1	knows that the sun provides energy for the Earth in the form of heat and light.
SC.B.1.2.4.3.1	knows that heat can be produced by chemical reactions, electrical machines, and friction.
SC.B.1.2.6.3.1	knows that when a warmer object comes in contact with a cooler one, the warm object loses heat and the cool one gains it until they are both the same temperature.

The investigations and experiences in this unit also address many of the Grade Level Expectations in Strand H, The Nature of Science.

Science in Florida

Fort Walton Beach

Dear Aunt Beth,

We are having a great time in Fort Walton Beach. The sun felt so hot today that I thought I was going to melt! Mom made me wear a lot of sunscreen. Now I know why Florida is the "Sunshine State."

The beach was full of energy. We all enjoyed the heat and light that came from the sun. Playing in the waves at the shore was fun. The sound of the waves put me to sleep.

Love,

Claire

The Sunshine State

USA

FCAT Writing

Writing Situation
Think about going for a swim. Explain why most people don't swim in the winter.

Experiment!

Keeping Food Cold To keep food cold in the hot sun, you use a cooler. Coolers are containers made of materials that don't allow heat to quickly pass through. What materials make the best coolers? For example, does a cooler made out of paper work better than a cooler made out of plastic? Plan and conduct an experiment to find out.

Chapter 2 Energy

Vocabulary

FCAT-Tested
energy
kinetic energy
potential energy
resource
nonrenewable
  resource
renewable resource

Other Terms
combustion
temperature
fossil fuels

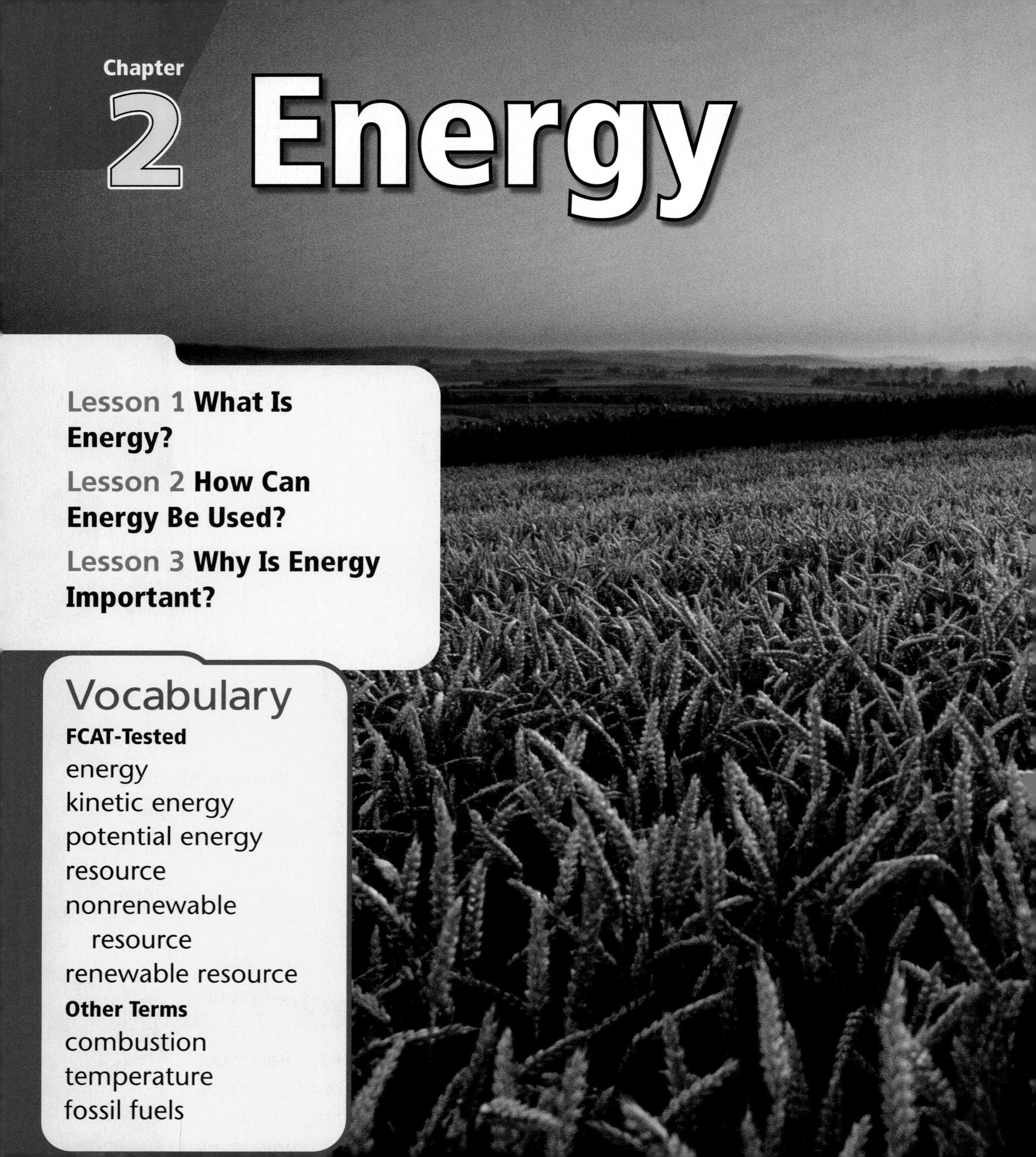

What do YOU wonder?

The sun gives off energy that helps this wheat grow. What other types of energy can you think of?

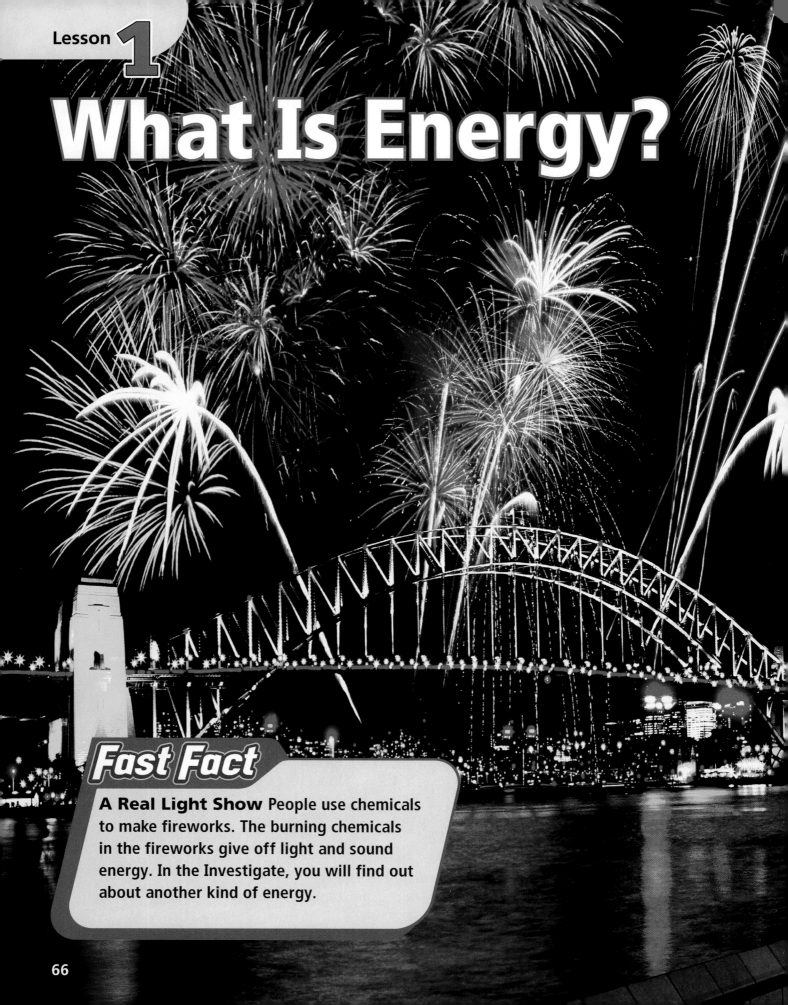

What Is Energy?

Fast Fact

A Real Light Show People use chemicals to make fireworks. The burning chemicals in the fireworks give off light and sound energy. In the Investigate, you will find out about another kind of energy.

Observing Temperature

Materials • thermometer • clock

Procedure

1. With your group, find a place outside that is sunny all day long.

2. In the morning, have a group member place the thermometer on the ground, face up.

3. Wait a few minutes until the temperature reading stops changing.

4. Each member of the group should read and record the temperature.

5. Observe the thermometer once an hour for several hours. Communicate your observations in a line graph that shows time and temperature.

Step 2

Step 5

Draw Conclusions

1. What changes did you observe? What caused these changes?

2. **Inquiry Skill** Scientists use their observations to infer why things happen. The rising temperature on the thermometer was caused by energy. Where can you infer that the energy came from?

Investigate Further

Do you think you would see similar changes on a cloudy day? Make a hypothesis. Plan and conduct a simple investigation to test it.

SC.H.1.2.2.3.1 following experimental design, **SC.H.1.2.2.3.2** using scientific instruments, **SC.H.2.2.1.3.2** uses graphs, **SC.H.3.2.2.3.1** collects data, **SC.H.3.2.2.3.2** presents scientific information

67

Reading in Science

SC.B.1.2.2.3.2 forms of energy, SC.B.1.2.3.3.1 sun energy/heat and light, SC.B.2.2.1.3.1 organisms need energy, LA.A.2.2.7 compare and contrast

VOCABULARY

energy p. 68

kinetic energy p. 70

potential energy p. 70

SCIENCE CONCEPTS

► what energy is

► what the relationship between kinetic energy and potential energy is

READING FOCUS SKILL

COMPARE AND CONTRAST

Look for ways in which forms of energy are different.

| alike |——| different |

Some Sources of Energy

Think about a moving car. As long as the car is moving, it must be getting energy. Gasoline is burned to supply the energy that makes the car move. **Energy** is the ability to make something move or change.

Now think about a boy riding a bike. The bike is moving, so the bike must be getting energy—but from where? The boy's muscles supply the energy to pedal the bike. Moving the pedals makes the bike move.

Moving water supplies the energy to turn the water wheel.

Lightning is a type of electric energy.

The boy needs energy to move his muscles. This energy comes from food. You need the energy from food to move your muscles. You also need energy to grow and change.

A seed sprouts and grows into a plant. The energy a plant needs to grow comes from sunlight.

Most of the energy on Earth comes from the sun. Its heat and light supply most of the energy we need.

★ COMPARE AND CONTRAST How is the energy you use to grow different from the energy the seed uses to grow?

You know there is sound energy from this clock, because the clapper is moving.

What types of energy does this picture show?

Electric energy causes this sign to light up.

Turning the crank tightens a spring inside the box.

Forms of Energy

You have just read about different kinds of energy. All kinds of energy can be grouped in two ways. **Kinetic energy** (kih•NET•ik) is the energy of motion. Anything that is moving has kinetic energy. A moving car has kinetic energy. A child moving down a slide has kinetic energy. A leg moving a bike pedal around and around has kinetic energy. If these things didn't have kinetic energy, they wouldn't move.

A child sitting at the top of a slide is not moving but still has energy. The child has potential energy. **Potential energy** (poh•TEN•shuhl) is energy of position. When the child moves, potential energy is changed into kinetic energy.

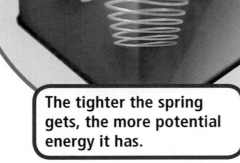

The tighter the spring gets, the more potential energy it has.

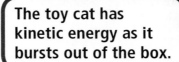

The toy cat has kinetic energy as it bursts out of the box.

A battery has potential energy. This energy can be transferred to other forms. When the battery is used to make something move, it releases kinetic energy.

 COMPARE AND CONTRAST What is the difference between kinetic energy and potential energy?

Science Up Close

How a Battery Works
Inside the battery are two powders. Each is mixed with a liquid to make a paste. The pastes are kept apart by a tube of fabric.

The two pastes have potential energy. When you put the battery in a circuit, the energy is changed into electric current.

One end of the battery touches a paste. The other end connects to the brass tube.

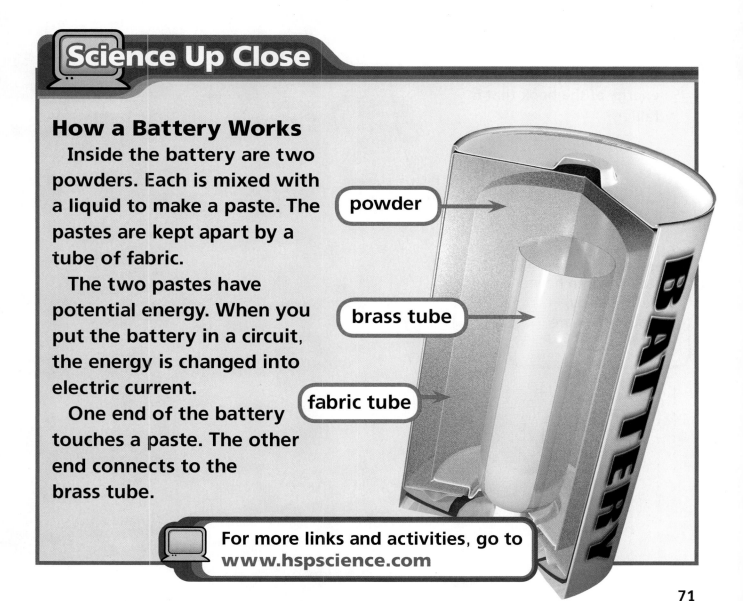

powder

brass tube

fabric tube

For more links and activities, go to www.hspscience.com

Energy Changes

Think about a book on a shelf. It has potential energy. Now suppose the book falls. As it falls, it's moving, so it has kinetic energy. Where did the kinetic energy come from? The potential energy of the book's position was changed to kinetic energy.

Now you put the book back on the shelf. As you lift it, it's moving. It has kinetic energy. When it's sitting on the shelf again, it has potential energy. The kinetic energy was changed to potential energy.

COMPARE AND CONTRAST **How is the energy of a book sitting on a shelf different from the energy of the book that is falling?**

These children have kinetic energy, because they are jumping.

1. COMPARE AND CONTRAST Copy and complete this graphic organizer.

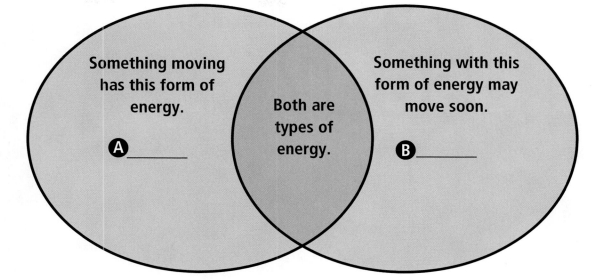

Something moving has this form of energy.

A_____

Both are types of energy.

Something with this form of energy may move soon.

B_____

2. SUMMARIZE Write two sentences that tell what this lesson is mainly about.

3. DRAW CONCLUSIONS A bike on its kickstand has potential energy. How could you change the energy to kinetic energy?

4. VOCABULARY Use each of the lesson vocabulary terms in a sentence that correctly shows its meaning.

FCAT Prep

5. Which type of energy do we get from the sun?

   A. potential

   B. electrical

   C. light

   D. kinetic

Links

Writing

Expository
Write a **friendly letter** telling a friend or relative what you learned about the different forms of energy.

Physical Education

Using Energy
Make up a 30-second physical fitness routine that uses kinetic and potential energy. Do your routine for the class, and identify the form of energy you have during each part of the routine.

For more links and activities, go to www.hspscience.com

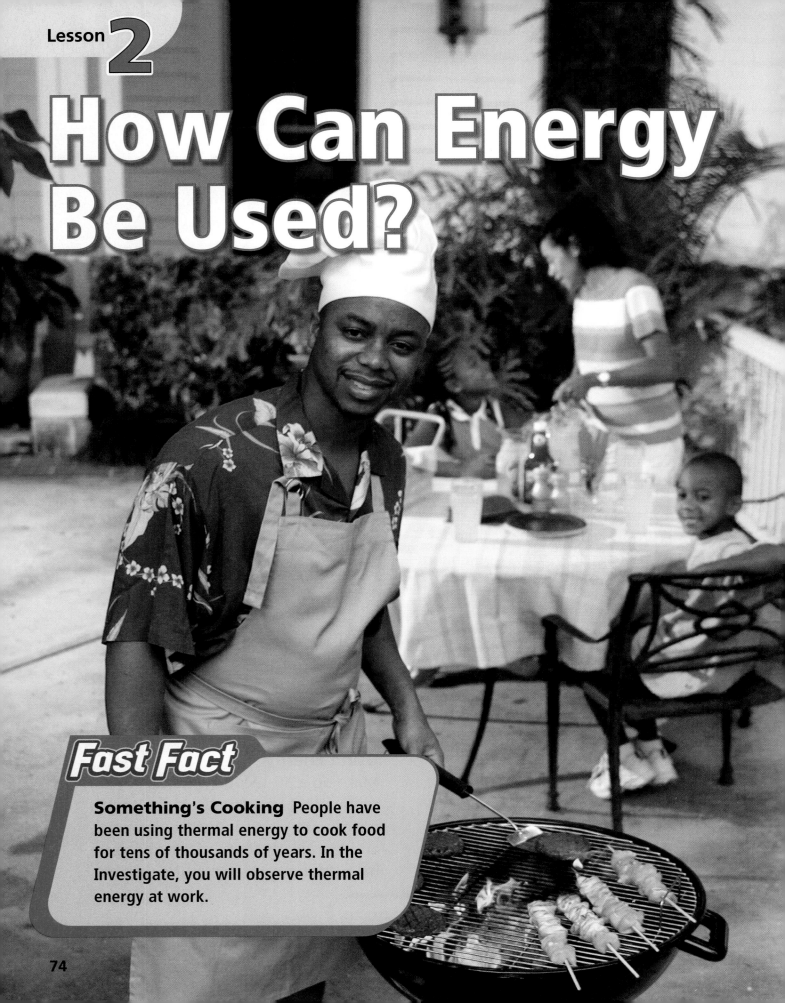

2

How Can Energy Be Used?

Fast Fact

Something's Cooking People have been using thermal energy to cook food for tens of thousands of years. In the Investigate, you will observe thermal energy at work.

The Heat Is On

Materials • **clear plastic cup** • **ice cubes** • **thermometer**

Procedure

1. Fill a clear plastic cup with ice cubes. Place a thermometer in the cup. Place the cup in sunlight.

2. After several minutes, **record** the temperature inside the cup.

3. Continue to **record** the temperature inside the cup every half hour for three hours.

4. **Communicate** the data from your table by making a bar graph.

Draw Conclusions

1. What did you **observe** about the temperature and the ice? What caused these changes?

2. **Inquiry Skill** Scientists use **observations** and data to **infer** why things happen. What can you **infer** happens to an object placed in sunlight?

Step 1

Step 4

Investigate Further

What do you think happens to the temperature of water placed in a freezer? Make a **hypothesis.** Then test it.

SC.H.1.2.2.3.1 following experimental design, **SC.H.1.2.2.3.2** using scientific instruments, **SC.H.2.2.1.3.1** makes inferences, **SC.H.2.2.1.3.2** uses graphs, **SC.H.3.2.2.3.1** collects data, **SC.H.3.2.2.3.2** presents scientific information

Reading in Science

SC.B.1.2.3.3.1 sun energy/heat and light, **SC.B.1.2.5.3.1** measuring gain/loss of energy, **LA.A.2.2.1** main idea and details

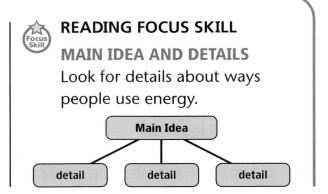

VOCABULARY

combustion p. 77
temperature p. 78

SCIENCE CONCEPTS
► how people use energy

READING FOCUS SKILL

MAIN IDEA AND DETAILS
Look for details about ways people use energy.

```
        Main Idea
   /        |        \
detail    detail    detail
```

Using Energy

Energy makes things move or change. Without it, we could not live.

The sun provides energy to plants to grow. You then get energy from eating the plants for food. After you eat, energy from the food moves through your body. The energy keeps you healthy and helps you grow.

Energy in your muscles lets you move. When you run or jump, energy moves from your leg muscles to make your body move.

It takes a lot of energy to make this big, heavy train move.

Machines get energy in many ways. One way to get energy is from combustion. **Combustion** (kuhm•BUHS•chuhn) is another word for "burning." When fuels burn, they give off heat.

A car engine burns gasoline. The gasoline gives off energy that makes the car move. Some stoves burn gas. The gas gives off energy that cooks your food. Wood burning in a fireplace also gives off energy.

 MAIN IDEA AND DETAILS What happens during combustion?

Where does the energy that moves the train come from?

Insta-Lab

Energy from Food
Think about all the activities a student like you could have done this morning, such as brushing teeth or packing a backpack. Food gives a person the energy to do these activities. List at least 10 activities someone might do each morning. Explain how someone might feel if he or she didn't have the energy from the foods.

Measuring Energy

You have read that there are different types and uses of energy. There are different ways to measure energy, too. The way energy is measured depends on the type of energy.

You have probably seen a thermometer like the one shown on this page. Thermometers are used to measure temperature. **Temperature** is the measure of how hot or cold something is. Not all energy is measured with a thermometer, though. For example, wind speed is measured with an anemometer.

 MAIN IDEA AND DETAILS What are some kinds of energy that can be measured?

Different Temperatures

Which requires more thermal energy, melting butter or boiling water?

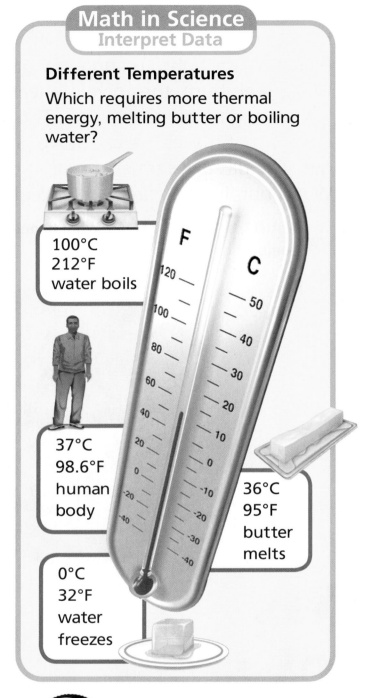

100°C
212°F
water boils

37°C
98.6°F
human body

0°C
32°F
water freezes

36°C
95°F
butter melts

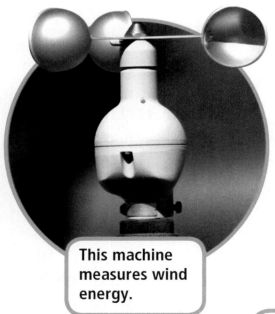

This machine measures wind energy.

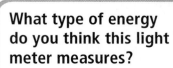

What type of energy do you think this light meter measures?

78

1. MAIN IDEA AND DETAILS Copy and complete this graphic organizer.

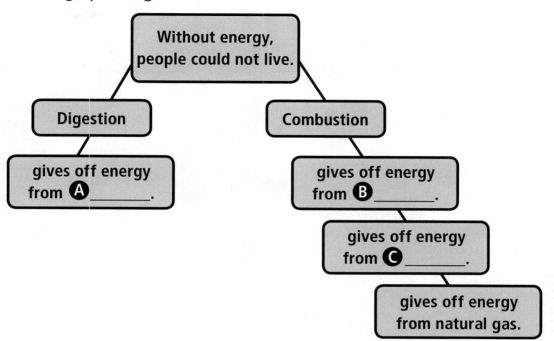

Without energy, people could not live.

Digestion

gives off energy from **A** _____.

Combustion

gives off energy from **B** _____.

gives off energy from **C** _____.

gives off energy from natural gas.

2. SUMMARIZE Write a summary of this lesson by writing the most important idea from each page.

3. DRAW CONCLUSIONS Matt tells his friend that he uses the sun's energy, even at night. How can this be?

4. VOCABULARY What word is a synonym of *combustion*?

FCAT Prep

5. Which type of energy does a thermometer measure?

  A. electric energy
  B. thermal energy
  C. light energy
  D. sound energy

Links

Writing

Expository
Find out how a light meter measures energy. Then write a **description** of what you learn. Share the description with a family member.

Math

Make a Graph
The average temperature of the human body is 37°C. Find the average body temperatures of three other animals of your choice. Make a bar graph to show your findings.

 For more links and activities, go to **www.hspscience.com**

Why Is Energy Important?

Fast Fact

Lighting Up the Night Places using the most electricity are the brightest in this satellite picture. Most electricity is produced by burning oil, coal, and natural gas. In the Investigate, you will explore another source of energy.

Make a Paper Windmill

Materials • white paper • ruler • scissors • pushpin • pencil with eraser

Procedure

1 Draw a 12.75-cm square with dotted lines and dots, as shown.

2 Use scissors to cut out the square.

3 Cut along each of the dotted lines to within 1.25 cm of the center.

4 Take each corner that has a dot, and fold it toward the center of the square to make a vane.

5 CAUTION: Pushpins are sharp! Put the pushpin through the center of all the folded corners and into the eraser of the pencil. Be sure the vanes turn freely.

6 You have just made a model of a windmill. Face your windmill into a strong breeze, or blow on it.

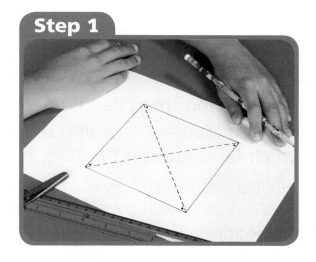

Step 1

Step 4

Draw Conclusions

1. What did you observe when you faced the paper windmill into the breeze?

2. Inquiry Skill Scientists use models to help them understand processes. How does a windmill work? What kind of energy turns a windmill?

Investigate Further

Fold each corner with a dot backward instead of forward. What do you predict will happen to your windmill in a breeze? Try it.

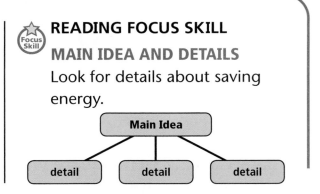

SC.B.2.2.2.3.1 natural resources, **SC.B.2.2.2.3.2** renewable/ nonrenewable resources, **SC.B.2.2.3.3.1** alternate energy sources, **LA.A.2.2.1** main idea and details

VOCABULARY

resource p. 83
fossil fuels p. 83
nonrenewable
resource p. 84
renewable
resource p. 84

SCIENCE CONCEPTS

▶ how important energy is
▶ why it's important to save energy

READING FOCUS SKILL

MAIN IDEA AND DETAILS

Look for details about saving energy.

```
        ┌──────────┐
        │ Main Idea │
        └──────────┘
       /      │      \
┌────────┐ ┌────────┐ ┌────────┐
│ detail │ │ detail │ │ detail │
└────────┘ └────────┘ └────────┘
```

The Importance of Energy

Every living thing needs energy. You are still growing. You're becoming bigger and taller, which takes energy. Walking, running, and playing use energy, too. Even when you are asleep, you're still breathing and your heart is still beating. That takes energy, too.

Communities also need energy. We use energy to cook our food. We use it to light our homes. We use it to run our cars.

 MAIN IDEA AND DETAILS What are three ways communities use energy?

These people are eating foods that will give them energy.

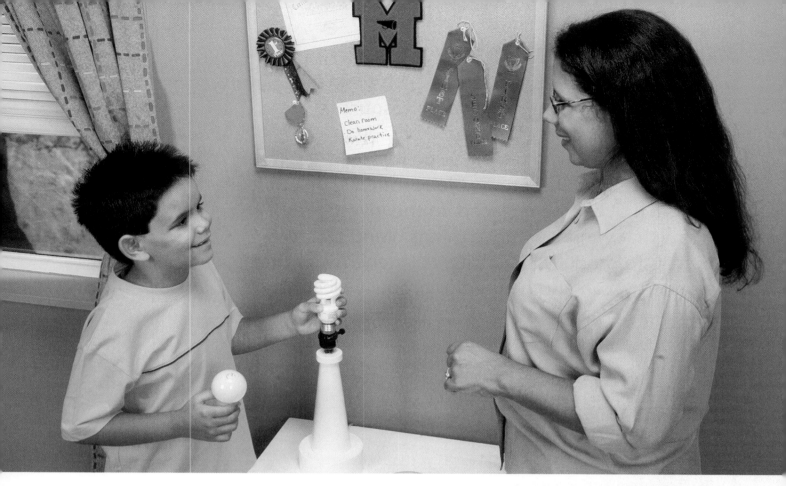

Ways to Save Energy

Coal, oil, and natural gas are all energy resources. A **resource** is something in nature that people can use. Energy resources are used to produce energy.

Coal, oil, and natural gas are called **fossil fuels**. They come from the remains of long-ago plants and animals. Fossil fuels can't be replaced. When they are used up, there will be no more. So it's important to save them and make them last longer. You save resources when you reduce the amount of energy you use.

MAIN IDEA AND DETAILS Why is it important to save energy?

▲ This boy is replacing an old light bulb with a new one. The new kind of bulb gives off the same amount of light as the old bulb but uses less energy.

Save Fossil Fuels
With a partner, design and make a table about fossil fuels. List as many fossil fuels as you can. Then list all the ways you can think of for people to use less of each fossil fuel. Share your table with your classmates.

Other Energy Resources

It took millions of years for fossil fuels to form. They are said to be **nonrenewable resources**, because no more fossil fuels can be made. *Nonrenewable* means "unable to be replaced."

Some resources are **renewable resources**, or resources that can be replaced. In the Investigate, you saw that wind can move things. Wind can turn windmills to produce electricity. Solar energy, or the sun's energy, can also be used to produce electricity.

MAIN IDEA AND DETAILS What are three nonrenewable resources?

This water is warmed by geothermal (jee•oh•THER•muhl) energy, or heat from deep within Earth. That same heat provides power to the city.

1. MAIN IDEA AND DETAILS Copy and complete this graphic organizer.

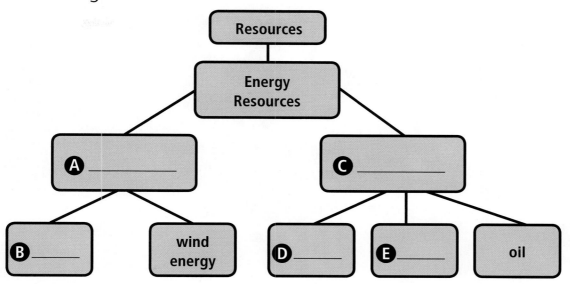

Resources

Energy Resources

A _____

C _____

B _____

wind energy

D _____

E _____

oil

2. SUMMARIZE Use your completed graphic organizer to write a lesson summary.

3. DRAW CONCLUSIONS As water plunges over Niagara Falls, it turns machines that produce electricity. Is moving water a renewable energy resource or a nonrenewable energy resource? Explain.

4. VOCABULARY Use each lesson vocabulary word in a sentence that correctly shows its meaning.

FCAT Prep

5. Which of the following is a nonrenewable energy resource?

A. electricity
B. coal
C. water
D. wind

Links

Writing

Persuasive
Some people think we should rely more on renewable energy resources than we do now. Write a **letter** to your local newspaper stating your opinion.

Literature

Saving Resources
Read a book about ways to save resources. Write a summary of the book to share with a first grader.

 For more links and activities, go to www.hspscience.com

SC.H.3.2.1.3.1 contributions of scientists, SC.H.3.2.3.3.1 scientific discoveries impact humans

Batteries Included

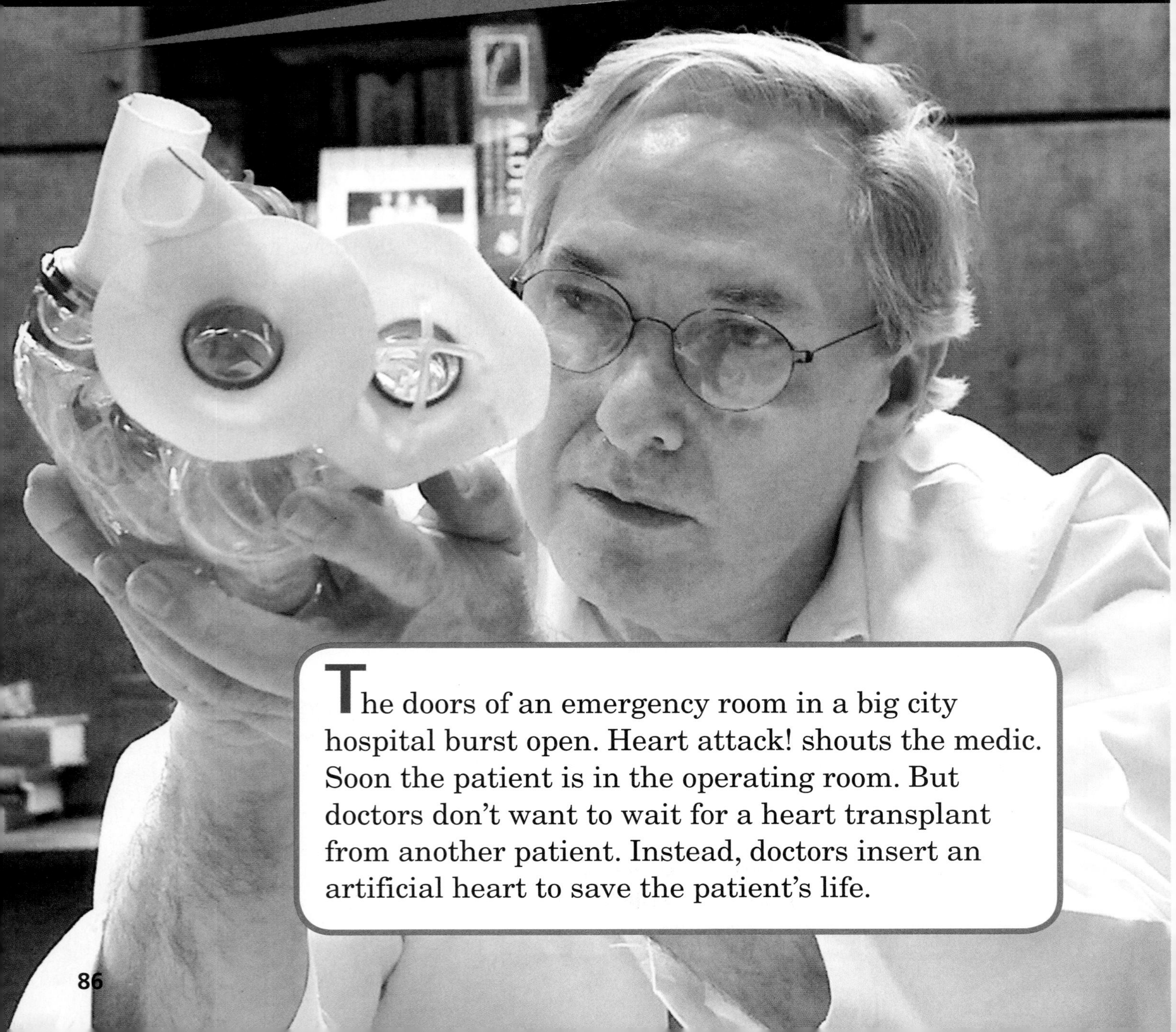

The doors of an emergency room in a big city hospital burst open. Heart attack! shouts the medic. Soon the patient is in the operating room. But doctors don't want to wait for a heart transplant from another patient. Instead, doctors insert an artificial heart to save the patient's life.

Although it hasn't happened yet, this type of scene could happen if the makers of the *AbioCor* are successful. The *AbioCor* is a battery-operated artificial heart that weighs about two pounds.

A Life-Saver

Scientists spent about 30 years designing the *AbioCor*. The replacement heart is different from earlier types of devices. This device fits completely inside the body of a patient. There is no need for wires to connect through the skin to an outside power source. This way a patient can be free to walk around without being hooked up to any machines.

Although the heart is not yet approved by the government, it is being tested in some patients. The first patient received an *AbioCor* about four years ago. Scientists hope that the government might soon approve the heart for use in humans.

THINK ABOUT IT

1. What other lifesaving devices might batteries be used in?

2. Why would patients want a replacement heart that runs on batteries instead of being plugged into a power source?

How It Works

The *AbioCor* gets its power from two lithium batteries. One battery is inside the patient and the other battery is outside the patient. Each battery has a set of coils. The outside battery pack can constantly recharge the inside battery. The outside battery does this by sending electricity from its coil, through the skin, to the coil of the inside battery.

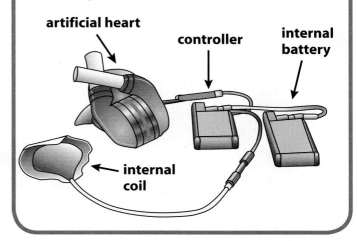

artificial heart

controller

internal battery

internal coil

Find out more! Log on to **www.hspscience.com**

A B C D E F F B C D E F

A Handy Idea

Ryan Patterson invented a special glove to help people who are deaf. Many people who are deaf use sign language to communicate. The glove can change sign language motions into written alphabet letters. The alphabet letters show up on a display screen.

Each finger of the glove has a computer chip on it. Tiny wires lead from the fingers to a small screen. The chips change the finger movements to alphabet letters. The letters are displayed on the screen. By the time he was 18, this young inventor had won many national science contests.

Spin-In Find out more! Log on to **www.hspscience.com**

SCIENCE Projects
for Home or School

You Can Do It!

Quick and Easy Project

Leaping Coin

Materials
- glass bottle
- quarter
- small bowl of water

Procedure

1. Put the bottle in a freezer for 10–15 minutes. Next dip the mouth part of the bottle in the water.

2. Wet the quarter by dipping it into the water. Put the quarter over the bottle's mouth.

3. Put your hands around the sides of the bottle, and keep them still. Record your observations.

Draw Conclusions
Why do you think this happened to the quarter?

Design Your Own Investigation

Learn About Solar Energy

What is solar energy? How can you measure it? Can you build a device that uses solar energy for power? Design one or more investigations that will help you find out more about solar energy. Then gather the materials you need, and carry out your investigations.

Review and FCAT Preparation

Vocabulary Review

Use the terms below to complete the sentences. The page numbers tell you where to look in the chapter if you need help.

energy p. 68
kinetic energy p. 70
potential energy p. 70
combustion p. 77
resource p. 83
fossil fuels p. 83
nonrenewable resource p. 84
renewable resource p. 84

1. Oil, coal, and natural gas are resources called _____.

2. A resource that can be replaced is said to be _____.

3. Energy of position is _____.

4. Gasoline gives off energy during _____.

5. Something in nature that people can use is a _____.

6. The ability to make something move or change is _____.

7. A resource that can't be replaced is a _____.

8. Energy of motion is _____.

Check Understanding

Write the letter of the best choice.

9. Where does the energy you need to grow come from?
   A. from potential energy
   B. from the food you eat
   C. from fossil fuels
   D. from wind energy

10. Which kind of energy does a book sitting on a shelf have?
    F. potential energy
    G. light energy
    H. speed energy
    I. kinetic energy

11. Which CD has kinetic energy?
    A. CD 1   **C.** CD 3
    B. CD 2   **D.** CD 4

12. MAIN IDEA AND DETAILS Which tool measures how hot or cold something is?
  F. an anemometer
  G. a light meter
  H. a sound meter
  I. a thermometer

13. Which kind of energy do people need to see things?
  A. sound energy
  B. light energy
  C. kinetic energy
  D. electrical energy

14. COMPARE AND CONTRAST Which resource can't be replaced?
  F. air
  G. oil
  H. water
  I. wind

15. Which resource is constantly being renewed?
  A. coal
  B. fossil fuels
  C. natural gas
  D. water

16. Which of the following takes millions of years to form?
  F. a plant
  G. a fossil fuel
  H. an energy need
  I. a hot spring

Inquiry Skills

17. Suppose it's a sunny July morning in your town. What hypothesis can you make about what will happen to the temperature? How could you check your hypothesis?

18. Suppose you have two ice cubes. You place one of the ice cubes outside in the direct sunlight and the other ice cube outside in the shade. Infer what will happen to each ice cube.

Read/Inquire/Explain

19. What changes can solar energy cause to a person lying in the sun?

20. List five ways you use energy in your home.

Chapter

3 Heat

Lesson 1 What Is Heat and How Is It Measured?

Lesson 2 How Does Thermal Energy Move?

Lesson 3 How Is Thermal Energy Used?

Vocabulary

FCAT-Tested
heat
friction

Other Terms
temperature
Celsius
thermal energy
conduction
conductor
insulator

What do YOU wonder?

This fire is part of a controlled burn. It was started by people who take care of the forest. Why might they have done this?

What Is Heat and How Is It Measured?

Fast Fact

Hot Times On average, the hottest days in the United States are in July and August. In the Investigate, you will make a model of a thermometer, which measures temperature.

Measuring Temperature

Materials
- I-L plastic bottle
- clear drinking straw
- red food coloring
- clear plastic cup
- metric ruler
- clay
- dropper
- water

Procedure

1. Fill a bottle with water. Add 10 drops of food coloring. Insert a straw $\frac{1}{4}$ of its length into the bottle, and seal the opening around the straw with clay.

2. Half-fill a cup with water and food coloring. Using the dropper, put water into the straw until you see water above the clay.

3. Using a pencil, mark the water level in the straw.

4. Take your "thermometer" to a different place. Leave it there for 15 minutes. Without squeezing the bottle, make a mark on the straw, and write the number 1 to measure the water level. Repeat this step three times, numbering the water level marks 2, 3, 4.

Step 1

Step 4

Draw Conclusions

1. What happened to the water level in the straw at each location?

2. **Inquiry Skill** Scientists use numbers to put things in order. Use the numbers you recorded to order the locations from warmest to coldest.

Investigate Further

The temperature outside may change from morning to afternoon. Predict how much it will change today. Use your thermometer to test your prediction.

SC.H.1.2.1.3.1 keeping accurate records, **SC.H.1.2.2.3.1** following experimental design, **SC.H.1.2.2.3.2** using scientific instruments, **SC.H.1.2.5.3.1** uses models, **SC.H.3.2.2.3.1** collects data

95

Reading in Science

SC.A.1.2.1.3.1 measurement, SC.B.1.2.2.3.1 heat and light,
SC.B.1.2.2.3.2 forms of energy, SC.B.1.2.3.3.1 sun energy/heat
and light, LA.A.2.2.1 main idea and details

VOCABULARY

temperature p. 96

Celsius p. 97

thermal energy p. 98

heat p. 98

SCIENCE CONCEPTS

▶ what heat is

▶ how temperature is measured

Focus Skill **READING FOCUS SKILL**

MAIN IDEA AND DETAILS Look for details about heat and temperature.

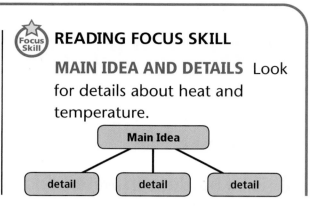

Measuring Temperature

Has anyone ever taken your body temperature? Have you ever checked the temperature outside? **Temperature** is the measure of how hot or cold something is. Temperature can be measured with a thermometer.

On these pages, you can see different types of thermometers. Many thermometers used today have equal divisions printed on them, much as rulers do. Instead of centimeters, degrees are used to divide thermometers. Two scales can be used on a thermometer, Fahrenheit or Celsius.

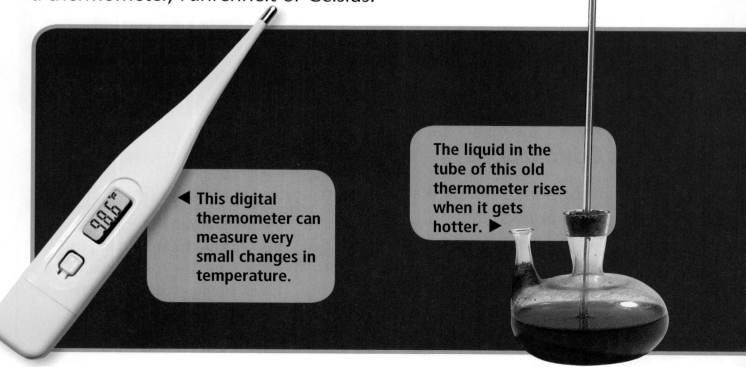

◄ This digital thermometer can measure very small changes in temperature.

The liquid in the tube of this old thermometer rises when it gets hotter. ▶

Scientists usually use the Celsius scale. **Celsius** is the metric temperature scale. On this scale, water boils at 100°C. It freezes at 0°C.

It's important to record the scale that is used to measure temperature. This way, temperature information can be shared and compared. Suppose one scientist sent data about temperatures to another scientist without telling which scale was used. What might happen?

 MAIN IDEA AND DETAILS What tool do you use to measure temperature?

Math in Science
Interpret Data

How Fast Does It Chirp?
The speed at which a cricket chirps depends on the temperature. Look at the table. As the temperature goes up, does a cricket chirp more quickly or more slowly?

Chirps Per Second	Approximate Temperature
1	11°C
2	19°C
3	28°C

◄ **This outdoor thermometer has big numbers that you can read through the window.**

The numbers on this meat thermometer go up to 200°F! ►

◄ **The number of floating bubbles changes as the temperature goes up or down.**

Heat

Think about sitting outside on a sunny day. The warmth from the sun might cause your skin temperature to go up.

Like all matter, your skin is made up of tiny particles. These particles are always moving. Temperature measures how fast the particles are moving. If the particles are moving very fast, the temperature goes up. When the temperature is high, the particles have more energy.

The form of energy that moves particles of matter is called **thermal energy**. The movement of thermal energy is called **heat**. Thermal energy always flows from hotter to cooler objects.

When you sit outside on a sunny day, the thermal energy moves from the sun to your skin. The particles in your skin move faster. You feel this as warmth.

◀ The particles in melted glass move freely. The man can change the shape of the hot glass.

98

What happens to the particles in an ice cube when you heat it? The energy from the heat makes the particles move faster. The temperature goes up. Next, the ice cube melts. After the ice becomes a liquid, the particles move even faster, and they are farther apart. If you keep heating the water, the particles will move so fast that they fly apart. The water then becomes a gas.

 MAIN IDEA AND DETAILS What is heat?

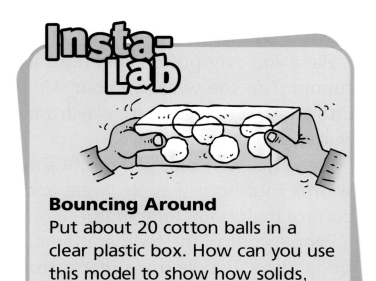

Bouncing Around
Put about 20 cotton balls in a clear plastic box. How can you use this model to show how solids, liquids, and gases are different?

When the glass cools, its particles move slowly. It becomes a solid with a fixed shape. ▶

Controlling Thermal Energy

Have you ever gotten cold right after you stopped running? As the sweat on your skin begins to change into a gas, it carries heat away from your body. This makes you feel cooler.

If you get too cold, you might shiver. The motion warms your body. People sweat and shiver to help control their body temperature.

People control the temperature outside their bodies, too. People use a *thermostat* to control the temperature in a room. It turns the heater or air conditioner off or on.

 MAIN IDEA AND DETAILS How does your body control its temperature?

Science Up Close

How a Thermostat Works

Inside the thermostat is a coil. It's made of strips of two different metals. Both strips expand as they get warmer. The strip on the inside of the coil expands faster. That makes the coil uncurl.

When the coil uncurls far enough, it flips a switch. The switch turns the heater off or the air conditioner on. As the room cools, the coil contracts. This moves the switch to the other position.

As the temperature in a room changes, the thermostat turns heating or cooling devices on or off.

 For more links and activities, go to www.hspscience.com

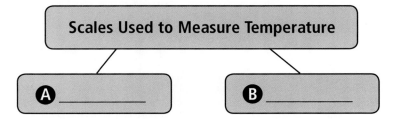

1. MAIN IDEA AND DETAILS Copy and complete the graphic organizer.

Scales Used to Measure Temperature

Ⓐ _____   Ⓑ _____

2. SUMMARIZE Use your completed graphic organizer to write a lesson summary.

3. DRAW CONCLUSIONS Why is it important to know which thermometer scale people use to measure temperatures?

4. VOCABULARY Write a definition of each vocabulary term in your own words.

FCAT Prep

5. Which of the following is a source of thermal energy?
- **A.** a thermostat
- **B.** a thermometer
- **C.** the sun
- **D.** a refrigerator

Links

Writing

Narrative

Write a personal **story** about a time you learned how warm the sun's rays can be. Maybe you had a great picnic outside with your family or you found out that crayons melt when they are left in sunlight too long.

Social Studies

Celsius Picture Book

Research more about Anders Celsius, a scientist from the country of Sweden. Write a picture book for a first grader to read. Make sure to add colorful pictures on each page of your book.

 For more links and activities, go to **www.hspscience.com**

How Does Thermal Energy Move?

Up and Down Each lamp has a light bulb in its base. Heat from the bulb warms the goo, which rises. When the goo cools at the top, it falls. That's one way thermal energy moves from one place to another. In the Investigate, you will observe another way.

Getting Warmer?

Materials • safety goggles • wooden spoon • plastic spoon • metal spoon
• 3 plastic foam cups • ceramic mug with handle
• plastic mug with handle • metal mug with handle • hot water

Procedure

1. CAUTION: **Put on safety goggles.**

2. Touch the three spoons. Record your observations.

3. CAUTION: Be careful with hot water. Fill three plastic foam cups with hot water. Place one spoon in each cup. Wait 1 minute.

4. Gently touch each spoon. Record your observations.

5. Touch the three mugs. Record your observations.

6. Fill each mug with hot water. Carefully touch each handle every 30 seconds for 2 minutes. Record what you observe.

Step 2

Step 6

Draw Conclusions

1. Compare your observations of the spoons and the mugs before and after the water was used.

2. **Inquiry Skill** Draw a conclusion about the way thermal energy travels through different substances. Write your conclusion down and compare it with a classmate's.

Investigate Further

Repeat the Investigate, using ice-cold water instead of hot water. Before you add the water, predict what will happen in each case.

SC.H.1.2.1.3.1 keeping accurate records,
SC.H.1.2.4.3.1 comparing/contrasting,
SC.H.2.2.1.3.1 makes predictions

103

Reading in Science

SC.B.1.2.6.3.1 temperature,
LA.A.2.2.1 main idea and details

VOCABULARY

conduction p. 105

conductor p. 105

insulator p. 106

SCIENCE CONCEPTS

▶ how thermal energy moves from one place or object to another

Focus Skill **READING FOCUS SKILL**

MAIN IDEA AND DETAILS Look for details about the movement of thermal energy.

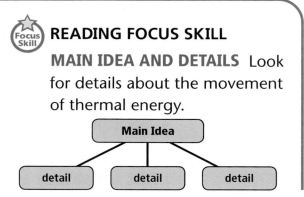

Ways Thermal Energy Moves

In the last lesson, you learned that heat is the movement of thermal energy. There are three ways thermal energy can move.

Sometimes, thermal energy travels from particle to particle in a solid. Or, particles of a gas or liquid can carry it from one place to another. It can even move through empty space. That's how heat from the sun reaches Earth.

Focus Skill **MAIN IDEA AND DETAILS** What are the three ways thermal energy can move?

Thermal energy moves from the fire through the air to cook the hot dogs. ▼

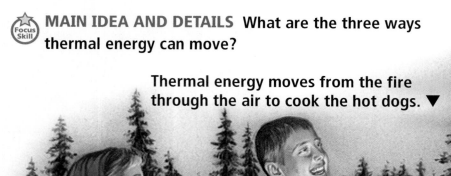

Conductors

To cook an egg, you put it in a pan and turn on the stove. The heat from the burner makes the pan hot. Soon, the thermal energy moves through the hot pan to the cold egg. The egg gains thermal energy from the pan. Eventually, the egg and the pan are the same temperature. The movement of thermal energy between objects that touch each other is **conduction**.

A pan is used for cooking because it is made of metal, such as iron or copper. Thermal energy moves easily through most metals. An object that thermal energy can move through easily is called a **conductor**.

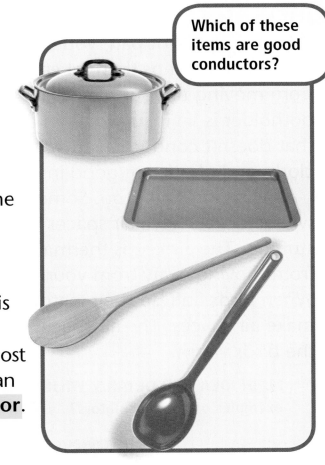

Which of these items are good conductors?

MAIN IDEA AND DETAILS What are two materials that are good conductors?

Heat moves from the burner to the pan to the food by conduction.

Insulators

To pick up a hot pan, you use a potholder. It keeps thermal energy from moving to your hand. The potholder is an **insulator**—an object that doesn't conduct heat well. Wood, cloth, and plastic are good insulators.

Air is an insulator, too. Some winter jackets have air spaces in their stuffing. The air keeps thermal energy from moving away from your body. When birds fluff up their feathers, they make air spaces. The air spaces keep the birds warm.

 MAIN IDEA AND DETAILS What are two examples of good insulators?

Feeling the Heat
Place small pieces of butter on top of a sponge, a piece of wood, and a metal jar lid. Float each object in a shallow pan of hot water. What happens to the butter? Why?

The cover wrapped around this pot is an insulator. ▼

Water seeps in between the wet suit and the surfer's skin. This water warms up and acts as an insulator, along with the wet suit.

106

1. MAIN IDEA AND DETAILS Copy and complete the graphic organizer.

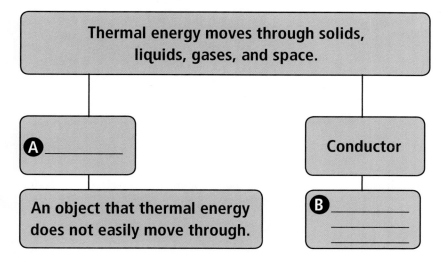

Thermal energy moves through solids, liquids, gases, and space.

A _____

An object that thermal energy does not easily move through.

Conductor

B _____

2. SUMMARIZE Write a summary of this lesson. Begin with this sentence: There are three ways heat can move.

3. DRAW CONCLUSIONS Tasha had a foam cup of hot cocoa. The cocoa stayed hot, and the cup didn't get too hot to hold. Explain why.

4. VOCABULARY Use the vocabulary words in this lesson to make a crossword puzzle.

FCAT Prep

5. Read/Inquire/Explain Make a list of 10 different kitchen items. Next to each item, write whether the item is a good conductor or not.

Links

Writing

Narrative

Write a **description** of what it feels like to sit by a campfire. Include adjectives to make your description exciting.

Math

Solve a Problem

At 10:52 A.M., LaShondra put a pot of water on the stove. The water in the pot began to boil at 11:07 A.M.. How long did it take the water to boil?

 For more links and activities, go to www.hspscience.com

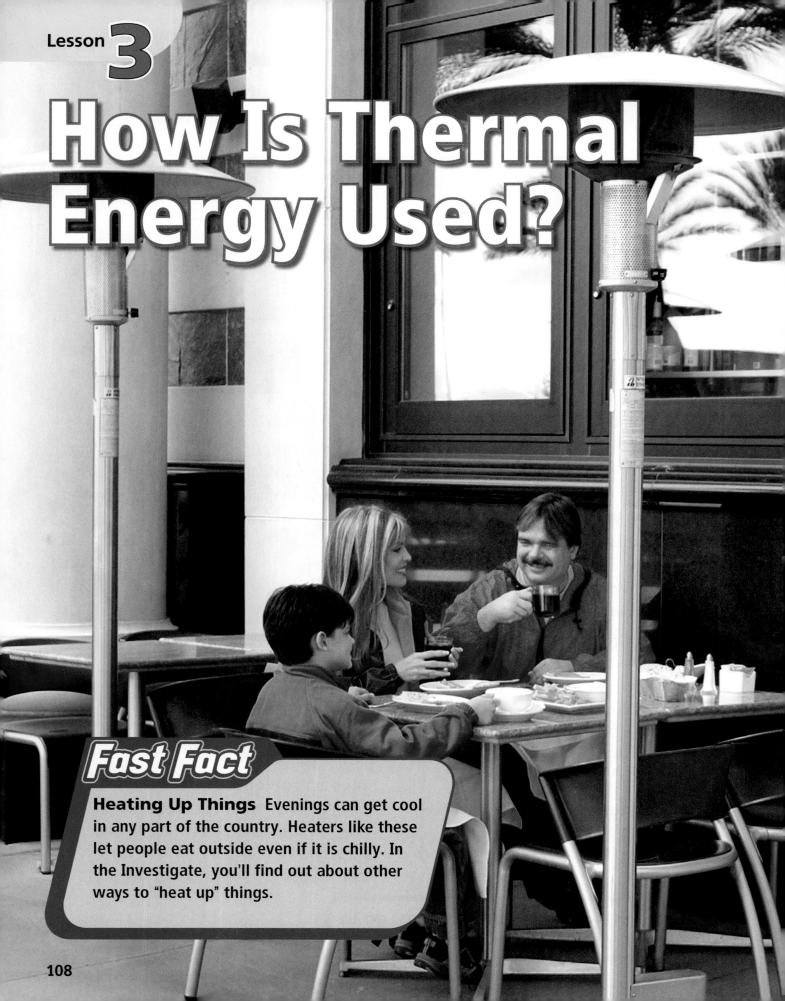

How Is Thermal Energy Used?

Fast Fact

Heating Up Things Evenings can get cool in any part of the country. Heaters like these let people eat outside even if it is chilly. In the Investigate, you'll find out about other ways to "heat up" things.

Where's the Heat?

Materials • metal button • wool • penny • paper

Procedure

1. Hold the palms of your hands together for 10 seconds. Do your hands feel warm or cold, dry or damp? **Record** what you **observe**.

2. **Hypothesize** what you would feel if you rubbed your hands together. Test your **hypothesis**. **Record** what you **observe**.

3. **Hypothesize** what would happen if you rubbed a button and a piece of wool together.

4. Rub a button and a piece of wool together for 10 seconds. Touch the button. Touch the wool. **Record** what you **observe**.

5. Repeat Steps 3 and 4, using a penny and a sheet of paper.

Step 2

Step 4

Draw Conclusions

1. What kind of changes did you **observe** in each step?

2. **Inquiry Skill** What knowledge and experiences did you use to help you **hypothesize**?

Investigate Further

How does the amount of time you rub things together affect the outcome? **Plan and conduct a simple investigation** to find out.

SC.B.1.2.4.3.1 how heat is produced,
SC.H.1.2.1.3.1 keeping accurate records,
SC.H.1.2.2.3.1 following experimental design

VOCABULARY	**SCIENCE CONCEPTS**	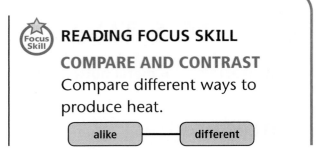 **READING FOCUS SKILL**
friction p. 110	▶ how heat can be produced	**COMPARE AND CONTRAST** Compare different ways to produce heat.

Focus Skill

alike ▬ different

Ways to Make Things Hot

How can you warm something up? You might put it in a hot oven or set it in the sun. What happens if you need something heated up that can't go in the oven, such as your hands? What if it isn't a sunny day? There are many other ways thermal energy can be produced.

In the Investigate, you produced thermal energy by using friction. **Friction** is the resistance between moving objects. Friction produces heat.

◀ Before matches were invented, people used machines like these to make fire by using friction.

A soldering iron changes electrical energy into thermal energy. You can use the heat to melt metals so they stick together.

Thermal energy can also be produced from electricity. An iron uses electricity to get hot. Heat from the iron helps remove the wrinkles in clothes. An electric blanket uses electricity to keep you warm during cold nights.

The mixing of chemicals can also produce thermal energy. Some heat packs produce thermal energy in this way. When the chemicals in the pack are mixed, the pack gets warm and is ready to be used.

COMPARE AND CONTRAST Compare and contrast how an iron and a heat pack produce thermal energy.

Insta-Lab

How Hot? Rub a block of wood with a piece of cloth for 30 seconds. Touch the wood. Record how hot the wood feels. Now rub the wood with sandpaper for 30 seconds. Touch the wood. Compare how hot the wood felt when rubbed with the cloth and the sandpaper.

Ways to Use Thermal Energy

People have used thermal energy for millions of years. Before ovens were invented, people used fire to cook food.

People use thermal energy today. If you have ever sat by a fire to get warm, you have used thermal energy. When you take a warm bath or shower, you use thermal energy to heat the water.

Scientists are researching ways that can save resources by using the sun for heat. Some people use solar panels to heat the water used in their homes.

COMPARE AND CONTRAST How do the ways people use thermal energy today contrast with the ways people used it in the past?

The machines on this page use thermal energy. ▼

1. COMPARE AND CONTRAST Copy and complete the graphic organizer.

Ways Thermal Energy Can Be Produced	Examples
Sun	**A** _____
Electricity	**B** _____
Chemicals	heating pack

2. SUMMARIZE Write two sentences that tell what this lesson is mainly about.

3. DRAW CONCLUSIONS Why was fire important to people before electricity was discovered?

4. VOCABULARY Write a sentence using the term *friction*.

FCAT Prep

5. Which of the following uses electricity to produce heat?
  A. the sun
  B. a match
  C. a clothes dryer
  D. a refrigerator

Links

Writing

Persuasive

Think about the electrical appliance that is the most important to you. Write a **paragraph** or two stating your opinion on why this appliance is important.

Math

Recognize a Pattern

A space heater produces 4 units of thermal energy in 2 hours and 12 units of thermal energy in 6 hours. How much thermal energy will it produce in 12 hours?

 For more links and activities, go to **www.hspscience.com**

SCIENCE Spin™ from WEEKLY READER®

Technology

SC.B.1.2.6.3.1 temperature,
SC.H.3.2.3.3.1 scientific discoveries impact humans,
SC.H.3.2.4.3.1 solving problems/new ideas

Technology Delivers HOT PIZZA

You know that thermal energy always moves from hot objects to cold objects. This means thermal energy moves from a hot pizza to the cooler air around it. In the process, the hot pizza gets cold. And who wants cold pizza?

We Want It Hot

A recent survey found that more than half of all take-out food was delivered to homes rather than picked up. Keeping pizza hot while the delivery person finds the right house is sometimes a problem. Customers want their food delivered fast, and they want it to arrive piping hot. Companies that deliver cold pizzas are soon out of business. So it's good news that science is helping pizza companies deliver your pizza hot to your door.

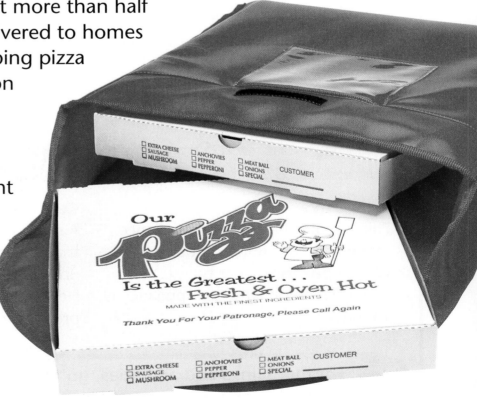

Our Pizza
Is the Greatest...
Fresh & Oven Hot
MADE WITH THE FINEST INGREDIENTS
Thank You For Your Patronage, Please Call Again

Keeping Thermal Energy In

The hot bag is made with three layers of material. The inside liner, made of nylon and vinyl, reduces condensation. It also has a shiny silver color to reflect the heat of the food back inside the container.

The middle layer is a dense foam. This layer is the insulator for the bag. Thermal energy doesn't move easily through the foam. That means the heat is trapped inside the bag. The foam also prevents air from moving into or out of the bag. Even though the inside of the bag is hot, the outside of the bag remains cool and easy to handle.

The outside of the bag is made of heavy vinyl. This makes the bag waterproof. The bag can be closed and sealed shut, keeping even more thermal energy in. The hot bag also has two small openings that allow steam to escape. They keep the pizza crust from becoming soggy on its trip to your home.

THINK ABOUT IT

1. What other types of fast-food companies could use the hot bag to help them in their deliveries?

2. Would these bags be helpful for delivering ice cream? Explain.

Spin In — Find out more! Log on to **www.hspscience.com**

A Measuring Milestone

Anders Celsius

When you look at a thermometer and you see a letter C, thank Anders Celsius. This Swedish scientist designed a scale of measuring temperatures more than 200 years ago. The Celsius scale is used in many countries today.

Celsius first stuck the bulb end of a thermometer into snow. Once the mercury stopped moving, he marked the level on the thermometer. He then stuck the thermometer into boiling water. Again, when the mercury stopped moving, he marked the thermometer.

Celsius divided the space between the two marks into 100 equal parts. On the Celsius scale, the freezing point of water is 0 degrees. The boiling point is 100 degrees.

Career   Insulation Workers

The job done by insulation workers is almost never seen, but it is always felt. Insulation workers install special materials in the walls and ceilings of buildings. The special material helps keep the heat inside when it's cold outside. It also helps keep cool air inside when it's hot outside.

Spin In

Find out more! Log on to www.hspscience.com

You Can Do It!

Quick and Easy Project

Color Matters

Procedure

1. Place the pieces of paper on a cookie sheet. Make sure the pieces of paper are all the same size.

2. Put an ice cube on each of the pieces of paper.

3. Place the cookie sheet in a sunny area.

4. Every three minutes, record what happens to the ice cubes.

Materials

- cookie sheet
- 3 pieces of paper: red, black, and white
- 3 ice cubes all the same size

Draw Conclusions

How did the different colors of paper change how fast the ice cubes melted? How might this help you when getting dressed to go and play outside on a warm day?

Design Your Own Investigation

Keeping Heat from Moving

Do insulators prevent the conduction of heat? Or do they just slow it down? Design an experiment that will help you find out. Then gather the materials you need, and do your experiment. Write a conclusion after you finish your experiment.

Review and FCAT Preparation

Vocabulary Review

Fill in each blank with a word from the list below. The page numbers after each word tell where to look in the chapter if you need help.

Celsius p. 97
thermal energy p. 98
heat p. 98
conductor p. 105
insulator p. 106
friction p. 110

1. An object that allows thermal energy to move easily through it is a _____.

2. The metric system uses a temperature scale called _____.

3. The form of energy that moves particles of matter is _____.

4. A potholder is an example of an _____.

5. Rubbing your hands together is an example of _____.

6. The flow of thermal energy from a warmer to a cooler substance is _____.

Check Understanding

Write the letter of the best choice.

7. How do particles in boiling water compare to particles in ice?
   A. They are moving slower.
   B. They are moving faster.
   C. There are more of them.
   D. There are fewer of them.

8. Why does a diver wear a wet suit?
   F. to keep from sinking
   G. to keep out cold
   H. to keep in thermal energy
   I. to keep from getting cuts

9. **COMPARE AND CONTRAST** In which beaker are particles moving the slowest?
   A. Beaker 1   C. Beaker 3
   B. Beaker 2   D. Beaker 4

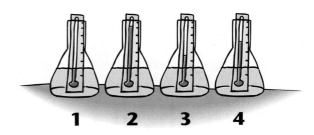

1   2   3   4

10. Which is a reasonable temperature for your classroom?
    F. 100°C   H. 0°F
    G. 20°C   I. 212°F

11. How many different ways can heat move from place to place?
   A. two
   C. five
   B. three
   D. six

12. Which object is a conductor?
   F. blanket
   H. sweater
   G. oven mitt
   I. metal spoon

13. **MAIN IDEA AND DETAILS** In the picture, between which items is conduction happening?
   A. the fire and the pot
   B. the wood and the pot
   C. the pot and the water
   D. the fire and the pot hanger

14. What must your hands do to produce friction?
   F. rub together
   G. be close together
   H. touch one another
   I. be insulators

15. What can you mix together to produce thermal energy?
   A. chemicals
   C. sticks
   B. liquids
   D. gases

16. Water boils at_____.
   F. 100°F
   H. 0°C
   G. 0°F
   I. 100°C

Inquiry Skills

17. You leave a pan full of hot water on the counter overnight. Predict how the temperature of the pan, the water, and the countertop will compare the next morning. Explain your prediction.

18. From the pictures, infer which day the water in the pool will be warmer. Explain.

Monday   Tuesday

Read/Inquire/Explain

19. Two pots of water are put on a stove. The pots are identical. The water in the pots is at the same temperature. Both burners are set at the same heat level. Five minutes later, the water in Pot 1 is boiling; the water in Pot 2 is not. What can you infer about Pot 2?

20. List five ways that you use thermal energy in your home.

Forces and Motion

PHYSICAL SCIENCE

 The chapters in this unit address these Grade Level Expectations from the Florida Sunshine State Standards.

Chapter 4 Forces and Motion

SC.C.1.2.1.3.1   describes the motion of various objects (for example, forward, circular, wave).

SC.C.1.2.2.3.1   understands the characteristics of waves (for example, crest, trough, length).

SC.C.2.2.2.3.1   knows that an object may move in a straight line at a constant speed, speed up, slow down, or change direction dependent on the net force acting on the object.

Chapter 5 Work and Machines

SC.C.2.2.1.3.1   knows the six types of simple machines (screw, inclined plane, wedge, pulley, lever, and wheel and axle).

The investigations and experiences in this unit also address many of the Grade Level Expectations in Strand H, The Nature of Science.

Science in Florida

Tampa

Dear Ryan,

    I had so much fun last night at the Florida State Fair in Tampa! I spun around and around on the tea cups. The faster we spun, the more I felt as if I were going to fall out of the ride.

    There was also a roller coaster that I was scared to ride. Dad went on it with me, and then I wanted to do it again!

See you soon,

Jamal

The Sunshine State

USA

FCAT Writing

Writing Situation
Think about recess. Write a story about what happened on the playground.

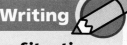

Experiment!

Make an Obstacle Course An obstacle course is full of forces and motion. To get through, you have to move up and down, back and forth, and left and right. Try building an obstacle course for a ball. Can you control how quickly a ball moves through your course? How does the ball move in different ways? Plan and conduct an experiment to find out.

121

Chapter 4

Forces and Motion

Vocabulary

FCAT-Tested

force
gravity

Other Terms

motion
distance
speed
weight
wave
crest
trough
wavelength

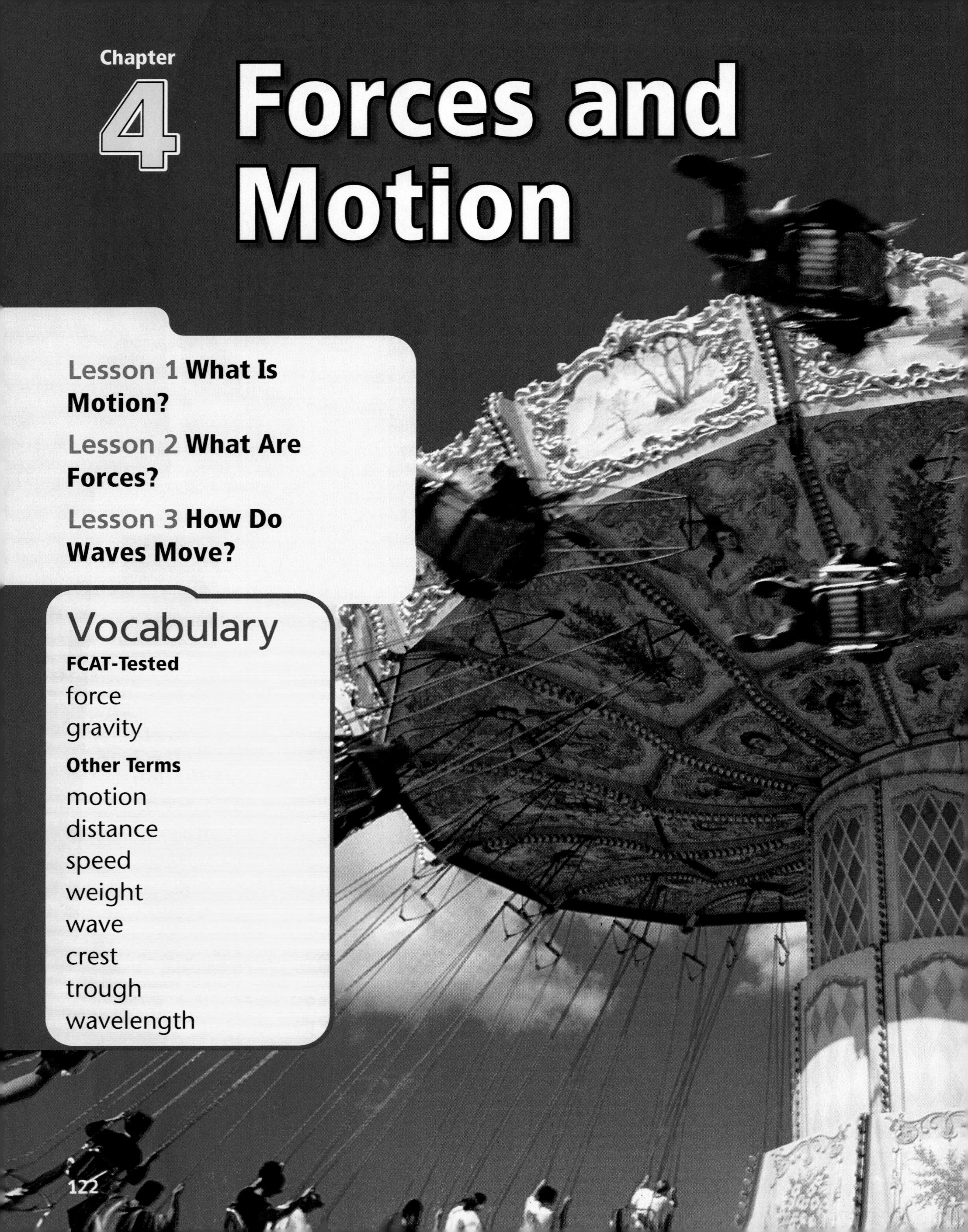

What do YOU wonder?

To build a ride like this one, you need to understand forces and motion. What causes the swings to move farther from the center pole? What brings them back to the center pole?

What Is Motion?

Fast Fact

Speedy Pinball In the game of pinball, a ball can reach a speed of 145 kilometers (90 mi) per hour! The ball moves in many directions. In the Investigate, you will experiment with several kinds of motion.

Make It Move

Materials • clay • string (about 25 cm long)

Procedure

1. Mold a piece of clay into a ball. Mold another piece into a ring.

2. Make the ball move in a straight line. Make it move at different speeds. **Record** your **observations**.

3. Make your ball zigzag. **Record** your **observations**.

4. Thread the string through the hole in the ring. Tie the string to the ring. Hold the string by the end. Make the ring swing back and forth and then in a circle. **Record** your **observations**.

5. **Communicate** your **observations** by making drawings of each movement.

Draw Conclusions

1. Make a table like the one shown. **Record** how you made the objects move.

2. **Inquiry Skill** When you **interpret data**, you explain what the data means. What did you do to make the objects move in different directions?

Step 4

Motion Table

Path of Motion	How the object was pushed or pulled
straight and fast	
straight and slow	
zigzag	
back and forth	
round and round	

Investigate Further

Plan an experiment with a different object, by itself and on the string. Try to move it each way you moved the ball and the ring.

SC.H.1.2.1.3.1 keeping accurate records,
SC.H.1.2.2.3.1 following experimental design,
SC.H.1.2.5.3.1 uses diagrams, **SC.H.3.2.2.3.1** collects data **125**

VOCABULARY

motion p. 127
distance p. 128
speed p. 130

SCIENCE CONCEPTS

▶ what motion is
▶ how distance and time affect speed

READING FOCUS SKILL

COMPARE AND CONTRAST Look for different ways to describe how objects move.

| alike | | different |

Types of Motion

Suppose you are on the playground. What kinds of motion do you see? A girl throws a ball forward. It curves up and then falls down. A boy bounces a basketball. It goes up and down. Some children run fast and zigzag as they play tag. Others go back and forth on swings or up and down on seesaws. Still others go round and round on a merry-go-round.

Straight-line motion

You can observe many kinds of motion on a playground. The next time you are on a playground, think about all the ways you move.

Back-and-forth motion

Zigzag motion

Round-and-round motion

An object can keep traveling in one direction, or it can change direction. Objects can move fast or slowly.

Every object has a position, or location. A school bus stops at the same position every day, so you know where to wait for it. You know the position of the cafeteria in your school. The cafeteria's position does not change. What is your position right now?

Motion is a change of position. To get to the cafeteria, you would need to change your position. You would need to *move.* When you ride a bike down the street, the bike changes position. It is in motion. If you park the bike in a bike rack, the bike is no longer changing position. It is no longer in motion.

COMPARE AND CONTRAST What is one way in which each kind of motion is different from the others? How are all kinds of motion the same?

Fast motion and slow motion

Distance, Direction, and Time

Suppose you are on a trip with your family. You ask, "How far do we have to drive to get to the next city?" What you want to know is the distance. **Distance** is how far it is from one location to another.

Distance is often measured in inches, yards, or miles. Scientists use units of centimeters, meters, and kilometers. You can use a ruler to measure distances.

An important thing to know about motion is its direction. Your family's car is going *east* from Chicago to New York. Your friend throws a ball *up* into the air.

Math in Science
Interpret Data

The graph shows the average speeds of different types of dogs. How much faster is the cocker spaniel than the basset hound?

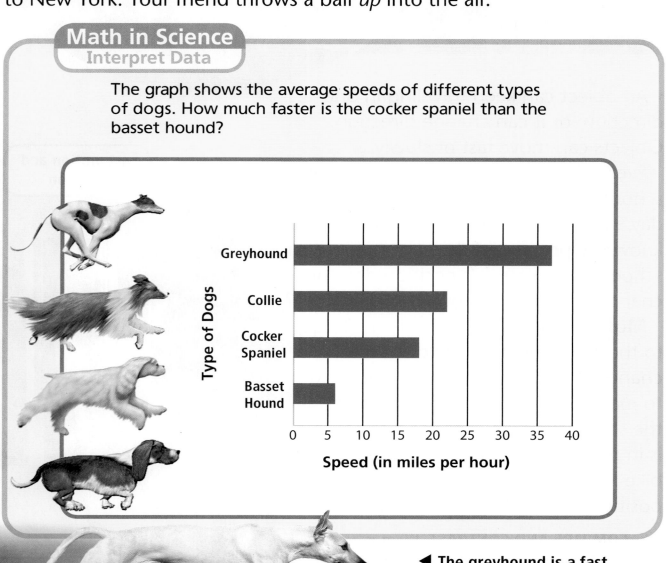

◄ The greyhound is a fast runner. It can cover a long distance in a short time.

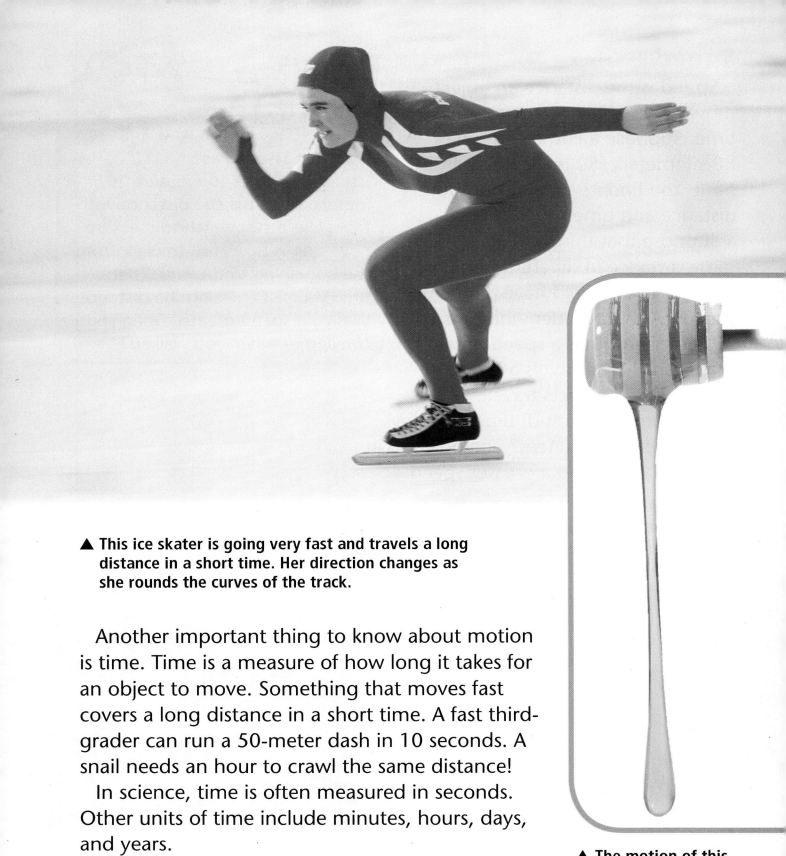

▲ This ice skater is going very fast and travels a long distance in a short time. Her direction changes as she rounds the curves of the track.

Another important thing to know about motion is time. Time is a measure of how long it takes for an object to move. Something that moves fast covers a long distance in a short time. A fast third-grader can run a 50-meter dash in 10 seconds. A snail needs an hour to crawl the same distance!

In science, time is often measured in seconds. Other units of time include minutes, hours, days, and years.

COMPARE AND CONTRAST You are walking home from school. Your parent is driving from your home to school. How is your motion different from your parent's?

▲ The motion of this honey is slow. Its direction is straight down.

Speed

Speed is the distance an object moves in a certain period of time. Suppose a lion could run 80 kilometers (50 miles) in one hour. You find its speed using both distance and time.

Suppose that things travel the same distance in different amounts of time. They would have different speeds. A third-grader who runs the 50-meter dash has a speed greater than a snail that travels 50 meters.

What if two objects traveled for the same amount of time but they went different distances? The object that traveled farther had a greater speed.

Insta-Lab

Getting There Fast
Use a meterstick to measure 10 meters. Mark off the distance with tape. Use a stopwatch to measure how long it takes you to walk from the beginning to the end. Then time yourself crawling the distance. Was your speed greater when you crawled or when you walked?

⭐ **Focus Skill**

COMPARE AND CONTRAST Suppose a zebra runs 15 kilometers in one hour. A grizzly bear runs 10 kilometers in one hour. Which animal has the greater speed?

A single beat of a hummingbird's wing takes less than a second.

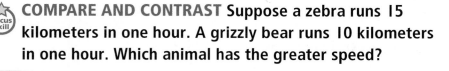

Plants turn toward the sun at such a low speed that you cannot see them move. This motion is measured in days.

1. COMPARE AND CONTRAST Draw and complete this graphic organizer.

Types of Motion	Straight-line	Zigzag	Round and Round	Back and Forth
Example	**A** _____	**B** _____	**C** _____	**D** _____

2. SUMMARIZE Use the vocabulary words to write a summary of the lesson.

3. DRAW CONCLUSIONS Would it be faster to zigzag or to walk in a straight line from one location to another? Why?

4. VOCABULARY Write a quiz question that uses all the vocabulary terms.

FCAT Prep

5. What changes when an object moves?
   - **A.** its direction
   - **B.** its height
   - **C.** its position
   - **D.** its shape

Links

Writing

Expository

Write a paragraph that **describes** the kinds of motion you see when you go outside at recess. Describe the speeds and distances of the people and things you observe.

Math

Solve Problems

Use a meterstick to measure the distance from one side of your classroom to the other. If you cross the classroom four times, how far will you walk?

 For more links and activities, go to www.hspscience.com

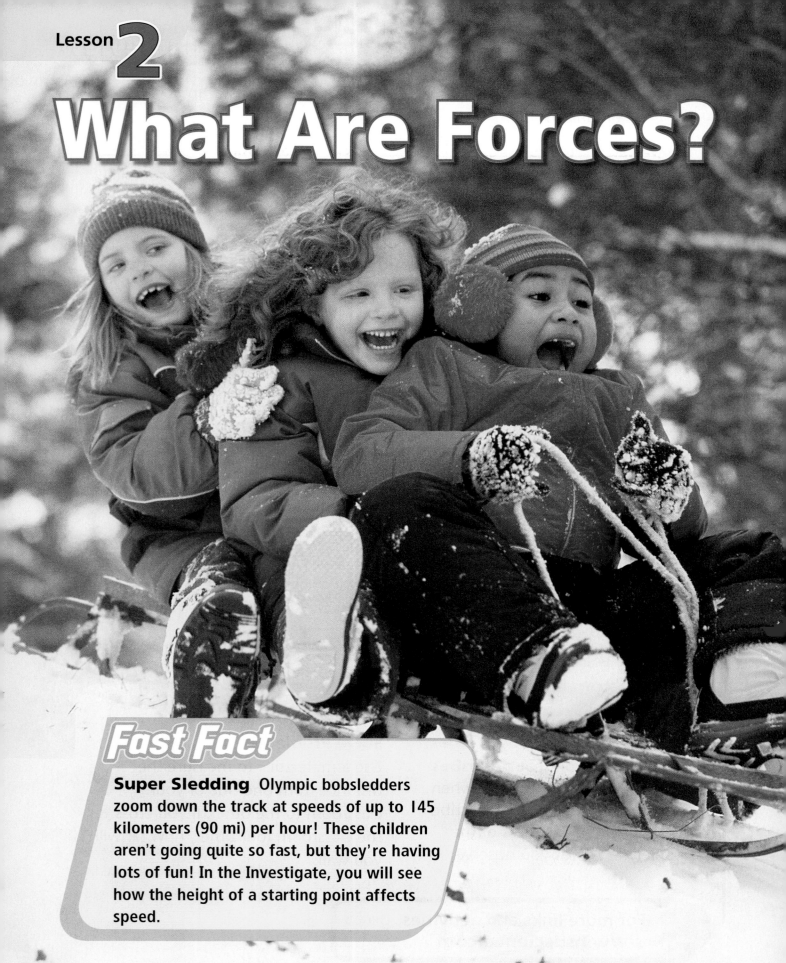

What Are Forces?

Fast Fact

Super Sledding Olympic bobsledders zoom down the track at speeds of up to 145 kilometers (90 mi) per hour! These children aren't going quite so fast, but they're having lots of fun! In the Investigate, you will see how the height of a starting point affects speed.

Speed Ramp

Materials • books • cookie sheet • block • metric ruler
• penny • rubber eraser

Procedure

1. Make a table like the one shown.

2. Stack the books about 5 cm high. **Record** how high the pile is.

3. Work with a partner. Place the penny, the block, and the eraser at the top of the cookie sheet. Hold the objects so they don't move.

4. Lay one end of the cookie sheet on the books to make a ramp. Let the objects go at the same time.

5. **Record** how fast each item traveled. Use words such as *fastest*, *slowest*, and *did not move*.

6. Add books to make the stack about 10 cm high. Repeat Steps 2–5.

7. Add books to make the stack about 15 cm high. Repeat Steps 2–5.

Speed Table		
	Height of Books	Speed
Penny		
Block		
Eraser		

Step 3

Draw Conclusions

1. **Compare** the speeds of the sliding objects. **Record** your **observations**.

2. **Inquiry Skill** When you **infer**, you make a guess based on what you **observe**. **Infer** why the speeds of the objects changed.

Investigate Further

Predict how your results would change if you coated the cookie sheet with oil. Try it. **Record** your **observations**.

SC.H.1.2.1.3.1 keeping accurate records, **SC.H.1.2.2.3.1** following experimental design, **SC.H.1.2.2.3.2** using scientific instruments, **SC.H.1.2.3.3.1** working collaboratively, **SC.H.1.2.4.3.1** comparing/contrasting, **SC.H.2.2.1.3.1** makes predictions

VOCABULARY

force p. 134
gravity p. 138
weight p. 138

SCIENCE CONCEPTS

▶ what the kinds of
  forces are
▶ what forces do

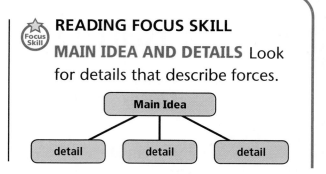

READING FOCUS SKILL

MAIN IDEA AND DETAILS Look
for details that describe forces.

Types of Forces

To move a ball, you can throw it, kick it, or hit it
with a bat. Any kind of push or pull is a **force**. You
must apply a force to make an object move. An
object will keep moving until another force stops it.
When you catch a moving ball, the force from your
hand stops the ball.

Friction is one force that stops things or slows
them down. When two objects rub together, there
is friction between them. Most rough surfaces make
more friction than smooth surfaces. You can slide
farther on ice than you can on dirt or grass.

The rocket is pushed
upward by the force of
its engines.

▲ When you open a
drawer, you are using
a pulling force.

Forces at Work

When the basilisk lizard runs fast across the water, it looks as if it is running above the water. If the forward force were stopped, the lizard would start to sink into the water.

For more links and activities, go to **www.hspscience.com**

Forces also make objects change directions. You apply a force to the handlebar to turn your bike. When you push one end of a seesaw down, the other end comes up.

Some forces do not even have to touch the object. A magnet can be used to push or pull objects made of iron or steel. This is called magnetic force. A magnet can pull a nail.

MAIN IDEA AND DETAILS A magnet picks up paper clips. What force is at work?

Insta-Lab

Amazing Paper Clips Put some water in a cup. Carefully lay a paper clip on the water's surface. Observe. Research surface tension. Then explain why the paper clip doesn't sink.

Ways That Forces Change Motion

Three things affect the motion of an object.

- the strength of the force
- the direction of the force
- the mass of the object

The stronger the force is, the greater the change in motion. If you toss a ball gently, it doesn't move fast or far. If you throw a ball hard, the ball moves faster and farther. You use more force on the ball when you throw it as hard as you can.

If an object is not moving and a force pushes or pulls it, the object will move in the direction of the push or pull. When you pull up on an object, it comes up. When you push an object to the right, it moves to the right.

The smaller the mass of an object is, the easier it is to move. It takes less force to pick up a pencil than to pick up a book, since a pencil has less mass.

The jogger pushes the stroller in the direction in which he wants it to go.

▲ Each of these people is using force to push the boat. When forces act in the same direction, they add up to make a greater force. The sum of all the forces is called the net force.

You can add all the forces that push or pull on an object. The sum is called the net force. Suppose you and a friend push the same way on a door. The net force on the door equals your push plus your friend's push.

MAIN IDEA AND DETAILS Name three things that affect the motion of an object, and tell what each one does.

When equal forces act in opposite directions, they cancel each other out. The net force is zero.

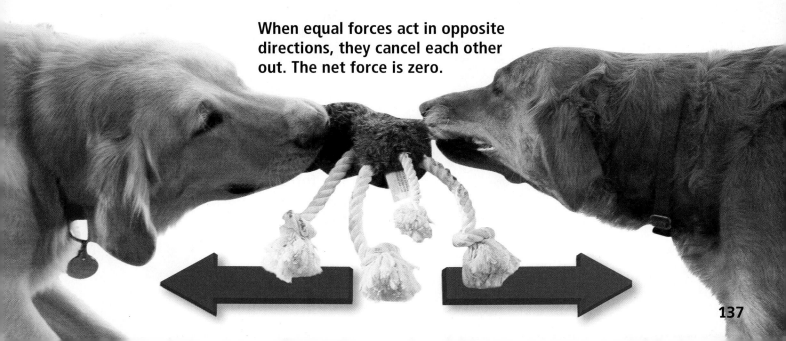

Gravity

When you throw a ball into the air, you know that it will come back down. **Gravity** is a force that pulls two objects toward each other. The ball comes back to Earth because Earth's gravity pulls on it.

Gravity is a very weak force between most objects. You don't feel the force of gravity between you and your desk. But Earth's gravity pulls very strongly. This is because Earth is so large.

The force of gravity depends on how much mass an object has. **Weight** is a measure of the force of gravity on an object. Objects with a large mass weigh more.

 MAIN IDEA AND DETAILS Does gravity pull a horse or a puppy harder? How do you know?

Why does the water fall back down to Earth after shooting up from the fountain?

The force of gravity pulls the roller coaster back to Earth for a thrilling ride!

138

1. **MAIN IDEA AND DETAILS** Copy and complete this graphic organizer.

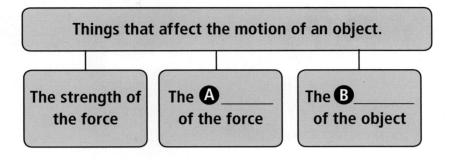

Things that affect the motion of an object.

| The strength of the force | The **A** _____ of the force | The **B** _____ of the object |

2. **SUMMARIZE** Write a summary of this lesson. Begin with the sentence *An object's motion changes because a force pushes or pulls it.*

3. **DRAW CONCLUSIONS** Why is it easier to ride a bike downhill than to ride it uphill?

4. **VOCABULARY** Use the terms *force, gravity,* and *weight* in sentences.

FCAT Prep

5. **Read/Inquire/Explain** Suppose you kick a ball sideways. In which direction will it move? Explain.

Links

Writing

Narrative

The moon is smaller than Earth, so the moon's gravity is weaker than Earth's. Write a **short story** about a day on the moon. How would the weaker gravity affect your motion?

Physical Education

Experiment with Forces

Gather several different sports balls. Throw them with different amounts of force. Push them in different directions. Then write a paragraph that describes your observations.

 For more links and activities, go to www.hspscience.com

How Do Waves Move?

Fast Fact

Waves! Water waves can be tiny, like these ripples in a pond. Waves in the ocean are much larger. The largest wave measured was 520 meters (1,700 ft) high. In the Investigate, you will see how two different kinds of waves move.

Two Kinds of Waves

Materials • rope about 2 meters long   • coiled spring toy

Procedure

1. Hold one end of the rope. Your partner will hold the other end. Let the rope hang loosely between you.

2. Move one end of the rope gently up and down as your partner holds the other end still. Then move the rope faster. **Observe** what happens.

3. Put the coiled spring toy on a table or on the floor. Have your partner hold one end still. Push the other end of the toy about 10 cm toward your partner. Then pull and push that end backward and forward. **Observe** what happens.

4. **Record** your **observations** by making diagrams for steps 2 and 3.

Step 2

Step 3

Draw Conclusions

1. How did the force you used on the rope affect it? What happened when you moved it faster?

2. **Inquiry Skill** When you **compare** things, you look at how they are alike. **Compare** the movements of the waves in the rope with the waves in the toy.

Investigate Further

What do you **predict** will happen when you move the coiled spring toy in the same way you moved the rope? Try it and see.

SC.H.1.2.1.3.1 keeping accurate records, SC.H.1.2.2.3.1 following experimental design, SC.H.1.2.3.3.1 working collaboratively, SC.H.1.2.4.3.1 comparing/contrasting, SC.H.1.2.5.3.1 uses diagrams, SC.H.2.2.1.3.1 makes predictions

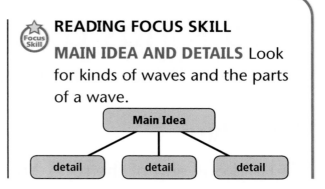
VOCABULARY

wave p. 142
crest p. 144
trough p. 144
wavelength p. 144

SCIENCE CONCEPTS

▶ what the types of waves are
▶ how to measure waves

READING FOCUS SKILL

MAIN IDEA AND DETAILS Look for kinds of waves and the parts of a wave.

```
        Main Idea
    ┌───────┼───────┐
 detail   detail   detail
```

Types of Waves

Even if you live far from the ocean, waves are all around you. There are many kinds of waves. Light travels in waves, and so does sound. Microwaves cook your food. A doctor uses X-ray waves to take pictures of the inside of your body.

A **wave** is a disturbance that travels through matter or space. Waves disturb matter by causing it to move. This is because waves carry energy. Waves can travel through solids, liquids, and gases. Some waves can travel through empty space.

Waves disturb the water particles. ▼

142

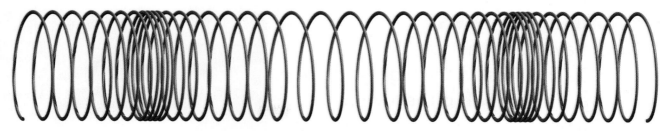

▲ A spring toy that is moved in and out makes a back-and-forth wave.

Sound waves from this xylophone (ZY•luh•fohn) bring sound energy to your ears. Sound waves are back-and-forth waves. ▶

Waves are made when something vibrates. Things that vibrate move back and forth. When you speak, your vocal cords vibrate quickly to make sound waves.

There are two types of waves. Some waves move up and down. Examples are radio waves and light waves. Some waves, like sound waves, move back and forth.

MAIN IDEA AND DETAILS
What is a wave?

Move It!
Sprinkle some tiny bread crumbs inside of a foil pie plate. Hold a cookie sheet next to the pie plate, and bang a large wooden spoon against the cookie sheet. Observe the crumbs. What makes them move?

Measuring Waves

Waves have parts that can be measured. The **crest** is the highest point of a wave. The **trough** is the lowest point of a wave. The greater the distance between these two points, the larger the wave is and the more energy it carries.

Forces affect the amount of energy that waves carry. A rock thrown into a pond will make bigger waves than a pebble will. Suppose you beat hard on a drum. The sound is louder than if you beat softly.

Scientists also measure another characteristic of waves. **Wavelength** is the distance from one point of one wave to the same point of the next wave.

Wavelength can be measured as the distance from one crest to the next crest or from one trough to the next trough.

 MAIN IDEA AND DETAILS What measurement tells how much energy a wave carries?

Measuring a wave is easy if you think of it as hills and valleys. ▼

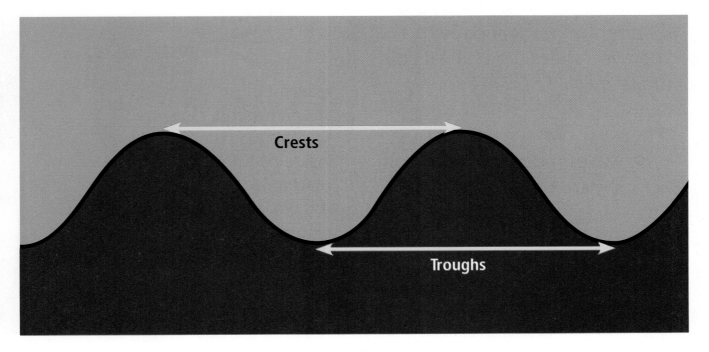

Crests

Troughs

1. MAIN IDEA AND DETAILS Copy and complete this graphic organizer.

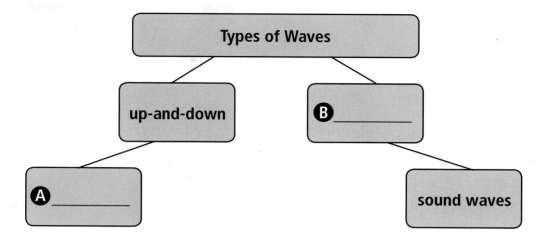

Types of Waves

up-and-down

B _____

A _____

sound waves

2. SUMMARIZE Write two sentences that tell what this lesson is mainly about.

3. DRAW CONCLUSIONS Why can ocean waves wash away rocks on the beach?

4. VOCABULARY Make a quiz question for each vocabulary term in this lesson. Provide the answers.

FCAT Prep

5. How can the length of a wave be measured?
   A. from trough to crest
   B. from crest to wavelength
   C. from crest to trough
   D. from crest to crest

Links

Writing

Narrative

Suppose you are a wave. Write a **description** of yourself. Tell what type of wave you are, how you move, and how your energy is measured. Describe how the amount of energy you carry can change.

Math

Measure Wavelength

Look at the two pictures of waves. Measure their wavelengths. How much longer is Wave A than Wave B?

A.

B.

For more links and activities, go to **www.hspscience.com**

145

Taking to the Air

Michael Moshier always believed he could fly. Now a lot of other people believe that he can, too.

Not long ago, Moshier flew about 60 cm (2 ft) into the air. That might not sound like much, but he flew with only the help of a special flying backpack that he invented, called the *SoloTrek*.

Straight Up

The *SoloTrek* was what scientists call a prototype, or a test version of something. It weighs about 147 kg (325 pounds) and is a personal flying machine. The machine is lifted into the air by two propellers, called ducts. The ducts force air in the direction they face. For example, if the pilot tilts the ducts to face forward, the aircraft flies forward. If the ducts are tilted to face upward, the aircraft flies up.

Bigger and Better

Since the *SoloTrek* prototype, Trek Aerospace has built several more test vehicles that can lift people or cargo. One new machine is called the *Dragonfly*. The *Dragonfly* is 4 m (13.1 ft) long and can carry a cargo of 205 kg (450 pounds), about the same weight as five third graders. The machine can fly at a maximum speed of about 378 km (235 miles) per hour.

Flying Solo

Dragonfly is being tested in both a piloted and an unpiloted version. An unpiloted version could someday be used by the military or firefighters to carry supplies to dangerous areas.

The company that makes *SoloTrek* has high hopes for its machines. The first purchases might be made by the military or firefighters. The company also hopes that families might someday buy these personal flying machines to get around town. Who knows—when you're old enough you might drive your kids to soccer practice in your own personal aircraft.

THINK ABOUT IT

1. During its test flight, how was the *SoloTrek* put into motion?

2. How would you use your own personal aircraft?

235 mph

450 pounds

Find out more! Log on to
www.hspscience.com

KIDS TAKE FLIGHT

Ten-year-old Michael Zollars recently went on the ride of his life. He and a pilot flew in a small airplane. "It was fun!" Michael said. "I got to take the controls for a while."

Michael was taking part in the Young Eagles program. The goal of the program was to give one million children free rides in private airplanes. The program ended on December 17, 2003, the 100th anniversary of the first powered flight made by the Wright brothers. Wilbur and Orville Wright built their first powered airplane, the *Flyer,* in 1903 and tested it at Kitty Hawk, North Carolina.

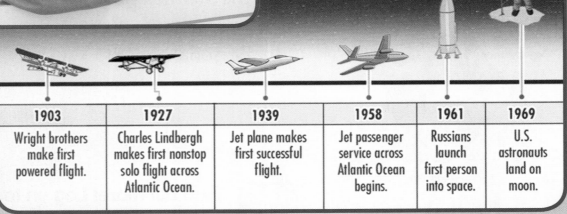

1903	1927	1939	1958	1961	1969
Wright brothers make first powered flight.	Charles Lindbergh makes first nonstop solo flight across Atlantic Ocean.	Jet plane makes first successful flight.	Jet passenger service across Atlantic Ocean begins.	Russians launch first person into space.	U.S. astronauts land on moon.

Find out more! Log on to
www.hspscience.com

You Can Do It!

Quick and Easy Project

Net Force

Materials
- book

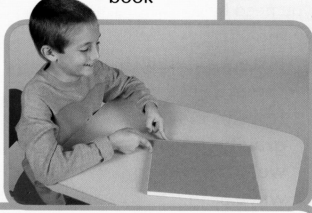

Procedure

1. Lay a book on a table or on the floor. Push on one side of the book. How does the book move?

2. Push on the side next to the side you just pushed. How does the book move?

3. Push on both of these sides at the same time. In which direction does the book move?

Draw Conclusions

Why did the book move in a new direction in Step 3?

What do you think would happen if you pushed on opposite sides of the book?

Design Your Own Investigation

Friction

Friction is a force that you can't see. It causes objects to slow down when two surfaces rub against each other. Design an investigation to find out more about friction. Find some surfaces that are smooth and some that are rough. Then choose an object, and try moving it across the different surfaces. Do smooth surfaces or rough surfaces cause more friction?

Review and FCAT Preparation

Vocabulary Review

Use the terms below to complete the sentences. The page numbers tell you where to look in the chapter if you need help.

motion p. 127
distance p. 128
speed p. 130
force p. 134
gravity p. 138
weight p. 138
wave p. 142
crest p. 144
trough p. 144
wavelength p. 144

1. The highest point of a wave is the _____.

2. A change in position is _____.

3. The measure of the force of gravity on an object is the object's _____.

4. A push or a pull is a _____.

5. The distance between one crest and the next crest is the _____.

6. The distance an object moves in a certain period of time is its _____.

7. A disturbance that travels through matter or space is a _____.

8. The lowest point of a wave is the _____.

9. The force that pulls two objects toward each other is _____.

10. How far an object moves is _____.

Check Understanding

Write the letter of the best choice.

11. A boy pushes a box across the floor. The box moves to the right. In which direction is the boy probably pushing?
    A. toward the left
    B. toward the right
    C. downward
    D. upward

12. What do waves carry with them from place to place?
    F. energy   **H.** speed
    G. motion   **I.** wavelength

13. **COMPARE AND CONTRAST** Two horses pull a wagon in the same direction with the same force. How does the net force compare to the force of each horse?

   A. The net force is twice the force of each horse alone.

   B. The net force is half the force of each horse alone.

   C. The net force is equal to the force of each horse alone.

   D. The net force is zero.

14. **MAIN IDEA AND DETAILS** To figure speed, what else do you need to know besides time?

   F. distance   **H.** motion

   G. force   **I.** wavelength

15. In the picture, the two girls start pushing the trunk with equal force. How does it move?

   A. It moves toward the right.

   B. It moves toward the left.

   C. It doesn't move.

   D. It moves slowly.

16. Which force holds your book on your desk?

   F. electricity

   G. gravity

   H. magnetism

   I. surface tension

Inquiry Skills

17. Interpret the data shown in the pictures. Which wave has the shortest wavelength? How do you know?

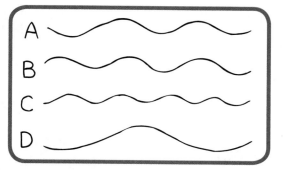

18. Compare two different types of waves.

Read/Inquire/Explain

19. Look around the room. Find three objects that can move, and describe their motions. Tell what forces are needed to make these objects move.

20. Weigh some objects in your classroom. Record the weights. Which object does gravity pull on the hardest? How do you know?

Chapter 5

Work and Machines

Vocabulary

FCAT-Tested

lever
fulcrum
wheel-and-axle
pulley
inclined plane

Other Terms

work
simple machine
wedge

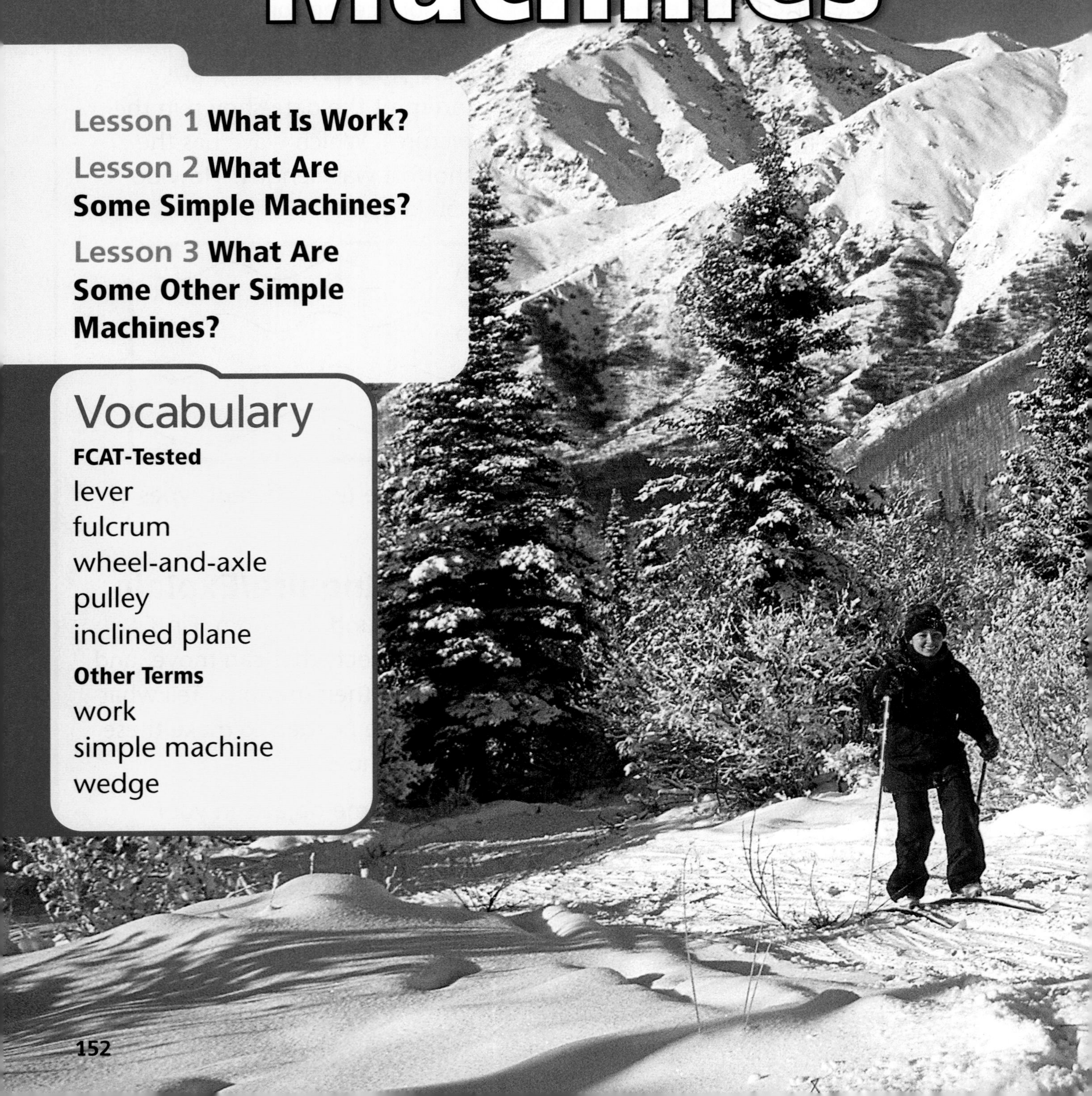

What do YOU wonder?

Simple machines can be found everywhere. What kinds of simple machines are being used here? What others can you think of?

What Is Work?

Fast Fact

Hard Work! This girl weighs less than the dog. However, she does work and uses simple machines to pull him through the park. In the Investigate, you will also use work to move an object.

Work with Me

Materials   • safety goggles   • graph paper   • checker   • drinking straw

Procedure

1 CAUTION: **Put on the safety goggles.** Work with a partner. On a piece of graph paper, make a start line. Place the checker on the graph paper behind the line.

2 Put one end of the straw in your mouth, and touch the other end to one edge of the checker. Blow hard through the straw.

3 Place the checker back at the same point on the paper. Have your partner press down on the checker while you repeat Step 2. **Record** your observations.

Draw Conclusions

1. Was the force of blowing on the checker the same or different each time? Explain.

2. Was the result the same or different each time? Explain.

3. **Inquiry Skill** Scientists often **measure** things during an experiment. How could you use the graph paper to measure how far the checker moved?

Step 2

Step 3

Investigate Further

Predict how using a stack of two checkers might affect your results each time. Try it!

SC.H.1.2.1.3.1 keeping accurate records,
SC.H.2.2.1.3.1 makes predictions

155

Reading in Science

SC.C.2.2 forces act on objects,
LA.A.2.2.1 main idea and details

VOCABULARY

work p. 158

SCIENCE CONCEPTS

▶ what scientists mean
by work

READING FOCUS SKILL

MAIN IDEA AND DETAILS

Look for details about work.

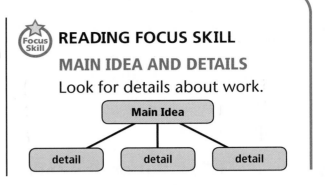

Different Types of Work

People use the word *work* all the time. Scientists do, too, but you might be surprised to find out what work means to a scientist.

Suppose your teacher asks you to solve a math problem in your head. You sit still and think hard. Then you get the answer. Your teacher says, "Good work!" However, a scientist would say that you did not do any work.

Suppose you want to open a jar. You twist the lid hard, but the lid doesn't move. You feel that you have done a lot of work. Again, however, a scientist would say you had done no work.

Is This Work?

3 + 5 - 2 + 1 = ?

◀ Solving a math problem isn't what scientists call work.

If the lid doesn't move, no work is being done. ▶

Now suppose you are playing soccer. A player passes the ball to you. As it rolls toward you, you pull your leg back. Then you kick hard. The ball flies up and forward. You make a goal!

As the crowd cheers, you say to yourself, "This is fun!" You do not think that you have done any work at all. Yet to a scientist, you have done work.

 MAIN IDEA AND DETAILS Which example shows what scientists call work?

Kicking a ball may seem like play, but scientists would say it was work.

One Type of Work

To a scientist, **work** is done only when a force is used to move an object. If you don't use a force, you don't do work. If nothing moves, you haven't done work.

Remember the math problem? You thought hard to solve it, but you didn't move anything. So to a scientist, you didn't do work.

Now think about opening the jar. You used a lot of force on the lid, but it didn't move. So to a scientist, you didn't do work on the jar.

What about the soccer game? Your muscles used force to lift your leg. Your foot used force to kick the ball. To a scientist, that was work.

⭐ **MAIN IDEA AND DETAILS** **What must happen for work to be done?**

How can you tell that work was done on the ball?

Measuring Work

Suppose you want to move a box full of toys across a room. To move such a heavy box, you will need to use a lot of force.

If you are not able to move the box alone, you might get a friend to help you. Then the force might be great enough to move it. You might also take out half of the toys. Then you might be able to move the box by yourself.

How could you measure how much work you had done? You would need to measure how much force you used and how far the object moved.

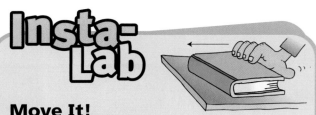

Move It!
Put a book on a desktop. Push gently on the side of the book. Slowly increase your force. Do the same thing with a stack of two books. Compare the force used to move two books with the force to move one book.

 MAIN IDEA AND DETAILS What two measurements tell you how much work is done?

Which picture shows the girl doing work? ▶

full, not moving

half full, moving

1. MAIN IDEA AND DETAILS Draw and complete this graphic organizer.

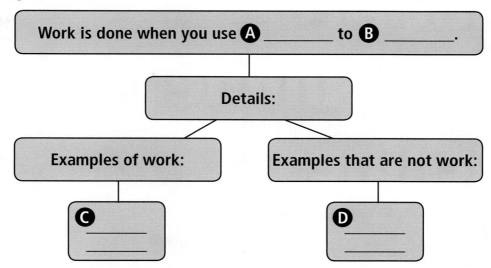

Work is done when you use **Ⓐ** _____ to **Ⓑ** _____.

Details:

Examples of work:

Ⓒ _____ _____

Examples that are not work:

Ⓓ _____ _____

2. SUMMARIZE Use the graphic organizer to write a lesson summary.

3. DRAW CONCLUSIONS Heather wants to carry her laundry basket to the washer. It is too heavy for her to pick up. What can she do to get the laundry to the washer?

4. VOCABULARY Write an example of work being done.

FCAT Prep

5. Which of these is **not** an example of work?
   A. sitting and reading
   B. playing fetch with a dog
   C. pulling a chair across a room
   D. pushing a box of books across the floor

Links

Writing

Expository
Think about community workers. List two or three workers who do things that scientists would call work. Write a **description** of how the workers' jobs include work.

Art

Working Art
Make a drawing of someone doing work. Then, on the back of your paper, list the ways you did work while you were making the drawing.

 For more links and activities, go to www.hspscience.com

What Are Some Simple Machines?

Fast Fact

Important Levers We use levers to do many things. Did you know that the nutcracker you use to crack a nut is a lever? In the investigate you will learn more about the importance of levers.

Help from Simple Machines

Materials
- measuring spoon
- jar lid
- white rice and brown rice, uncooked
- forceps
- two paper plates

Procedure

1. Measure out one tablespoon of white rice. Place it in the jar lid. Do the same with the brown rice.

2. Mix the two types of rice in the lid.

3. Use your fingers to separate the types of rice. **Record** your observations.

4. Put the rice you separated back in the lid. Mix the rice again.

5. This time, use the forceps to separate the types of rice. **Record** your observations.

Draw Conclusions

1. Which way of separating the rice grains was easier? Why?

2. Which would be a safer way of handling food, using your fingers or using forceps?

3. **Inquiry Skill** Would using fingers or forceps make a difference if time was important in completing this task? Repeat the Investigate and **measure** the time.

Step 3

Step 5

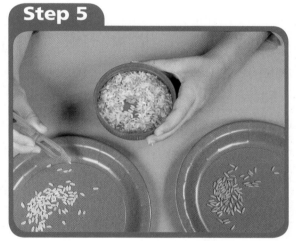

Investigate Further

You have measured how long it takes to separate the rice. **Compare** your time with 4 other classmates by making a bar graph. Were there differences? Why do you think so?

VOCABULARY

simple machine p. 165

lever p. 166

fulcrum p. 166

wheel-and-axle p. 168

pulley p. 170

SCIENCE CONCEPTS

▶ what simple machines are

▶ how levers, wheels-and-axles, and pulleys make work easier

READING FOCUS SKILL

Focus Skill

MAIN IDEA AND DETAILS
Look for details.

```
        Main Idea
    ┌───────┼───────┐
 detail   detail   detail
```

Simple Machines

Imagine that the lawn is covered with leaves. Your job is to clear them away. You grab a handful of leaves and put them in a trash bag. Then you pick up another handful of leaves, and another, and another. This is going to take a very long time!

The job might go faster if you used a machine. A machine is anything that changes the way work is done. For example, a leaf blower is a machine. This machine would make clearing up the leaves easy and fast.

Other examples of machines include cars, dishwashers, and bicycles. These machines have many parts. All the parts together make the machines work.

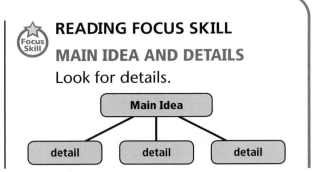

This leaf blower has an engine. The engine supplies the force to do the work.

Not all machines have a lot of parts. If you don't have a leaf blower, you could use a rake to help you clear up the leaves. A rake is a machine, even though it has no engine. A rake is an example of a simple machine.

A **simple machine** has few or no moving parts. The rake has no moving parts. To use a simple machine, you apply only one force. To use a rake, you pull on it with one hand.

MAIN IDEA AND DETAILS What is a simple machine?

◀ With the rake, the boy provides the force that gets the work done.

Math in Science
Interpret Data

Gavin raked all the leaves in the yard. Then he scattered them across the yard and used a leaf blower. How much time could he have saved by using the leaf blower the first time?

Clearing Leaves			
Leaf Blower	🍂		
Rake	🍂	🍂	🍂

Key: Each 🍂 = 1 hour

The Lever

A rake is a lever. A **lever** is a bar that pivots, or turns, on a fixed point. A fixed point is a point that doesn't move. The fixed point on a lever is called the **fulcrum** (FUHL•kruhm).

Think about how you hold a rake when you use it. One hand holds the end of the handle. That hand stays still. It is the fulcrum. The other hand pulls the middle of the handle. The end of the rake gathers the leaves.

Your hand moves the middle of the rake's handle a certain distance. The end of the rake moves a greater distance, so it gathers more leaves. That's what makes the work easier.

Do all levers work this way? No, but a broom and a fishing pole are levers that work this way. So is your arm. Your elbow joint is the fulcrum.

A broom is a lever that helps you clean up an area more easily. Where is the fulcrum? ▼

fulcrum

Insta-Lab

I Wonder

Where is the best place on a broom to put your hands? Try placing both your hands at the top of the stick and then at the bottom of the stick. What would happen if you separated your hands? Which way would allow you to sweep up more leaves?

A shovel is a lever that changes the direction and strength of a force. You push down on the handle with a certain force. A greater force moves the blade up, taking the rock with it.

fulcrum

Levers work in different ways, depending on where the fulcrum is and where you apply the force. In the Investigate, you used forceps. The fulcrum of the forceps was the hinge.

Suppose you want to move a large rock. You push the blade of a shovel under the rock. The ground is the fulcrum. You push down on the handle, and the blade comes up, bringing the rock with it. A crowbar works this way, too.

A nutcracker is also a lever. Its fulcrum is where its arms connect. When you push the other ends of the arms together, the force cracks the nut that is between them.

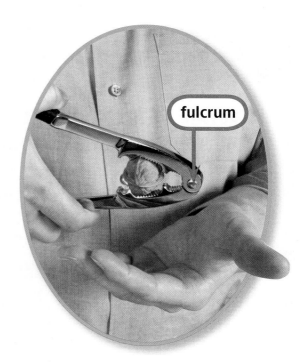

fulcrum

▲ A nutcracker doesn't change the direction of the force you apply. It increases the strength of that force.

 MAIN IDEA AND DETAILS Why are a rake, a shovel, and a nutcracker all classified as levers?

The Wheel-and-Axle

Another type of simple machine is the wheel-and-axle. The **wheel-and-axle** is made up of a wheel and an axle that are connected so that they turn together.

You know that a bicycle has wheels, and you might know that it has axles. However, since the wheels and the axles of a bicycle aren't connected and don't turn together, they are not what a scientist would call a simple machine.

The doorknob shown on this page is an example of a wheel-and-axle. The wheel is the knob, and the rod that is connected to the knob is the axle. The knob and the rod form a simple machine, since they are connected and they turn together.

Science Up Close

A Wheel-and-Axle: The Doorknob

The knob part of a doorknob is a wheel. The rod connected to it is an axle. When you turn the knob, the axle turns, too. As it does, it pulls back the catch, and the door opens.

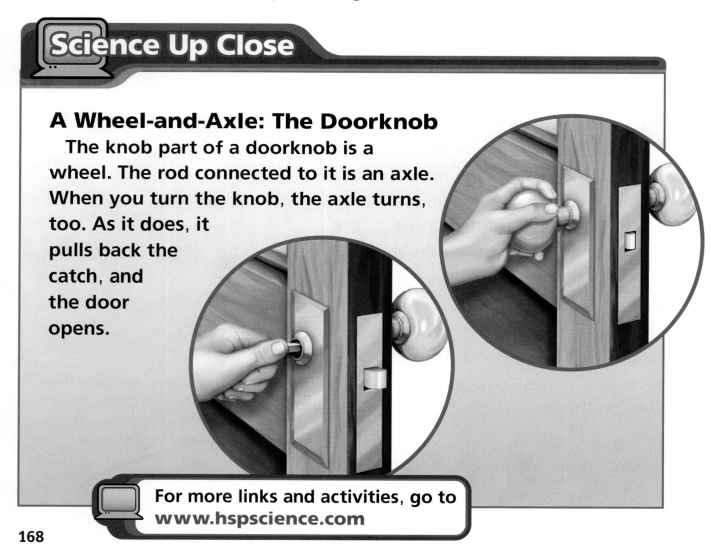

For more links and activities, go to **www.hspscience.com**

▲ Without a screwdriver, it would be very difficult to tighten screws.

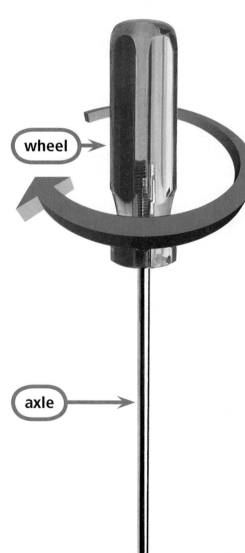

The handle of the screwdriver is the wheel that turns the axle—the shank. ▼

wheel

axle

A screwdriver is another example of a wheel-and-axle. The metal shank is the axle. The handle is the wheel. The shank would be very hard to turn by itself. You would have to apply a lot of force. The handle allows you to turn the shank with less force, making the work easier.

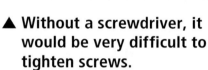 **MAIN IDEA AND DETAILS** How does a wheel-and-axle make work easier?

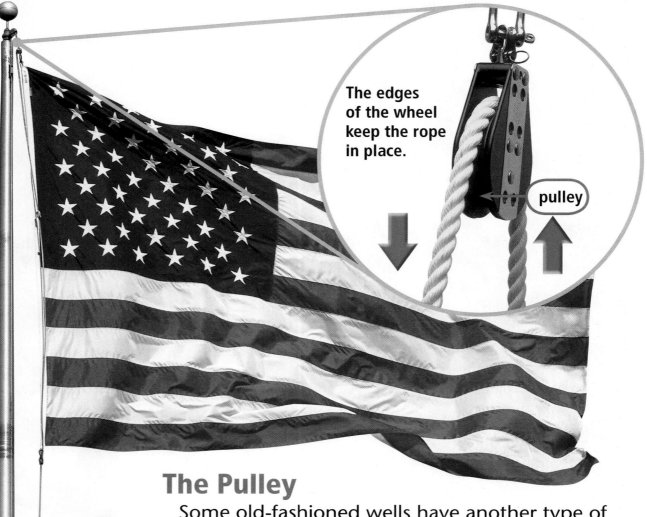

The edges of the wheel keep the rope in place.

pulley

rope

◄ **You pull down on the rope, and the flag moves up.**

The Pulley

Some old-fashioned wells have another type of simple machine. A bucket is attached to a rope. The rope is part of a simple machine called a pulley.

A **pulley** is a wheel with a rope around it. You pull one end of the rope one way, and the other end moves in the opposite direction.

The bucket in the well is attached to one end of the rope. It would be hard to raise the bucket by pulling up on the rope. With the pulley, you can pull down instead, which is easier, and the bucket comes up.

Some window curtains and blinds have pulleys. So do flagpoles. You wouldn't want to climb to the top of the pole in order to raise the flag. With a pulley, you don't have to.

 MAIN IDEA AND DETAILS How does a pulley work?

170

1. MAIN IDEA AND DETAILS Draw and complete this graphic organizer.

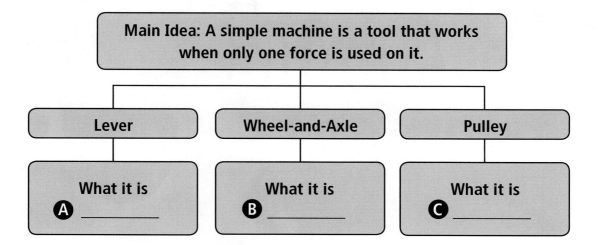

Main Idea: A simple machine is a tool that works when only one force is used on it.

Lever	Wheel-and-Axle	Pulley
What it is Ⓐ _____	What it is Ⓑ _____	What it is Ⓒ _____

2. SUMMARIZE Write a sentence that tells the most important information in this lesson.

3. DRAW CONCLUSIONS What simple machine can you use to move a basket of fruit from the ground into a treehouse?

4. VOCABULARY Write one example of each kind of simple machine you learned about in this lesson.

FCAT Prep

5. Which simple machine would you use to open a paint can?
   A. lever
   B. lever and pulley
   C. pulley
   D. wheel-and-axle

Links

Writing

Expository
Write to a first grader explaining **how to** raise a flag by using a pulley. Draw pictures to go with your writing.

Health

Body Levers
Find a diagram of a human arm, copy it, and label it to show how the arm works as a lever. What other body parts work that way?

 For more links and activities, go to www.hspscience.com

What Are Some Other Simple Machines?

Fast Fact

Watch Out! An ice fisher must be careful when walking out onto the ice to drill using an auger. To hold the weight of one adult, the ice must be at least 5 centimeters (2 in.) thick. In the Investigate you will be measuring force using a spring scale.

172

Inclined to Help

Materials • safety goggles • board • chair • tape measure
• string • toy car • spring scale

Procedure

1 CAUTION: **Put on safety goggles.** Use the board to make a ramp from the floor to the chair seat. Measure to find the distance from the floor to the seat. Measure straight up and along the ramp. Record both distances.

2 Tie a loop of string to the toy car. Attach the spring scale to the string.

3 Hold on to the spring scale, and lift the car from the floor straight up to the chair seat. Record the force shown on the scale.

4 Hold on to the spring scale, and slowly pull the car up the ramp from the floor to the chair seat. Record the force shown on the scale.

Work Data					
	Distance (cm)	Times	Force (newtons)	Equals	Work (newton-cm)
No Ramp		x		=	
Ramp		x		=	

Draw Conclusions

1. How did the ramp affect the force needed to lift the car?

2. How did the ramp affect the distance?

3. **Inquiry Skill** Scientists interpret data to draw conclusions. What conclusions can you draw from your data?

Step 4

Investigate Further

What might affect the force needed to lift the car? **Plan and conduct a simple investigation** to test some variables.

SC.H.1.2.1.3.1 keeping accurate records, SC.H.1.2.2.3.1 following experimental design, SC.H.3.2.2.3.1 collects data

VOCABULARY

inclined plane p. 174

wedge p. 176

screw p. 178

SCIENCE CONCEPTS

▶ how inclined planes, wedges, and screws are used

READING FOCUS SKILL

COMPARE AND CONTRAST

Look for ways inclined planes, wedges, and screws are alike and different.

> alike ——— different

The Inclined Plane

Suppose you wanted to get to the top of this hill. You could take a straight path to ride up it. That would be easier than climbing up a cliff, but you still might be very tired after riding up the straight path.

Instead, you could ride up a path that winds around the hill. The path is longer than the straight route, but it's easier to ride up a gentle slope.

Both routes are inclined planes. An **inclined plane** is a simple machine that makes moving and lifting things easier.

> Going up the straight path doesn't take as long, but it is more work. Taking the winding path is less work, but it takes longer.

Ramp

Suppose you need to put a box of books on a shelf. You try to lift the box, but it's too heavy. So you lean a board against the shelf. Then you drag the box to the end of the board. A hard push moves the box up the board. Soon it's on the shelf.

You have used the board as a ramp. A ramp is an example of an inclined plane. People use ramps to make it easier to get things out of basements or onto trucks.

▲ Pushing this chair up the ramp is easier than lifting it directly into the truck.

COMPARE AND CONTRAST How is a ramp like a path up a hill?

A ramp can make getting into buildings easier for people with physical disabilities. ▶

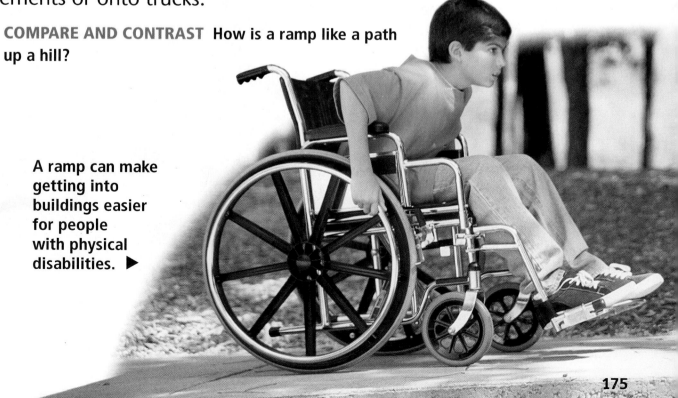

The Wedge

Suppose you want to put a slice of tomato on your sandwich. How can you get one thin slice off a whole tomato? That's easy—use a sharp knife.

To slice the tomato, you press down on the knife. The knife splits the tomato into two pieces. In a moment, they are separated from each other.

A knife is a simple machine known as a wedge. A **wedge** is made up of two inclined planes placed back-to-back. Wedges are used to force two things apart or to split one thing into two.

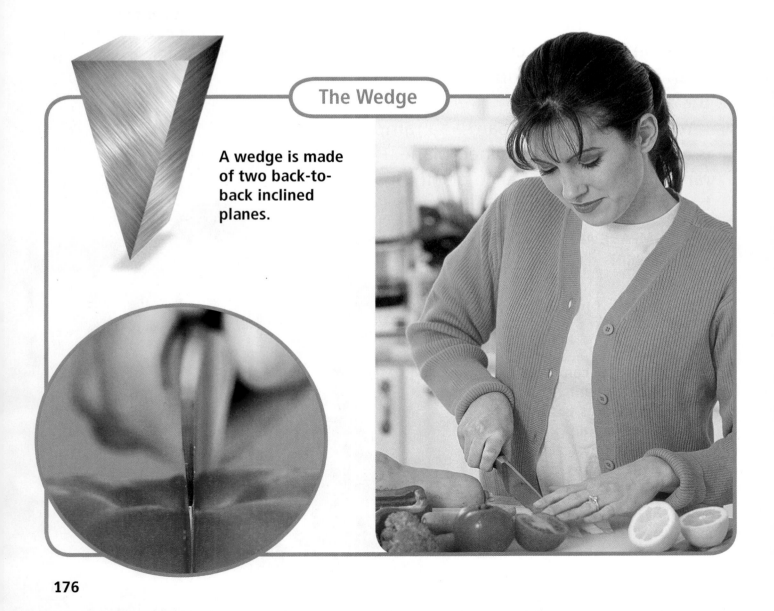

The Wedge

A wedge is made of two back-to-back inclined planes.

It's easy to see the wedge shape of this ax.

A chisel is a wedge, too. This man uses a chisel to separate small pieces of limestone from the big piece.

An ax is also a wedge. It can split a log into two pieces.

The ax head looks like two ramps. To move something up a ramp, you push the object up. To move a wedge down through an object, you push the wedge down. In both cases, something slides along a ramp.

COMPARE AND CONTRAST How are a wedge and an inclined plane alike? How are they different?

The Screw

Suppose you want to hold two pieces of wood together. You could use a nail, but since a nail is smooth, it might slip out of the wood. It might be better to use a screw.

A **screw** is a simple machine you turn to lift an object or to hold two or more objects together. It is like a nail with threads around it. The threads make it hard to pull the screw out of the wood.

A nail goes straight into the wood. A screw moves around and around as it goes in. A screw travels farther than a nail does, but it takes much less force to get it in.

 COMPARE AND CONTRAST How are a screw and an inclined plane alike? How are they different?

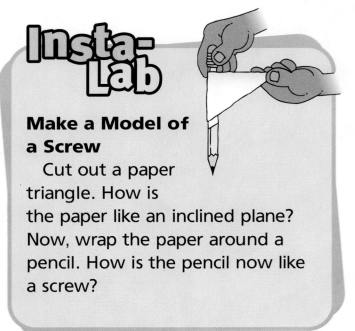
Some screws have threads that are far apart. Others have threads that are close together and wind around the screw more times. It's easier to turn these screws, but it takes longer. ▼

The screw's threads hold the pieces of wood together.

1. COMPARE AND CONTRAST Draw and complete this graphic organizer.

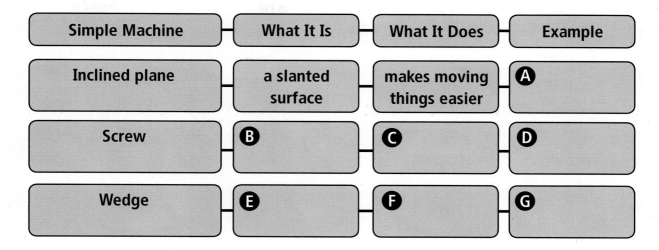

Simple Machine	What It Is	What It Does	Example
Inclined plane	a slanted surface	makes moving things easier	Ⓐ
Screw	Ⓑ	Ⓒ	Ⓓ
Wedge	Ⓔ	Ⓕ	Ⓖ

2. SUMMARIZE Use the graphic organizer to write a lesson summary.

3. DRAW CONCLUSIONS Matthew is putting together a bench. Explain why it might be better for him to use screws than to use nails.

4. VOCABULARY Write a paragraph using the terms *inclined plane*, *wedge*, and *screw* correctly.

FCAT Prep

5. Your friend lives at the top of a hill. Which simple machine would you most likely use to go to your friend's house?
   A. inclined plane
   B. pulley
   C. wedge
   D. lever

Links

Writing

Narrative
Write a **story** about an imaginary place that doesn't have simple machines. Your story can be funny or serious. Remember to give your place a name.

Social Studies

Egyptian Pyramids
Read about how the ancient Egyptians built the pyramids. Find out which simple machines scientists believe they used and how they probably used them.

 For more links and activities, go to www.hspscience.com

SCIENCE Spin from WEEKLY READER®

Technology

SC.H.3.2.1.3.1 contributions of scientists, SC.H.3.2.3.3.1 scientific discoveries impact humans, SC.H.3.2.4.3.1 solving problems/new ideas

Say Hello to ASIMO

How would you like having a robot around the house to help you with chores, such as cleaning your room? That reality may be closer than you think. Meet ASIMO, the world's most advanced humanoid robot.

This 4-foot, 115-pound robot is almost lifelike. Balancing on two legs, ASIMO can walk, climb stairs, and even dance. This robot has two arms and two hands, so it can shake hands, hold objects, turn on light switches, and open doors. It can also recognize faces and voices.

Engineers for a company in Japan spent more than 16 years developing ASIMO. Their goal was to build a robot that would improve people's lives. "ASIMO was created for the purpose of someday helping people in need," said Koichi Amemiya, president of the company.

Scientists hope *ASIMO* will be able to help out with chores around the house, such as taking out the garbage.

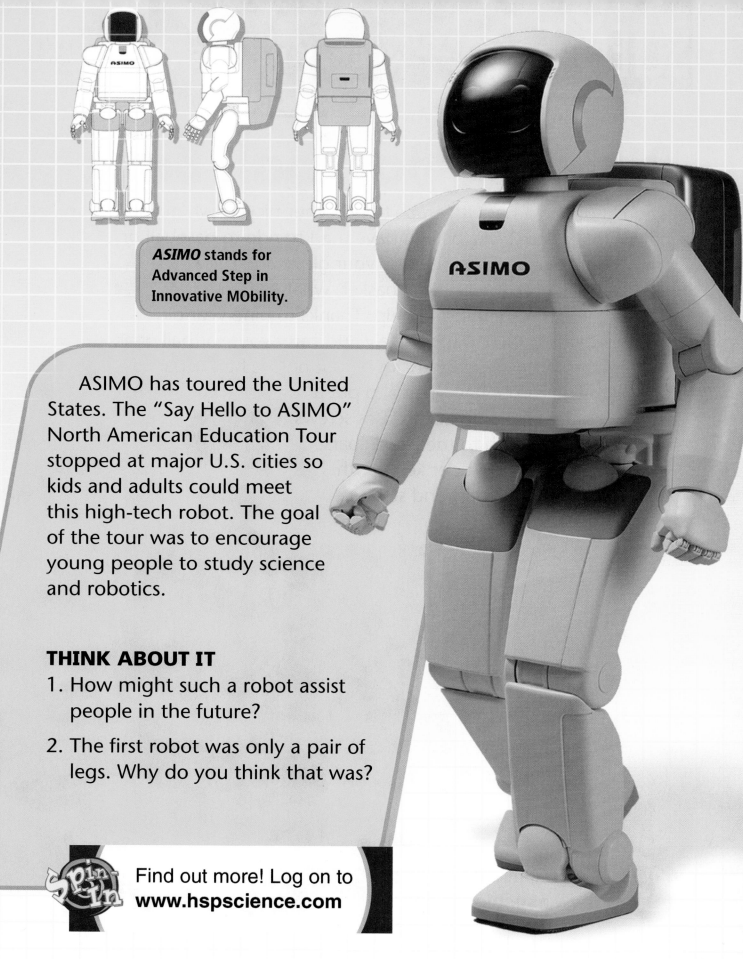

ASIMO stands for Advanced Step in Innovative MObility.

ASIMO has toured the United States. The "Say Hello to ASIMO" North American Education Tour stopped at major U.S. cities so kids and adults could meet this high-tech robot. The goal of the tour was to encourage young people to study science and robotics.

THINK ABOUT IT

1. How might such a robot assist people in the future?

2. The first robot was only a pair of legs. Why do you think that was?

Find out more! Log on to
www.hspscience.com

Bikes and Baseball Bats

You know how hard it can be to ride your bicycle when you have a lot to carry. Maybe you have tried to ride to baseball or softball practice and had to carry your glove and bat at the same time. If you don't have a basket, what can you do?

Now there is something to help. Thanks to nine-year old Austin Meggitt, you can ride safely and carry your softball gear. Austin invented a carrier that can be put on the handlebars of any bike. The carrier has a place to put a baseball bat, glove, and ball. It uses screws and clamps to attach to the handlebars. This invention lets the rider keep both hands on the handlebars and stay safe while riding.

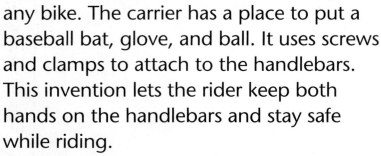

Find out more! Log on to
www.hspscience.com

You Can Do It!

Making an Elevator

Procedure

1 Tape the pulley wheel to the underside of a box.

2 Pass the string over it.

3 Tape a paper cup to each end of the string.

4 Place pennies in one cup and then in the other. Watch your elevator move.

Materials

- pulley
- 2 paper cups
- string
- pennies
- tape
- box

Draw Conclusions

How does the balance of weight affect the movement of your elevator?

Design Your Own Investigation

How Do Simple Machines Work?

Exactly how does a wedge work? How does a lever work? Do different levers work in different ways? How would you build a model of each of these simple machines? Sketch ideas for ways to build wedges and levers with wooden blocks. Then use your sketches as guides to build the simple machines.

Vocabulary Review

Use the terms below to complete the sentences. The page numbers tell you where to look in the chapter if you need help.

work p. 158

simple machine p. 165

lever p. 166

fulcrum p. 166

pulley p. 170

inclined plane p. 174

wedge p. 176

screw p. 178

1. A wheel with a rope that goes around it is a _____.

2. A bar that pivots on a fixed point is a _____.

3. Two inclined planes placed back-to-back form a _____.

4. Anything that makes work easier and has few or no moving parts is a _____.

5. Using a force to move an object is known as _____.

6. A slanted surface that makes it easier to move objects is an _____.

7. When you use a shovel to pry up an object, the ground acts as a _____.

8. Threads wrapped around a post form a _____.

Check Understanding

Write the letter of the best choice.

9. **MAIN IDEA AND DETAILS** Which of the following is an example of work?
   A. holding a baseball
   B. packing a lunch box
   C. pushing against a wall
   D. thinking about homework

10. **COMPARE AND CONTRAST** Compare the simple machines. Which of the following is **not** a lever?
    F. broom   H. rake
    G. crowbar   I. ramp

11. How is the screwdriver being used in this picture?

    A. as a lever
    B. as an inclined plane
    C. as a wedge
    D. as a wheel-and-axle

12. What type of simple machine is a nutcracker?

  F. axle   **H.** lever
  G. inclined plane **I.** screw

13. What simple machine can you use to lift a can of paint to the second floor as you stand on the ground?

  A. pulley   **C.** wedge
  B. ramp   **D.** wheel-and-axle

14. What simple machine is made up of an inclined plane that winds around a post?

  F. fulcrum   **H.** wedge
  G. screw   **I.** wheel-and-axle

15. Leo is using a chisel to shape a piece of wood. What simple machine is he using?

  A. lever   **C.** ramp
  B. pulley   **D.** wedge

16. Which of these objects at a playground is an example of a lever?

  F. ladder   **H.** slide
  G. seesaw   **I.** swing

Inquiry Skills

17. Your teacher asks you to use classroom items to put together a simple machine. You see a ruler and a rubber eraser. What two simple machines could you make using these items? Draw what they would look like. Compare.

18. You kicked a soccer ball as far as you could. Explain how you could use a jump rope to measure how far the ball was kicked.

READ INQUIRE EXPLAIN Read/Inquire/Explain

19. Angie and her family have reached the airport late. They must hurry to catch their flight. Is Angie doing work as she pulls her suitcase up a ramp? Explain.

20. In this picture, Kyle is pushing a large bundle of newspapers up a ramp. What could he do to lessen the amount of force he needs to apply?

Processes That Shape the Earth

EARTH SCIENCE

The chapters in this unit address these Grade Level Expectations from the Florida Sunshine State Standards.

Chapter 6

Minerals and Rocks

SC.D.1.2.1.3.1   knows that smaller rocks come from the breaking and weathering of bedrock and larger rocks.

Chapter 7

Forces That Shape the Land

SC.D.1.2.1.3.1   knows that smaller rocks come from the breaking and weathering of bedrock and larger rocks.

SC.D.1.2.4.3.1   understands the processes of weathering and erosion.

SC.D.1.2.5.3.1   knows that land forms change over time (for example, earthquakes, volcanoes).

Chapter 8

The Water Cycle

SC.D.1.2.2.3.1   knows that approximately 75 percent of the surface of the Earth is covered by water.

SC.D.1.2.3.3.1   understands the stages of the water cycle (for example, evaporation, condensation, precipitation).

Chapter 9

Conserving Resources

SC.D.2.2.1.3.1   knows that reusing, recycling, and reducing the use of natural resources improve and protect the quality of life.

The investigations and experiences in this unit also address many of the Grade Level Expectations in Strand H, The Nature of Science.

Science in Florida

NATIONAL HURRICANE CENTER

Miami

Dear Sheila,

Our class took a field trip to the National Hurricane Center in Miami. We met the scientists who keep us safe by predicting the path a hurricane will take. They showed us the computers they use.

In class we learned about the water cycle. When you drink water today, you could be drinking the same water that was once rain in a hurricane!

Sincerely,

Maria

The Sunshine State

USA

FCAT Writing

Writing Situation

Think about thunder and lightning. Write a story about being in stormy weather.

Experiment!

Hurricane Damage Hurricanes can be dangerous storms if you are not prepared. Scientists and engineers have designed buildings to withstand the strong winds of a hurricane. What types of structures are the most stable? For example, are short and wide buildings safer than tall and skinny buildings? Plan and conduct an experiment to find out.

Chapter 6

Minerals and Rocks

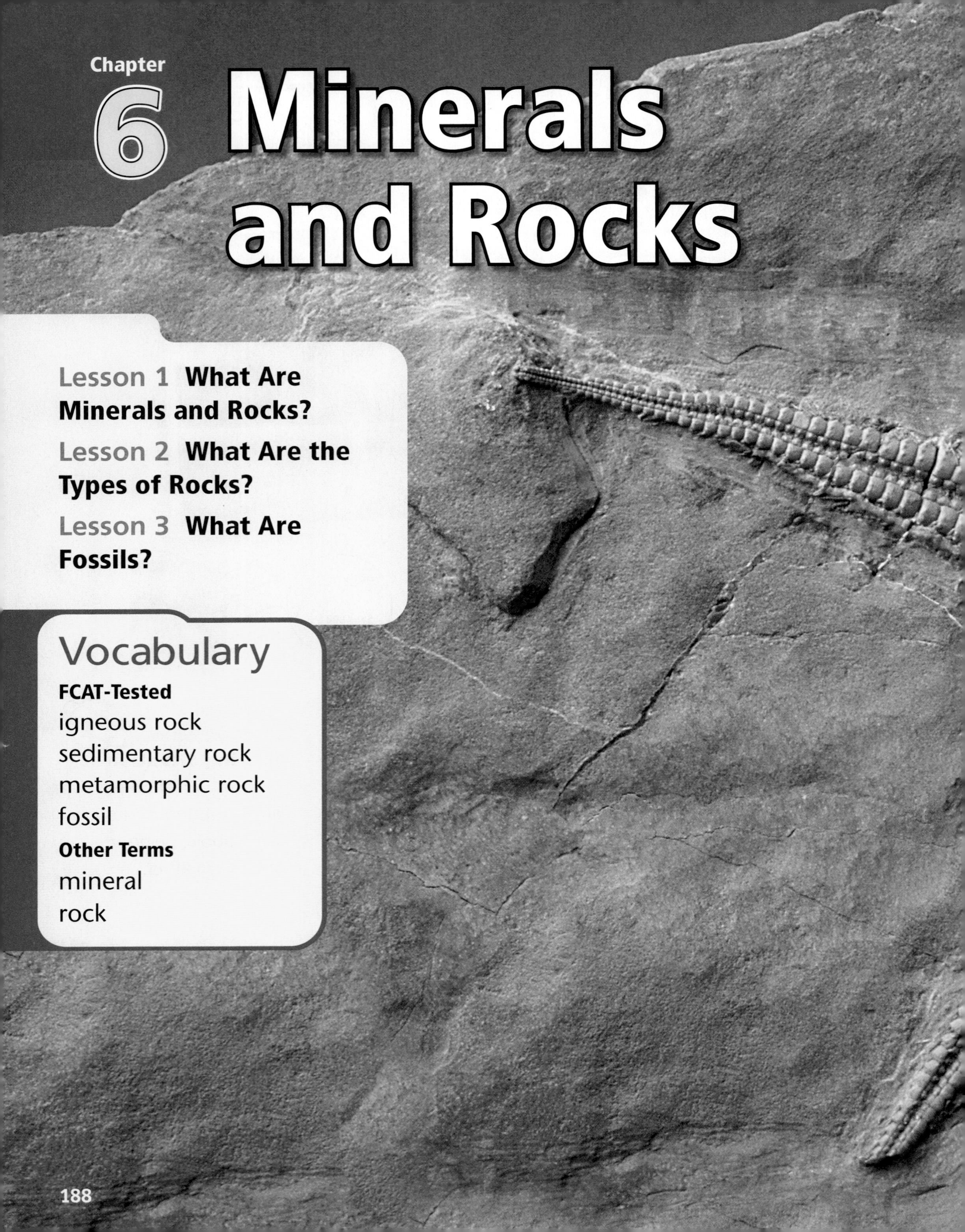

Vocabulary

FCAT-Tested

igneous rock
sedimentary rock
metamorphic rock
fossil

Other Terms

mineral
rock

What do **YOU** wonder?

A starfish fossil like this one gives clues that tell about both the starfish and the rock around it. What do you think scientists could learn from this fossil?

189

1

What Are Minerals and Rocks?

Fast Fact

Hard Minerals Not all minerals are the same. One of the ways minerals differ is in their hardness. Some minerals are hard enough to cut steel. In the Investigate, you will learn more about the hardness of minerals.

Testing Minerals

Materials • safety goggles • minerals labeled A through G

Procedure

1. Make a table like the one shown.

2. CAUTION: **Put on safety goggles.** A harder mineral scratches a softer mineral. Try to scratch each mineral with Sample A. Record which minerals Sample A scratches.

3. A softer mineral can be scratched by a harder mineral. Try to scratch Sample A with each of the other minerals. Record the minerals that scratch Sample A.

4. Repeat Steps 2 and 3 for each mineral.

5. Using the information in your table, order the minerals from softest to hardest.

Mineral Table		
Mineral to Test	**Minerals It Scratches**	**Minerals That Scratch It**
Sample A		
Sample B		
Sample C		
Sample D		
Sample E		
Sample F		
Sample G		

Draw Conclusions

1. Which mineral was hardest? Which was softest? How do you know?

2. **Inquiry Skill** Scientists often put objects in order. How did you decide how to order the minerals? How can putting minerals in order of hardness help you identify them?

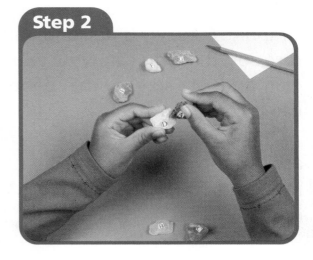

Step 2

Investigate Further

Test the hardness of each mineral again. This time, use a penny and your fingernail. Classify the minerals by what scratches them.

VOCABULARY

mineral p. 192

rock p. 196

SCIENCE CONCEPTS

▶ what minerals and rocks are

Focus Skill

READING FOCUS SKILL

MAIN IDEA AND DETAILS

Look for main ideas about minerals and rocks.

Main Idea

detail   detail   detail

Minerals

You might know that minerals are found in some of the foods you eat. You may have even seen someone wearing minerals. If an object is solid, formed in nature, and has never been alive, it is likely to be a **mineral**. There are many different minerals, and no two kinds are exactly alike. Gold, for example, is shiny. Graphite (GRAF•yt) is dull and dark, and it is so soft that you can write with it. Yet diamonds are so hard that people use them to cut steel.

Only about 100 minerals are common. One of the most common minerals is quartz.

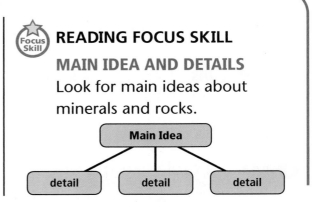
Mica

Garnet

◀ Notice the differences between the minerals in their natural settings and after they have been cut and polished.

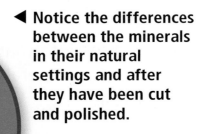
Quartz

Amethyst

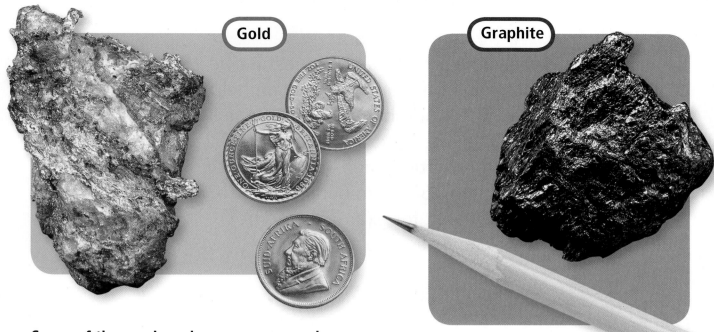

Gold

Graphite

Some of these minerals you use every day.

Halite

You use minerals throughout the day. If you put salt on your food, you are using a mineral. Minerals are also in many of the things around you. For example, quartz is used to make the glass in a window. Iron that is used in buildings comes from minerals, such as hematite. Minerals such as gold and diamond are often used to make jewelry. If you have a penny dated before 1983, it is made mostly of copper. Copper comes from minerals.

 MAIN IDEA AND DETAILS What are three ways minerals are used?

Ways to Identify Minerals

In the Investigate, you learned that hardness is one property of minerals. How hard a mineral is can help identify that mineral. The scale shown on this page is a tool scientists use to tell the hardness of a mineral.

Minerals have other properties, such as color, that can also help identify them. Some minerals can have more than one color. Quartz, for example, can be pink, purple, white, clear, or even black.

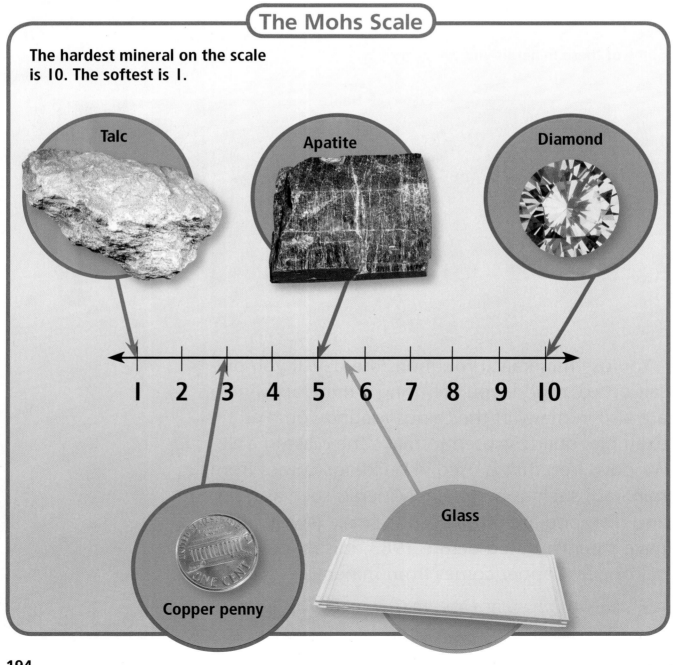

The Mohs Scale

The hardest mineral on the scale is 10. The softest is 1.

Talc

Apatite

Diamond

1 2 3 4 5 6 7 8 9 10

Copper penny

Glass

A streak test is one way to identify a mineral. ▼

Streak is another way to identify minerals. Streak is the color of the powder left behind by a mineral when it is rubbed against a rough white tile. The streak is usually the same color as the mineral. However, the streak can be a different color than the mineral's outside color.

 MAIN IDEA AND DETAILS What are two ways to identify minerals?

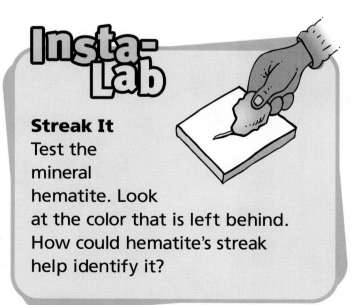

Insta-Lab

Streak It
Test the mineral hematite. Look at the color that is left behind. How could hematite's streak help identify it?

The Texas State House

▲ Builders use granite because it is beautiful and very strong.

Rocks

Earth is made mostly of rocks. A **rock** is a naturally formed solid made of one or more minerals. Look at the rock on this page. It is made of several minerals.

Earth has three main layers. The outside layer, which we live on, is the crust. The crust sits on the mantle. The mantle is so hot that some of the rocks flow like taffy. At the center of Earth is the metal core. The core is divided into two parts. The inner core is solid, and the outer core is so hot that it is liquid.

Focus Skill **MAIN IDEA AND DETAILS** What is rock made of?

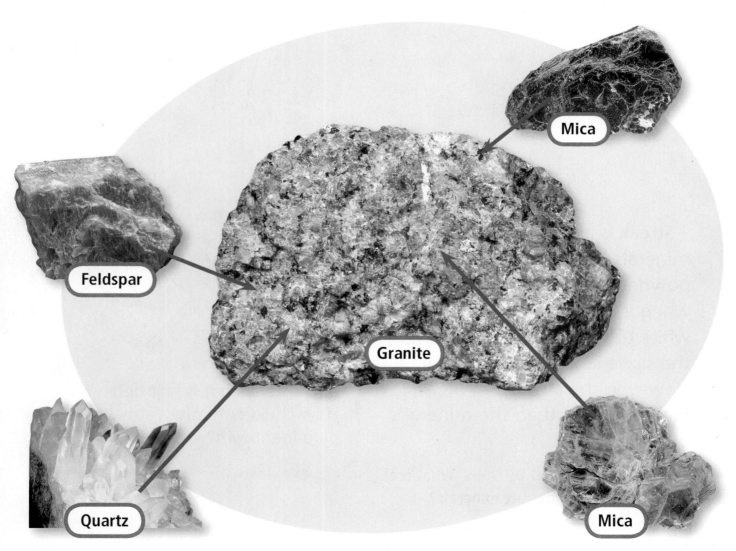

Mica

Feldspar

Granite

Quartz

Mica

1. MAIN IDEA AND DETAILS Draw and complete this graphic organizer.

```
        ┌─────────────────────────────┐
        │  Main Idea: Minerals and Rocks │
        └─────────────────────────────┘
              /                    \
  ┌──────────────────┐    ┌──────────────────┐
  │ A mineral is Ⓐ ____. │    │ A rock is Ⓑ ____. │
  └──────────────────┘    └──────────────────┘
```

2. SUMMARIZE Use the graphic organizer to write a summary of the lesson.

3. DRAW CONCLUSIONS Why is it better to identify a mineral by its hardness than by its color?

4. VOCABULARY Write at least two sentences comparing and contrasting a rock and a mineral.

FCAT Prep

5. Which is true of all minerals?
   A. They are all hard.
   B. They were never alive.
   C. They are made of rocks.
   D. They were once animals.

Links

Writing

Expository
Look at the rocks where you live. Choose one that looks interesting to you. Write a **description** of the rock. Make sure to tell about the color of the rock, how it feels, and what it looks like.

Social Studies

The Changing Penny
The United States penny has changed through the years. Research the different materials the penny has been made of. Make a poster to share your findings.

 For more links and activities, go to **www.hspscience.com**

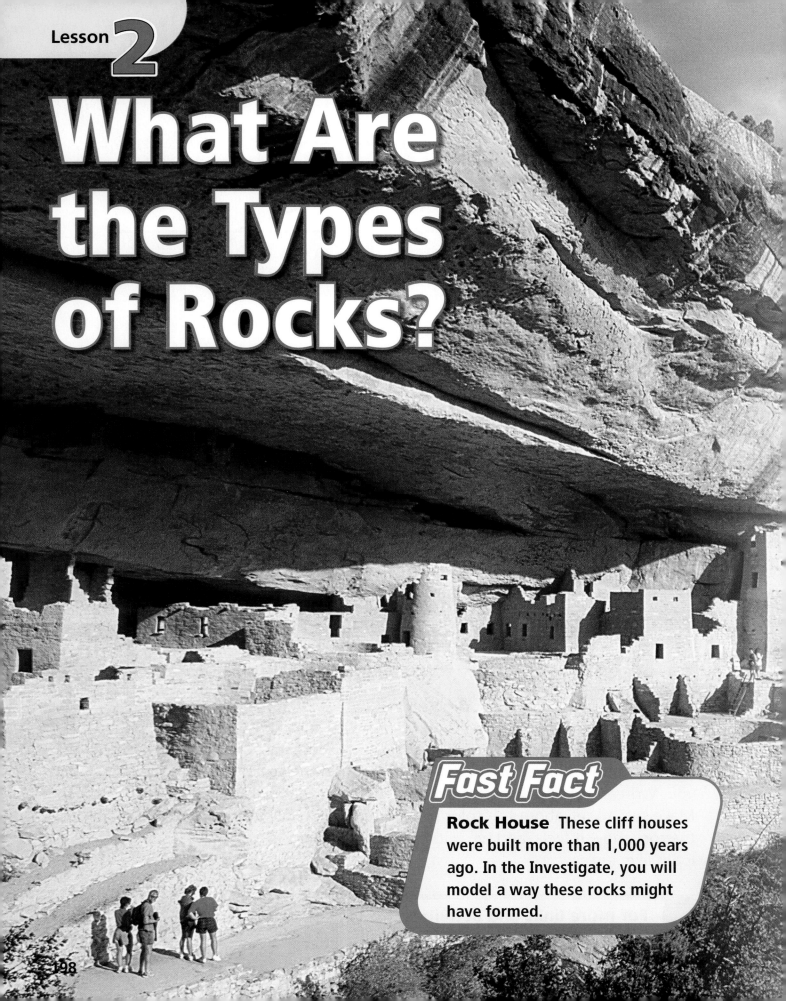

What Are the Types of Rocks?

Fast Fact

Rock House These cliff houses were built more than 1,000 years ago. In the Investigate, you will model a way these rocks might have formed.

Make a Model Rock

Materials
- newspaper
- sand
- wax paper
- gravel
- paper or plastic cup
- white glue
- plastic spoon
- water
- hand lens

Procedure

1. Spread newspaper over your work area. Place a smaller sheet of wax paper on the newspaper.

2. Place 1 spoonful of sand in the cup.

3. Add 1 spoonful of gravel to the cup. Stir the sand and gravel.

4. Add 1 spoonful of glue to the cup.

5. Stir the mixture until it forms a lump. You may need to add a little water.

6. Pour the mixture onto the wax paper, and let it dry. You have made a model of a rock.

Step 4

Step 6

Draw Conclusions

1. Use the hand lens to observe the dried mixture you made. What does the mixture look like?

2. **Inquiry Skill** Scientists often use models to understand processes they can't easily observe. Rocks can form when sand and gravel are somehow cemented or glued together. How is the model you made like a rock?

Investigate Further

Try to make models of rocks using different materials. Explore how changing the materials changes the rock.

VOCABULARY

igneous rock p. 200
sedimentary rock
p. 201
metamorphic rock
p. 201

SCIENCE CONCEPTS

▶ what the three types
of rocks are
▶ how rocks form

READING FOCUS SKILL

COMPARE AND CONTRAST
Look for the words *alike* and
different when reading about
types of rocks.

alike ——— different

Types of Rocks

Suppose you want to start a rock collection.
How would you group the rocks? By color, by
grain size, by whether they have layers? Rocks
can look very different, but there are just three
main types of rocks. The three types of rocks
are grouped by how they form.

Igneous (IG•nee•uhs) **rock** is rock that was
once melted and then cooled and hardened.
Some igneous rocks cool quickly and look like
glass. Other igneous rocks cool more slowly
and have large grains.

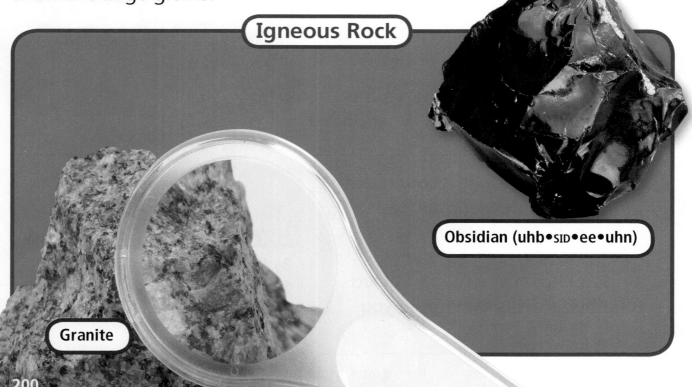

Igneous Rock

Obsidian (uhb•SID•ee•uhn)

Granite

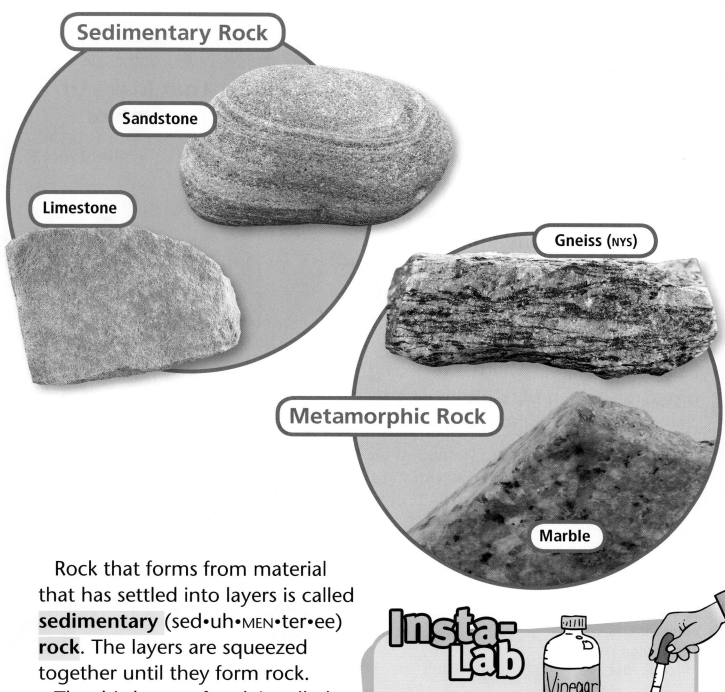

Sedimentary Rock

Sandstone

Limestone

Gneiss (NYS)

Metamorphic Rock

Marble

Rock that forms from material that has settled into layers is called **sedimentary** (sed•uh•MEN•ter•ee) **rock**. The layers are squeezed together until they form rock.

The third type of rock is called metamorphic rock. **Metamorphic** (met•uh•MAWR•fik) **rock** is rock that has been changed by temperature and pressure.

 COMPARE AND CONTRAST How is metamorphic rock different from igneous rock?

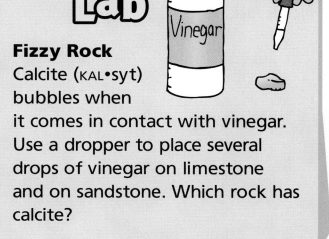

Insta-Lab

Fizzy Rock
Calcite (KAL•syt) bubbles when it comes in contact with vinegar. Use a dropper to place several drops of vinegar on limestone and on sandstone. Which rock has calcite?

How Rocks Form

The three types of rock form differently. Melted rock can reach Earth's surface through a volcano. Then it cools and becomes igneous rock.

Sedimentary rock, by contrast, begins with the breaking of rocks. Wind and water break rock into bits. Then the wind and water carry the bits of rock and soil away. The bits settle into layers. After a long time, the layers harden into rock.

Metamorphic rock forms deep in Earth's crust in yet another way. The pressure and temperature there change rock into metamorphic rock.

Focus Skill **COMPARE AND CONTRAST Contrast the ways the three types of rock form.**

Vents in volcanoes bring melted rock to the surface, where it cools. The cooled rock is igneous rock. ▶

202

▲ Wind and water break rock into small bits. Then wind and water carry away the bits of rock. Layers of these bits of rock form and, under pressure, become sedimentary rock.

◄ Rock inside Earth softens from Earth's high temperature. Pressure in Earth's crust then squeezes the rock. The rock changes into metamorphic rock.

The Rock Cycle

Over time, one kind of rock can become any other kind. The process of rocks changing from one kind of rock to another kind of rock is called the rock cycle. The diagram on the right page shows this cycle.

Wind and water break down all kinds of rocks to form sedimentary rocks. Any kind of rock that melts and cools can become an igneous rock. Any rock can end up in Earth's crust and be pressed and heated. Then that rock can become metamorphic rock.

 COMPARE AND CONTRAST How are all rocks alike and different?

This Colorado mountain range has all three kinds of rocks. ▼

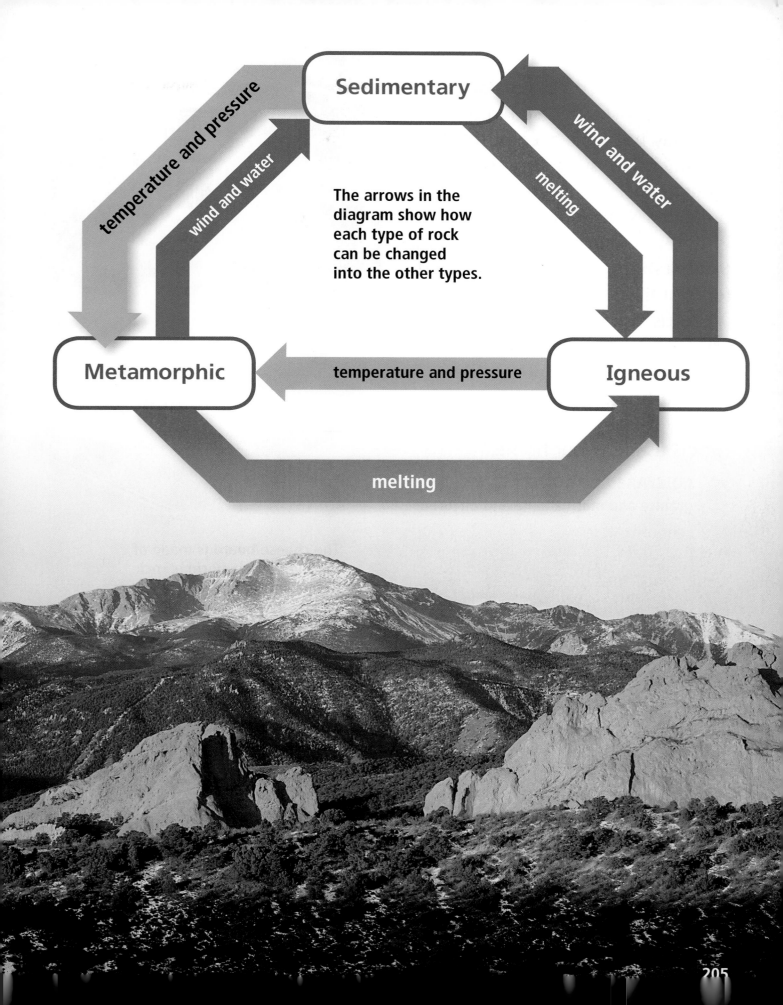

The arrows in the diagram show how each type of rock can be changed into the other types.

Sedimentary

temperature and pressure

wind and water

wind and water

melting

Metamorphic

temperature and pressure

Igneous

melting

How People Use Rocks

You often see rocks outside. However, rocks are used in places you may not have even noticed.

Many rocks, such as granite, an igneous rock, are used to make buildings. Crushed sedimentary rock is used to make cement and bricks. Slate, a metamorphic rock, is used for roof tiles.

Rock is also used in art. Some artists carve marble, which is a metamorphic rock, into statues. Other artists use granite for statues. See if you can find any place where rock is used in your home.

 COMPARE AND CONTRAST How are granite and marble alike and different?

The cheese board is made of marble, a metamorphic rock. Mount Rushmore is made up of mostly igneous and metamorphic rock. Stones for houses come from all three types of rock.

1. COMPARE AND CONTRAST Copy and complete this graphic organizer.

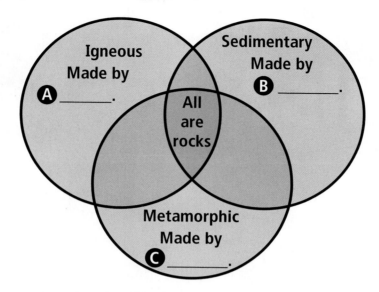

2. SUMMARIZE Write one or more sentences that tell the most important information about this lesson.

3. DRAW CONCLUSIONS Why are few sedimentary rocks found deep inside Earth?

4. VOCABULARY Write a definition for *metamorphic rock*.

FCAT Prep

5. Read/Inquire/Explain Suppose you're walking near a river. You see a dark gray rock that has layers like thick pages in a book. You pick up the rock, and some of the "pages" start to separate in your hands. What type of rock do you think it is? Explain.

Writing

Expository
Interview someone who works with rocks or minerals. Find out how he or she uses them. Write a **report** about what you learn, and share your report with the class.

Drama

Rock Cycle Play
With four other classmates, write a play about the rock cycle. Your play can be funny or serious. Perform the play for the class.

 For more links and activities, go to **www.hspscience.com**

What Are Fossils?

Fast Fact

Learning from the Past Animals like this one no longer exist, but their fossils show that they look similar to some of the animals alive today. In the Investigate, you will find out about how some fossils form.

Make a Model Fossil

Materials
- seashell
- small plastic bowl
- petroleum jelly
- white glue
- modeling clay

Procedure

1. Coat the outside of the seashell with a thin layer of petroleum jelly.

2. Press the seashell into the clay to make a model of a fossil.

3. Remove the seashell carefully from the clay.

4. Place the clay with the seashell's shape in the plastic bowl.

5. Drizzle white glue into the imprint. Fill it completely. This also makes a model of a fossil.

6. Let the glue harden for about a day. When it is hard, separate the hardened glue from the clay.

Step 2

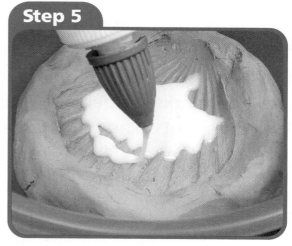

Step 5

Draw Conclusions

1. You made two models of fossils. How do the fossils compare?

2. **Inquiry Skill** Scientists use models to better understand how things happen. How do you think pressing the seashell into the clay models how a fossil forms?

Investigate Further

Use at least four other once-living materials such as fallen leaves to make models of fossils. Which materials make the best fossils?

VOCABULARY

fossil p. 210

SCIENCE CONCEPTS

▶ what fossils are
▶ how fossils form

READING FOCUS SKILL

MAIN IDEA AND DETAILS Look for information about different kinds of fossils.

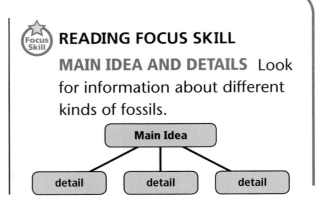

Fossils

Think about the "fossils" you made in the Investigate. Did they look like the shell you used? How were they different from the shell? A **fossil** is a trace or the remains of a living thing that died a long time ago. There are many different kinds of fossils.

Some fossils, such as bones and teeth, look like the actual parts of animals. Slowly minerals replaced the bones.

Other fossils, such as dinosaur tracks in mud, are only marks left behind. These marks are called imprints. The mud hardened, and in time it changed to rock. Some imprints are of animal parts, such as feathers. Other imprints are of leaves.

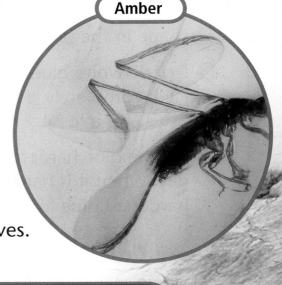

Amber

Cast

Mold

A mold is the shape of a once-living thing left in sediment when the rock formed. The organism that made the mold dissolved, leaving only a cavity shaped like the organism.

A cast forms when mud or minerals later fill a mold. The cast has the actual shape of the organism itself. You made a model of a fossil mold and a fossil cast in the Investigate.

Plant fossils are not as common as animal fossils. That's because the soft parts of plants are easily destroyed as rocks form.

 MAIN IDEA AND DETAILS What are three kinds of fossils?

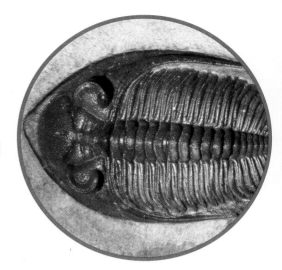

▲ This fossil shows a trilobite (TRY•luh•byt), a kind of animal that died out more than 200 million years ago.

◀ In petrified (PEH•truh•fyd) wood like this, minerals replaced the once-living plant.

Dinosaur tracks give clues to the animal's size and shape.

How Fossils Form

Places that have a lot of sedimentary rocks are better for fossil hunting than other places. Why? It's because what's left of a once-living thing is sometimes buried in the particles that form sedimentary rock. Fossils often form in limestone and shale.

Few fossils form in metamorphic and igneous rock. The pressure and temperature that form these rocks often destroy plant and animal parts before they can become fossils.

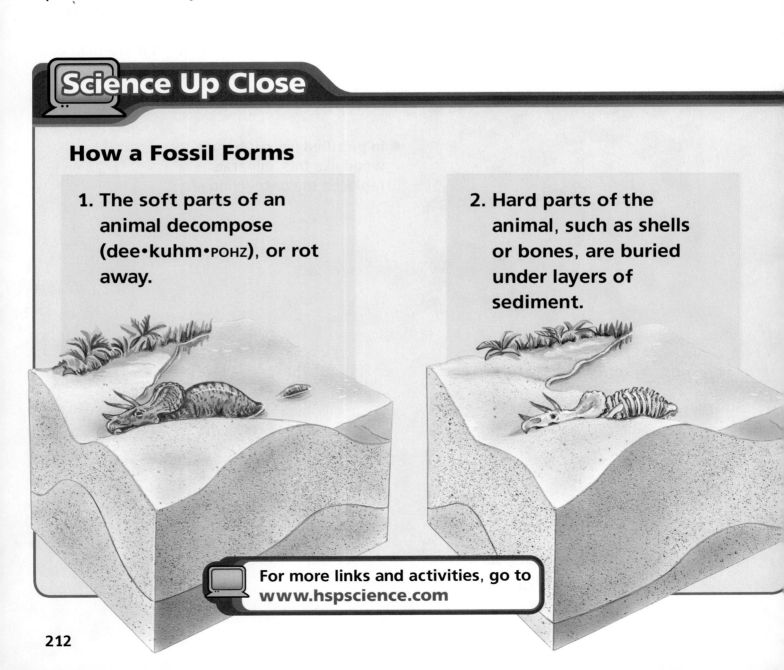

Science Up Close

How a Fossil Forms

1. The soft parts of an animal decompose (dee•kuhm•POHZ), or rot away.

2. Hard parts of the animal, such as shells or bones, are buried under layers of sediment.

For more links and activities, go to www.hspscience.com

The Science Up Close shows how a fossil might have begun forming millions of years ago. After dying, the animal was quickly covered by layers of sediment. If the animal had not been covered quickly, another animal might have eaten it. After millions of years, the layers of sediment became sedimentary rock. What was left of the animal is now a fossil.

MAIN IDEA AND DETAILS Why are more fossils found in sedimentary rocks than in other rocks?

This shows what the triceratops (try•SAIR•uh•tahps) fossil below might look like. ▼

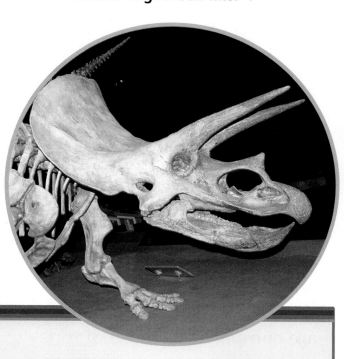

3. **Over a long time, the bones and sediment turn to rock.**

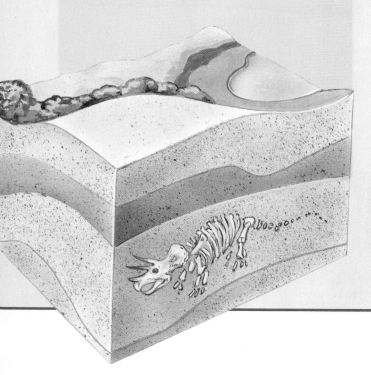

4. **Movement of Earth's crust brings the rock closer to the surface. Wind and rain wear away the rock. Then, people can see the fossils.**

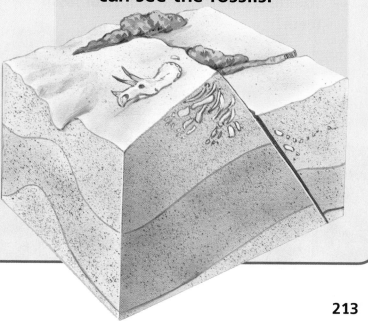

213

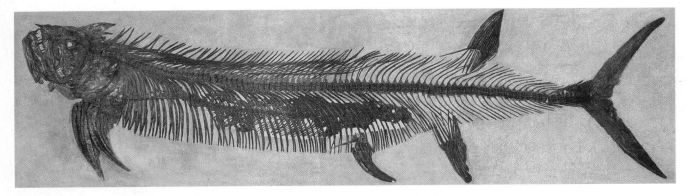

▲ What can a scientist tell about this fossil?

Learning from Fossils

Scientists today use fossils to learn about animals and plants that no longer exist. For example, scientists learn what kind of foods animals ate by looking at the shapes of fossil teeth. The teeth are compared to those of today's animals.

Fossils also help scientists tell what a place was like long ago. For example, fossil clams in a place show that a sea once covered the area.

Focus Skill **MAIN IDEA AND DETAILS** What can scientists tell from the shapes of fossil teeth?

Fossil Find

Press a hard object, such as a paper clip, into a ball of clay. Then remove the object. Trade clay imprints with a partner. Don't tell what object you used to make your imprint. Try to tell what object your partner used to make his or her imprint.

▼ Why do scientists dig up dinosaurs very carefully?

Focus Skill

1. MAIN IDEA AND DETAILS Copy and complete this graphic organizer about fossils.

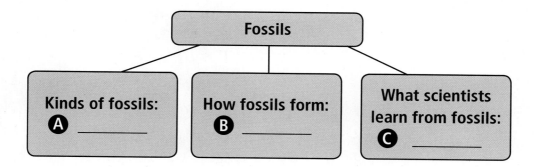

Fossils

Kinds of fossils:
A _____

How fossils form:
B _____

What scientists learn from fossils:
C _____

2. SUMMARIZE Use the graphic organizer to write a summary of the lesson.

3. DRAW CONCLUSIONS After walking through mud with his tennis shoes, Kyle notices an imprint of his track. Has Kyle made a mold or a cast?

4. VOCABULARY Write a sentence that tells the meaning of *fossil*.

FCAT Prep

5. Which is one thing scientists learn from fossils?
   A. how rocks form
   B. what sediments are
   C. what animals are like today
   D. about once-living things that no longer exist

Links

Writing

Narrative

Find out about a kind of dinosaur. Write a **story** about what life was like for the dinosaur. Include information about where the animal lived, its size, and what it ate.

Math

Word Problem

Write a word problem using information from this table. Have a classmate solve it.

Name of Dinosaur	Length
Stegosaurus	9 m (30 ft)
Brachiosaurus	25 m (82 ft)

For more links and activities, go to **www.hspscience.com**

SC.H.3.2.2.3.1
collects data

STUCK IN THE MUCK

Nearly 30,000 years ago, a thirsty woolly mammoth walked into a small pool to get a drink of water. The mammoth's feet sank into the dark pool, which was really a tar pit. Unable to get out of the sticky tar, the mammoth starved to death. Over time, the mammoth was covered by the tar.

Today, those tar pits are known as the La Brea (BRAY•ah) site in Los Angeles. The tar oozes up from beneath the Earth's surface. Each summer, scientists spend two months digging through La Brea's Pit 91 looking for fossils.

Digging Into the Past

Scientists have unearthed thousands of fossils from Pit 91. "The information we captured will tell us more about what life was like in this area 35,000 years ago," scientist Chris Shaw told Weekly Reader.

Digging in the pit is a slow and careful process. The bottom of the pit is divided into a grid so that scientists can pinpoint the exact spot of each fossil. After scientists take measurements, drawings, and pictures, the fossils are collected using small hand

tools. Those tools include dental picks, trowels, small chisels, and brushes.

The Search Continues

Shaw can't wait until next summer to start looking for more fossils. "The coolest thing about doing fieldwork," he said, "is realizing that the fossil you're touching has not seen the light of day for 35,000 years."

THINK ABOUT IT

1. Why would scientists divide the bottom of Pit 91 into a grid?
2. Why do scientists have to be careful when digging up fossils?

Brrrrrr!

About 30,000 years ago, Earth was in an ice age. The weather was much cooler then, and a mile-thick layer of ice, or glacier, covered much of what is now the United States. By digging in the pit, scientists have learned that many cold-weather animals lived near the tar pits. Woolly mammoths, saber-toothed cats, camels, llamas, and even lions once roamed the area.

Find out more! Log on to
www.hspscience.com

Digging Rocks

Mai-Li Chung loves collecting rocks. Her favorite ones are those with bright colors.

Mai-Li has collected rocks from all over the world. She is holding her prize piece of pyrite, which she found in Virginia.

"I hope to be able to have a rock from each state," says Mai-Li. "I want to find a pink quartz and an opal."

Find out more! Log on to
www.hspscience.com

You Can Do It!

Quick and Easy Project

Minerals in Sand

Procedure

1. Spread 1 tablespoon of sand on a sheet of white paper.

2. Observe the colors and shapes of the sand grains by using the hand lens. Each type of mineral grain has a different color and shape.

3. Use the toothpick to move the grains of each kind of mineral into a separate pile.

Materials

- sand
- sheet of white paper
- hand lens
- toothpick
- mineral descriptions
- measuring spoons

Draw Conclusions

Identify all the different minerals you can. Use the descriptions your teacher gives you. Which mineral is most common?

Design Your Own Investigation

Fossil Models

You have learned how some different kinds of fossils were formed. Make models to show how different kinds of fossils form. Use leaves, shells, clay, syrup, and other materials to make your models. Write down the steps you used to make each model. Have someone else use your steps to make his or her own model. Compare the two models.

Review and FCAT Preparation

Vocabulary Review

Match the terms to the definitions below. The page numbers tell you where to look in the chapter if you need help.

mineral p. 192
rock p. 196
igneous rock p. 200
sedimentary rock p. 201
metamorphic rock p. 201
fossil p. 210

1. Trace or remains of a living thing that died long ago

2. Rock that was once melted and then cooled and hardened

3. An object that is solid, has never been alive, and was formed in nature

4. A rock formed from material that settled in layers

5. A solid made of one or more minerals

6. A rock changed by temperature and pressure

Check Understanding

Write the letter of the best choice.

7. **MAIN IDEA AND DETAILS** Which tells a way most minerals are identified?
   A. beauty   **C.** smell
   B. heat   **D.** streak

8. **COMPARE AND CONTRAST** How are casts different from molds?
   F. Casts are only found in the mantle.
   G. Casts are plant fossils. Molds are animal fossils.
   H. Casts are materials that fill up a mold.
   I. Casts are fossils. Molds are not.

9. Which do the drawings show?

   A. how a fossil forms
   B. how a mineral forms
   C. how igneous rocks form
   D. how to classify kinds of rocks

10. Which is most important in forming igneous rocks?
- **F.** fossil models
- **G.** melting
- **H.** cool temperatures
- **I.** dead plants and animals

11. Which is an imprint fossil?
- **A.** a petrified tree
- **B.** a dinosaur footprint
- **C.** a dinosaur bone
- **D.** an insect trapped in sap

12. Which process is shown in the drawing?

- **F.** how sediments build up
- **G.** how imprint fossils form
- **H.** how metamorphic rocks form
- **I.** how sandstone forms

13. Which would be needed to form sedimentary rocks?
- **A.** a volcano
- **B.** casts and molds
- **C.** pressure and temperature
- **D.** wind and water

14. Which is **not** a way to identify a mineral?
- **F.** by its outside color
- **G.** by its hardness
- **H.** by doing a streak test
- **I.** by trying to break it

15. What is the hardest mineral on the Mohs Scale?
- **A.** apatite
- **C.** diamond
- **B.** copper
- **D.** talc

16. Which could a scientist infer about a place that has fish fossils?
- **F.** The place was once land.
- **G.** That place is a sea now.
- **H.** That place was once a sea.
- **I.** The fish did not live in water.

Inquiry Skills

17. How could you make a model to show the way sedimentary rocks form?

18. What could you use to order minerals by hardness?

READ INQUIRE EXPLAIN Read/Inquire/Explain

19. A scientist finds two fossils at different depths. Which fossil is probably older? Explain.

20. A scientist finds a dinosaur tooth that is flat, like a cow's tooth. What kind of food can the scientist infer the dinosaur ate? Why?

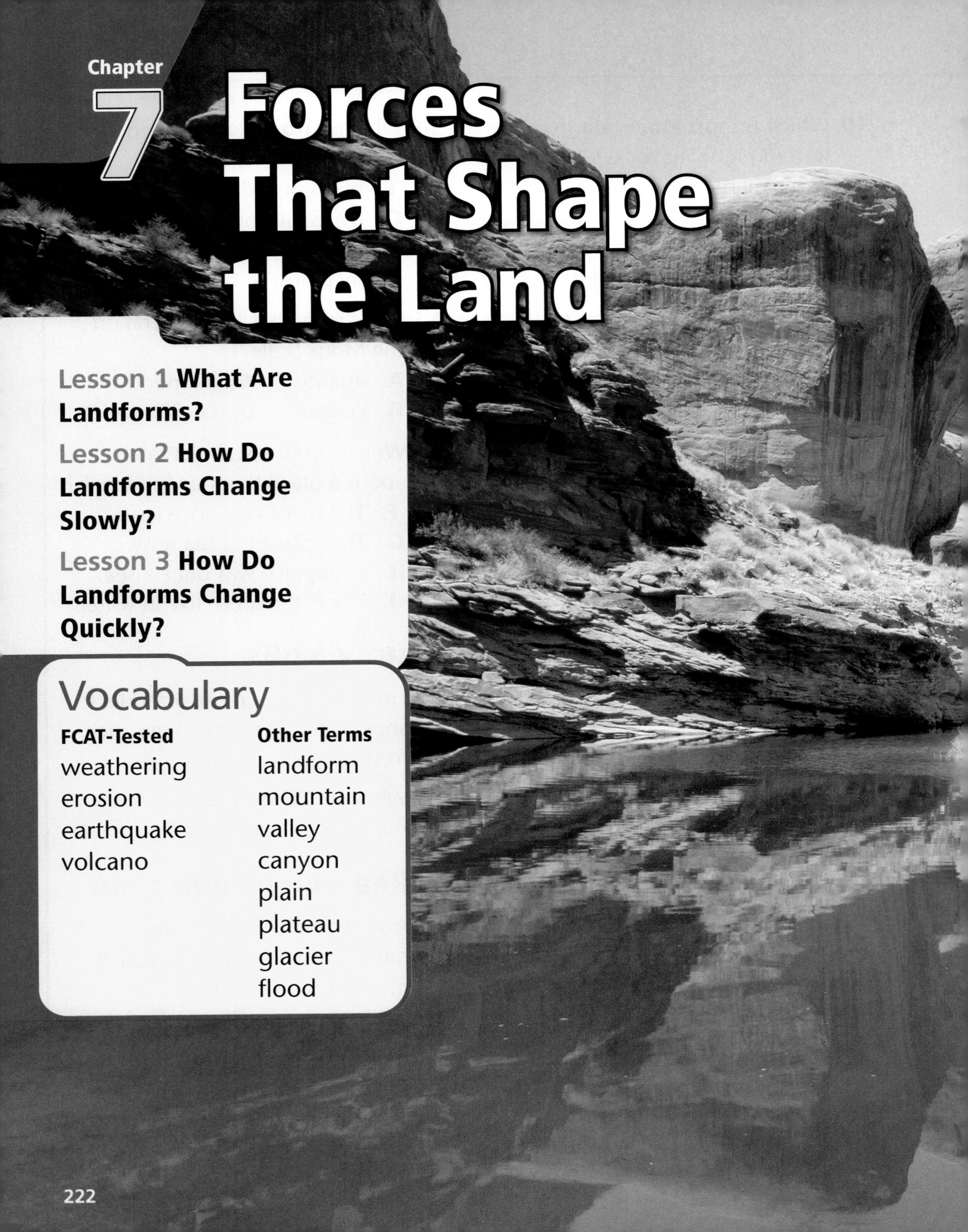

Chapter 7

Forces That Shape the Land

Lesson 1 **What Are Landforms?**

Lesson 2 **How Do Landforms Change Slowly?**

Lesson 3 **How Do Landforms Change Quickly?**

Vocabulary

FCAT-Tested	**Other Terms**
weathering	landform
erosion	mountain
earthquake	valley
volcano	canyon
	plain
	plateau
	glacier
	flood

What do YOU wonder?

Rainbow Bridge in Utah is the largest natural stone bridge in the world. Its top is 88 meters (288 ft) above the river below. It is almost as high as the Statue of Liberty. What do you think formed the bridge?

What Are Landforms?

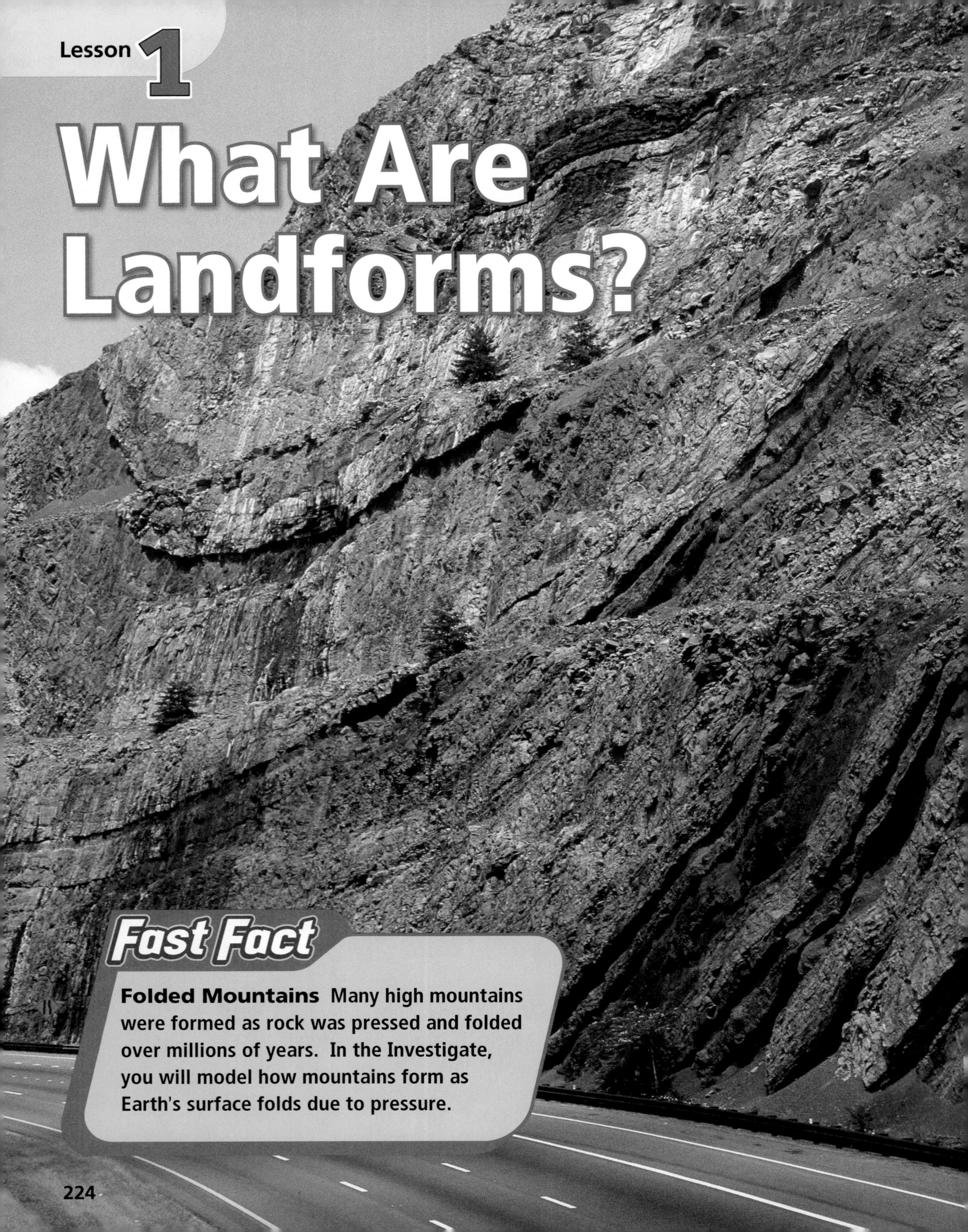

Fast Fact

Folded Mountains Many high mountains were formed as rock was pressed and folded over millions of years. In the Investigate, you will model how mountains form as Earth's surface folds due to pressure.

Folds in Earth's Crust

Materials • 4 paper towels • water in a plastic cup

Procedure

1. Stack the paper towels on a table. Fold the stack in half.

2. Sprinkle water on both sides of the towels. They should be damp but not very wet.

3. Place your hands on the ends of the damp towels.

4. Slowly push the ends toward the center. **Record** your **observations**.

Step 2

Draw Conclusions

1. What happened as you pushed the ends of the towels together?

2. How did the height of the towels change as you pushed the ends?

3. **Inquiry Skill** Scientists **use models** to understand how things happen. How does this model help you understand how some mountains form?

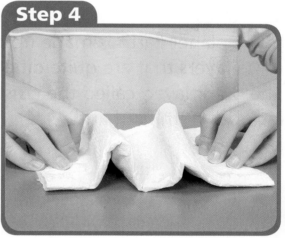

Step 4

Investigate Further

Other mountains form when two sections of Earth's crust push against each other. How would you **use a model** to show this?

VOCABULARY

landform p. 226
mountain p. 227
valley p. 228
canyon p. 228
plain p. 229
plateau p. 230

SCIENCE CONCEPTS

▶ the layers Earth has
▶ what landforms are

READING FOCUS SKILL

COMPARE AND CONTRAST
Look for ways landforms are
alike and different.

alike ———— different

Surface Features

Maybe you live in a flat area. Perhaps
you live in a hilly place. Flat areas and
hills are types of landforms. A **landform**
is a natural shape on Earth's surface,
which includes both dry land and
ocean floors. The ocean bottom has
mountains and valleys, just as the
land does.

The planet Earth is made up of
three layers that are quite different.
The outer layer, called the crust,
includes both land and water
features.

 COMPARE AND CONTRAST How are
the layers of Earth different from one
another?

Crust

Mantle

Core

Earth has three layers. The
outside layer is the rocky crust.
The mantle in the middle is
very hot rock. The outer part of
the core is liquid metal and the
center is solid metal.

Mountains

Earth's highest landforms are mountains. A **mountain** is a place on Earth's surface that is much higher than the land around it. A mountain is at least 600 meters (about 2,000 ft) high. High landforms that are smaller than mountains are hills. In the Investigate, you saw how Earth's crust can fold to form mountains.

There are different kinds of mountains. Some are rocky and pointed, while others are rounded. Some mountains are low. Others are very high and have snow on their tops all year long. The longest mountain range on Earth is in the ocean.

 COMPARE AND CONTRAST How are some mountains different from others?

This island is the top of a mountain. The rest of the mountain is under the water.

The Grand Tetons are mountains in Wyoming. They formed when forces pushed up a block of Earth's crust. ▼

Valleys

A **valley** is a low area between higher landforms, such as mountains. Some valleys are deep and narrow. They are V-shaped. Some valleys are wide and have flat bottoms. They are U-shaped. Their walls are far apart. Oceans have valleys, too.

A **canyon** is a valley with steep sides that have been carved by forces of nature. The biggest canyon in the United States is the Grand Canyon. It is 1.6 kilometers (1 mi) deep. The Colorado River wore away rock to form it. Canyons can even be found in the ocean.

COMPARE AND CONTRAST How is a valley different from a mountain?

Rivers can wear away rock and soil to form valleys. ▼

It took millions of years for water to carve this canyon. ▼

The Great Plains of North America stretch for thousands of kilometers in the United States and Canada. Short grasses grow on much of the Great Plains.

Plains

A **plain** is a wide, flat area on Earth's surface. Most plains are lower than the land around them. The plants that grow on dry plains are mostly grasses. Plains that get more rainfall may have many trees.

A huge plain lies in the middle of the United States. This region is called the Great Plains. It is a dry area, but it has rich soil. Farmers grow crops such as wheat, corn, and oats there.

Plains are also found along some oceans, lakes, and rivers. The plains near ocean coasts are called coastal plains. Coastal plains in the eastern United States are very wide. They have flat, sandy beaches.

 COMPARE AND CONTRAST How is a coastal plain the same as the Great Plains?

Plateaus

A **plateau** (pla•TOH) is a flat area higher than the land around it. Most plateaus are wide. In some places, plateaus have very steep sides.

Plateaus can wear away and get smaller. A small plateau is a mesa (MAY•suh). *Mesa* means "table" in Spanish. Mesas look like tables made of rock. A mesa can wear away until it is just a flat-topped rock column called a butte (BYOOT).

Streams and rivers can cut deep valleys in plateaus. These valleys become canyons. The Grand Canyon is in the Colorado Plateau.

COMPARE AND CONTRAST How are a plateau and a mesa alike? How are they different?

Insta-Lab

Make a Landform
Use clay to make a model of a landform in this lesson. What features make this landform different from others?

Water and wind wear away plateaus. They may become mesas, like the one you see here. ▼

230

1. COMPARE AND CONTRAST Copy and complete the graphic organizer below.

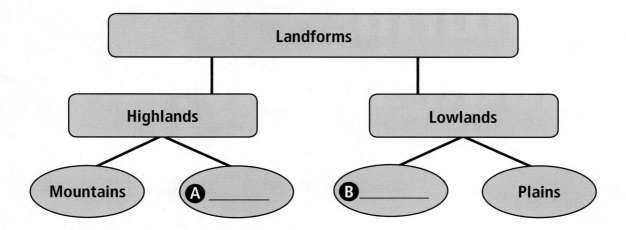

Landforms

Highlands

Lowlands

Mountains

A _____

B _____

Plains

2. SUMMARIZE Write a sentence that summarizes the main idea of this lesson.

3. DRAW CONCLUSIONS How are plateaus and mountains alike? How are they different?

4. VOCABULARY Make a crossword puzzle using the vocabulary terms from this lesson.

FCAT Prep

5. Which type of landform is in the middle of North America?

A. a mountain

B. a plain

C. a plateau

D. a valley

Links

Writing

Expository

Look for some landforms in your area. Write a paragraph **describing** where they are and what they look like.

Math

Construct a Bar Graph

Research the heights of four mountains. Make a bar graph showing their heights.

 For more links and activities, go to **www.hspscience.com**

Lesson 2

How Do Landforms Change Slowly?

Fast Fact

Rock Shapes Moving water and wind can wear down rock into unusual shapes. What may happen to the top part of this rock in time? In the Investigate, you will model how water breaks down rock.

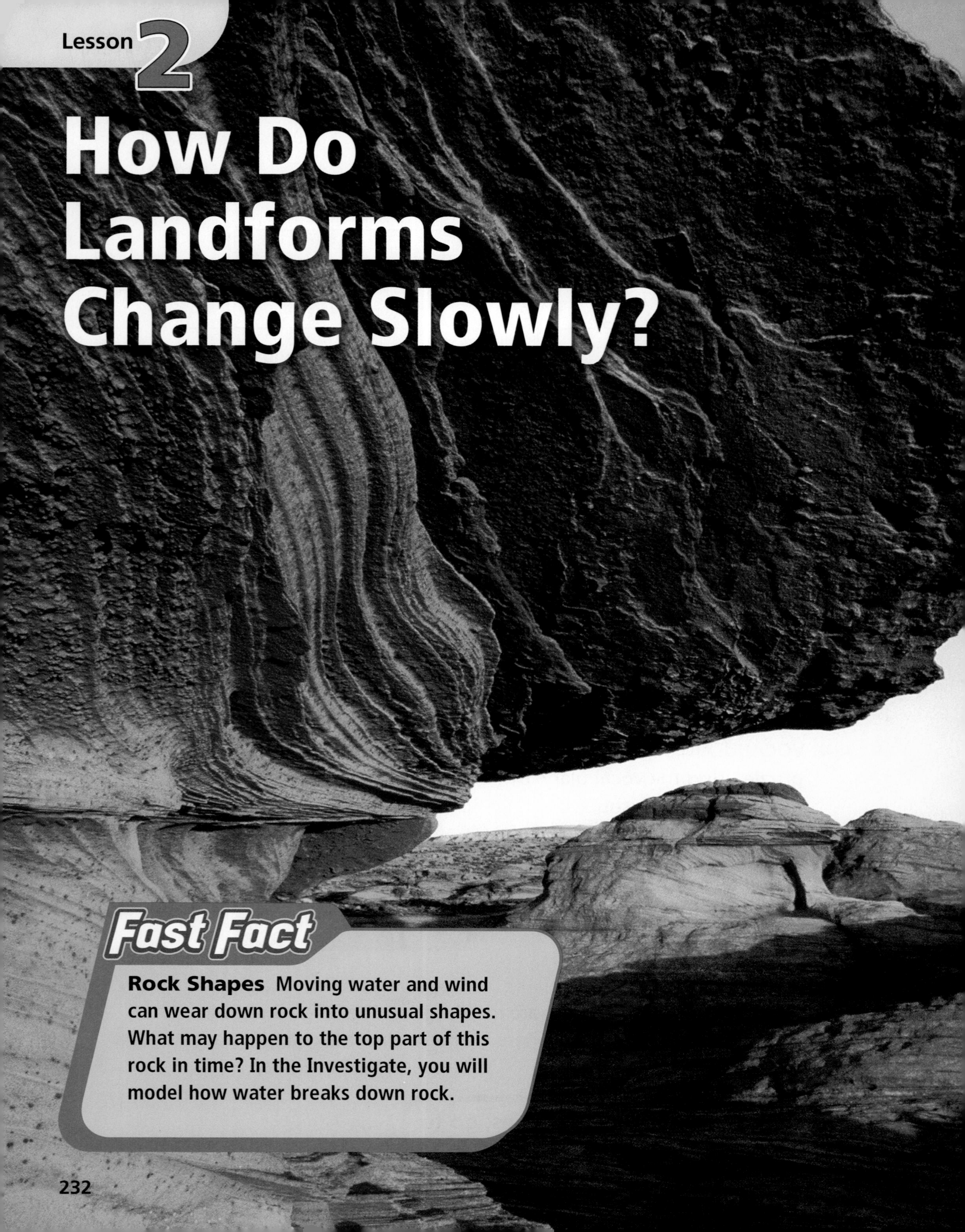

Water at Work

Materials
- balance
- extra masses for the balance
- water
- clear jar with lid
- small pieces of brick

Procedure

1. **Measure** the mass of the brick pieces. Record your results.

2. Fill the jar three-fourths full of water.

3. Put the brick pieces into the jar of water. Put the lid on the jar.

4. Take turns with a partner to shake the jar for 10 minutes. Do this three times a day for one week. Then **measure** and **record** the mass of the brick pieces.

Step 3

Step 4

Draw Conclusions

1. Do the brick pieces look different after a week of shaking them? If so, how are they different?

2. **Compare** the mass of the brick pieces before and after the shaking. Did the mass of the brick pieces change? If so, how did it change?

3. **Inquiry Skill** Scientists **interpret data** to understand how things work. Use your data to tell what happened to the brick pieces.

Investigate Further

Do large pieces of rock weather faster than small ones? **Plan and conduct an investigation** to test your prediction.

SC.H.1.2.2.3.1 following experimental design, **SC.H.1.2.3.3.1** working collaboratively, **SC.H.1.2.4.3.1** comparing/contrasting

233

Reading in Science

 SC.D.1.2.1.3.1 weathering of rocks, **SC.D.1.2.4.3.1** weathering, erosion, **SC.D.1.2.5.3.1** land forms change, **LA.A.2.2.1** sequence

VOCABULARY

weathering p. 234
erosion p. 236
glacier p. 238

SCIENCE CONCEPTS

▶ what weathering does
▶ what erosion does

READING FOCUS SKILL

SEQUENCE Look for the steps that lead to erosion.

How Rocks Are Broken Down

Earth's surface is rock. Rock wears down and breaks apart. The way rocks are broken down into smaller pieces is called **weathering** (WETH•er•ing).

Water causes weathering. Wind also breaks rock down. It picks up sand and then smashes it against rocks. This chips the rocks slowly. Ice breaks down rock in a different way. You can see how it does this on the next page. Plant roots can grow in cracks in rock and widen them, too.

Weathering happens slowly. It can take thousands of years for rocks to be broken down to become sand and soil.

 SEQUENCE How does wind break down rocks?

Water flows through cracks in rock. It slowly wears down the rock edges into rounded shapes.

Weathering has cracked this rock. The layers on the surface have broken off. ▼

How Ice Cracks Rock
Water in the form of ice can break down rock and concrete.

1 Water goes into a crack.

2 The water freezes and becomes ice. Frozen water takes up more space than liquid water. It pushes against the sides of the crack.

3 The crack becomes wider and breaks the concrete or rock.

For more links and activities, go to
www.hspscience.com

How Rock Pieces Move

After rocks are broken down, erosion moves the pieces. **Erosion** (ih•ROH•zhuhn) is the movement of weathered rock. Creep is a very slow type of erosion that moves rocks and soil. It can bend fences and walls over time.

Moving water is the cause of much erosion. Rainfall loosens sand and rock. It carries the sand and weathered rocks into rivers. The rivers carry the materials downstream.

When the water's flow slows down, the materials drop. Rivers drop sand along their banks. This is one way the shape of a river can change.

Plants help hold soil in place. They keep water from washing the sand away from farmlands.

Rivers drop sand and rock at their mouths. The sand and rock build up to form a landform called a delta. ▼

Rivers erode soil along their banks. This muddy river is carrying a lot of soil. ▼

Wind erosion blows sand into huge mounds called dunes. Dunes form in deserts and along sandy coasts.

Creep is very slow movement of rocks and soil. It happens too slowly to be seen. But it can bend fences and walls.

Wind causes erosion, too. The stronger the wind, the more soil it can carry. When the wind slows down, the soil drops and makes landforms.

In deserts, wind forms big piles of sand called dunes. Sand dunes can be taller than a 20-story building.

Erosion is often slow. It can take hundreds or even thousands of years to change the land.

SEQUENCE **What must happen before rock can be eroded?**

Growing Ice
Fill $\frac{1}{2}$ of a small plastic cup with water, and mark the water line. Put the cup in a freezer. When the water is frozen, check the mark. Is the ice at the same level? Measure how much the ice "grew." How does this relate to weathering?

How Glaciers Change the Land

Glaciers (GLAY•sherz) also shape the land through erosion. A **glacier** is a huge block of moving ice. Glaciers form where it is so cold that snow never melts. The snow piles up and turns to ice.

As glaciers move, they pick up rocks and soil. When they melt, they drop the rocks and soil, which form hills and ridges. Glaciers scrape the surface as they move. They make valleys wider.

 SEQUENCE How does a glacier form a hill?

Glaciers cover $\frac{1}{10}$ of Earth's surface. They form high in mountains and in areas near the poles. ▼

Which glacier is the longest? Where is it?

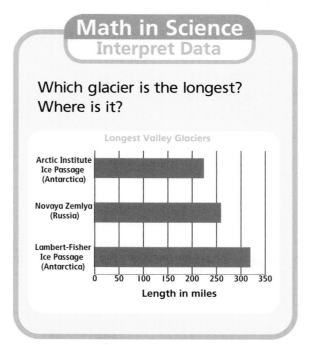

Longest Valley Glaciers

Arctic Institute Ice Passage (Antarctica)

Novaya Zemlya (Russia)

Lambert-Fisher Ice Passage (Antarctica)

Length in miles

Glaciers can carve deep grooves into rock. They can even form valleys.

1. SEQUENCE Copy and complete the graphic organizer below.

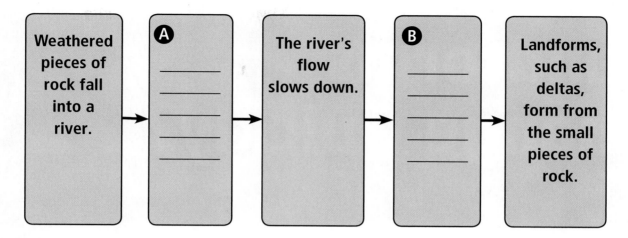

| Weathered pieces of rock fall into a river. | **A** _____ _____ _____ _____ _____ | The river's flow slows down. | **B** _____ _____ _____ _____ _____ | Landforms, such as deltas, form from the small pieces of rock. |

2. SUMMARIZE Summarize how water causes erosion.

3. DRAW CONCLUSIONS Would a tree root pushing up part of a sidewalk be an example of weathering or erosion? Explain.

4. VOCABULARY Draw a picture of a glacier. Then write a caption that explains what a glacier is.

FCAT Prep

5. Read/Inquire/Explain
Jamie visits her grandmother every summer. She sees that her grandmother's fence has moved from where it was. Explain how this may have happened.

Links

Writing

Narrative
Glaciers covered much of the land during the last Ice Age. Research the Ice Age. Then write a **story** about what a day might have been like for people living at that time.

Math

Solve Problems
If a delta grows by 3 meters each year, how much will it grow in 5 years? How much will it grow in 10 years?

 For more links and activities, go to www.hspscience.com

How Do Landforms Change Quickly?

Fast Fact

A Tall Volcano Mount Etna, shown in the picture, is the tallest active volcano in Europe. It is 3,350 m (10,990 ft) high. In the Investigate, you will make a model of a volcano.

A Model Volcano

Materials • 2 plastic jars • soil • safety goggles • measuring spoons • water • lab apron • flour • measuring cup • large tray • baking soda • dropper • white vinegar • wax paper • red and green food coloring

Procedure

① **CAUTION: Put on safety goggles and a lab apron.** Cover the tray with wax paper. Put a jar in the middle.

② Mix $\frac{1}{2}$ tsp flour and 1 tsp baking soda in the jar. Add 10 drops of red food coloring.

③ Dampen the soil a little, and pack it around the jar in a cone shape. Make the top of the soil even with the top of the jar.

④ Slowly pour $\frac{1}{4}$ cup vinegar into the jar. **Observe**. Remove the jar carefully. Wait 15 minutes.

⑤ Repeat Steps 2 through 4 with green food coloring and the other jar. **Record** your **observations**.

Draw Conclusions

1. What happened when you poured the vinegar into the jar? What does the mixture represent?

2. Inquiry Skill Scientists use models to understand how things happen in nature. How did your model help you learn how volcanoes change the land?

Step 3

Step 4

Investigate Further

Learn about different types of volcanic eruptions. Choose one type. **Plan and conduct an investigation** to model it.

SC.H.1.2.2.3.1 following experimental design, **SC.H.1.2.5.3.1** uses models

VOCABULARY

earthquake p. 242
volcano p. 244
flood p. 246

SCIENCE CONCEPTS

▶ how earthquakes and volcanoes change the land
▶ how floods change the land

READING FOCUS SKILL

CAUSE AND EFFECT Look for the effects of earthquakes.

| cause | → | effect |

Earthquakes

An **earthquake** is the shaking of Earth's surface. It is caused by movement in Earth's crust. Earth's crust is made up of rock. In some places, the rock has large cracks in it called faults.

When Earth's crust suddenly moves along these faults, the area above the fault can shake. The shaking of Earth's crust during an earthquake can cause many things to happen at Earth's surface.

Earthquakes can change landforms. They make big cracks in Earth's surface. They create uneven areas of ground.

Earthquakes can cause great damage. These homes in San Francisco tilted when the ground moved under them. ▼

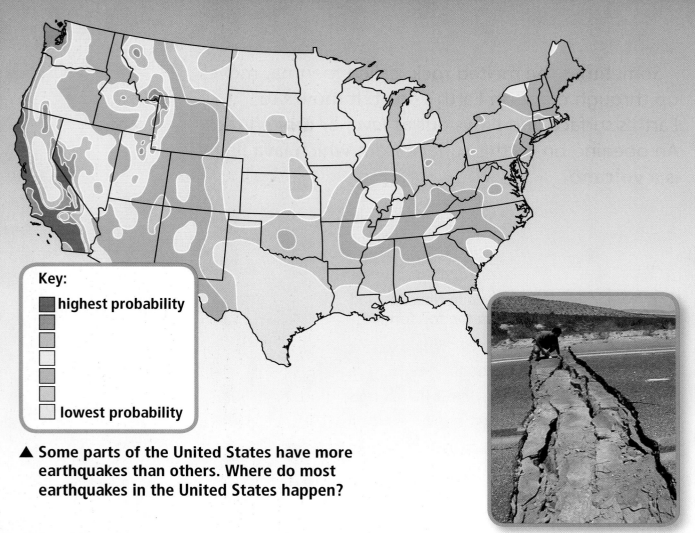

Key:
- highest probability
- lowest probability

▲ Some parts of the United States have more earthquakes than others. Where do most earthquakes in the United States happen?

Earthquakes can cause quick erosion. Near the coast, they can destroy beaches. In the mountains, they can cause large amounts of rock or soil to slide downhill. These movements are called landslides.

Earthquakes destroy buildings and other kinds of property. The landslides they cause can cover entire streets of houses. Even in undamaged homes, people may be without water or electricity for days after an earthquake.

CAUSE AND EFFECT What causes earthquakes?

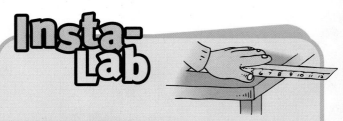

▲ The movement of the ground can split roads and damage bridges.

Insta-Lab

Where's the Energy?
Hold one end of a ruler down on a desk. Pull the other end up. What will happen if you let the free end go? Let it go. Was your prediction correct? Infer why this happens.

Volcanoes

Sometimes the melted rock, called magma, moves up through cracks in Earth's crust. It moves to Earth's surface and flows out as *lava*, or molten rock. An opening on Earth's surface from which lava flows is a **volcano**.

Heat from inside this volcano in New Zealand creates steam. The crater at the top formed during a past eruption.

When volcanoes erupt, they change Earth's surface quickly. The lava, ash, and rock they send out cover the land around them. Volcanoes also send out clouds of gas and ash that roll down the volcano's sides. The hot gas and ash burn down buildings and trees, affecting both human communities and animal habitats.

A volcano is a type of mountain. Lava and rock build up on its sides each time it erupts. The volcano mountain slowly becomes taller.

CAUSE AND EFFECT What effects does an erupting volcano have on land?

A river of lava flows down the sides of the volcano.

These houses are almost buried in lava and ash.

Floods

You know that water can change the land slowly. It can also change the land quickly. Sometimes so much rain falls that rivers and streams cannot hold all the water. The water flows over their banks, causing a flood. A **flood** is a large amount of water that covers normally dry land.

Floods sweep over the land. They destroy buildings and wash away bridges, roads, and crops. Floods also carry soil. When the floodwaters go down, they leave the soil along banks of rivers. Farmers can grow crops in this fertile soil.

 CAUSE AND EFFECT What causes a flood?

▲ **Droughts happen when an area does not get enough rain. The dryness and heat cause cracks in the soil.**

A river has flowed over its banks. It has flooded houses on a nearby plain. ▼

1. CAUSE AND EFFECT Copy and complete the graphic organizer below.

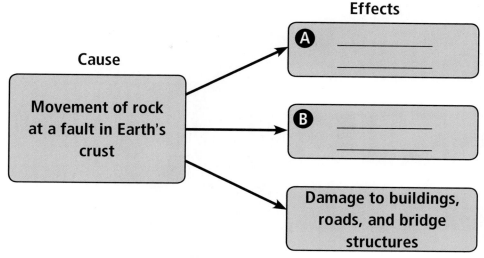

Effects

Cause

Movement of rock at a fault in Earth's crust

A _____
_____

B _____
_____

Damage to buildings, roads, and bridge structures

2. SUMMARIZE Write a short summary of the lesson. Begin with the sentence *Earth's surface can change quickly.*

3. DRAW CONCLUSIONS Suppose you lived in an area where earthquakes happen. What would you need to do to keep safe during an earthquake?

4. VOCABULARY Use a vocabulary term in a sentence correctly.

FCAT Prep

5. Which of these is an effect of earthquakes?
   A. burned forest
   B. large cracks in Earth
   C. gas clouds
   D. crops washed away

Links

Writing

Expository

Imagine that you are a TV reporter watching a volcano erupt. Write a **report** describing what you see. Make sure your information is correct.

Social Studies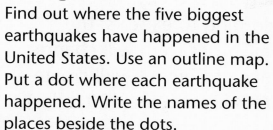

The Big Ones

Find out where the five biggest earthquakes have happened in the United States. Use an outline map. Put a dot where each earthquake happened. Write the names of the places beside the dots.

 For more links and activities, go to **www.hspscience.com**

SC.H.3.2.3.3.1 scientific discoveries impact humans

The Great Dam

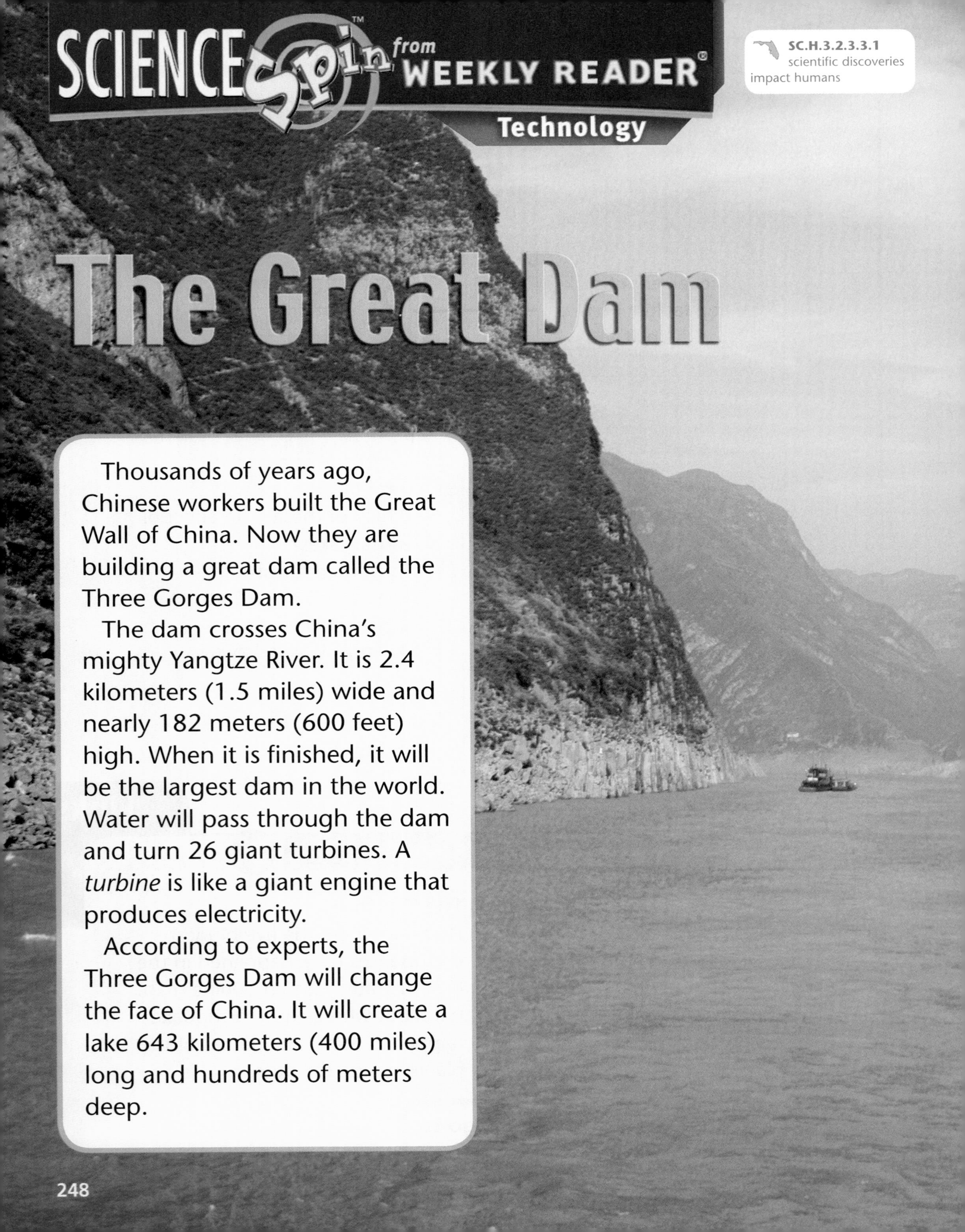

Thousands of years ago, Chinese workers built the Great Wall of China. Now they are building a great dam called the Three Gorges Dam.

The dam crosses China's mighty Yangtze River. It is 2.4 kilometers (1.5 miles) wide and nearly 182 meters (600 feet) high. When it is finished, it will be the largest dam in the world. Water will pass through the dam and turn 26 giant turbines. A *turbine* is like a giant engine that produces electricity.

According to experts, the Three Gorges Dam will change the face of China. It will create a lake 643 kilometers (400 miles) long and hundreds of meters deep.

The Three Gorges Dam will hopefully help stop flooding by the Yangtze River. ▼

Why Build a Dam?

To build the dam, officials had to construct a coffer dam. This is a temporary dam that sends the river around the building site.

Chinese officials hope the dam will stop the Yangtze River from flooding. For centuries, flooding of the river has been a problem. Floods in China have killed more than a million people over the past 100 years.

Not everyone is happy about the dam. Some people say the dam will hurt the environment. They fear that the new giant lake caused by the dam will collect a lot of pollution from towns and factories along the Yangtze. Any people or animals living near the lake might be harmed by that pollution.

THINK ABOUT IT

1. How will the Three Gorges Dam change the landscape of China?

2. Why would people want a dam built? Why would people not want a dam built?

Find out more! Log on to **www.hspscience.com**

SCIENCE Spin™ from WEEKLY READER®

SC.H.3.2.1.3.1
history of science/
contributions of scientists

People

Measuring Movements

Every so often, the news reports about an earthquake. During the report, you will probably hear the words "Richter scale." That's not a giant scale to weigh people. The Richter scale measures the overall strength of an earthquake.

That scale was created by Charles Richter (1900–1985). Richter was a *seismologist*, a scientist who studies earthquakes and the structure of the Earth. Seismologists try to determine where and when an earthquake may occur next.

Career   Volcanologist

Volcanologists are scientists that study volcanoes. They watch volcanic sites and gather information about the Earth. Volcanologists help keep people safe who live near volcanoes. They warn them of possible eruptions so they can leave the area.

Find out more! Log on to
www.hspscience.com

You Can Do It!

Quick and Easy Project

Shake the Earth

Procedure

1. Cover the top of the gelatin with plastic wrap.

2. Use the croutons to make buildings on the gelatin.

3. Move the pan up and down and from side to side. Tap one end as you move it. Observe the movement of the gelatin.

Materials

- baking pan filled with gelatin
- plastic wrap
- large croutons

Draw Conclusions

Did the movement damage your "buildings"? Record your observations. How does this model an earthquake?

Design Your Own Investigation

Find Changes to the Land

Look for changes that have happened quickly to the land where you live. The changes can be natural. They can also be changes caused by people. Design a way to show how the land changed. You might use before and after photos or drawings. Or you might just show the effects of the changes. Then write a description of what happened.

Review and FCAT Preparation

Vocabulary Review

Use the terms below to complete the sentences. The page numbers tell you where to look in the chapter if you need help.

canyon p. 228
plateau p. 230
weathering p. 234
erosion p. 236
glacier p. 238
earthquake p. 242
volcano p. 244
flood p. 246

1. The movement of weathered rock and soil is _____.

2. An opening in Earth's surface from which lava flows is a _____.

3. A valley with steep sides is a _____.

4. A huge block of moving ice is a _____.

5. The shaking of Earth's surface is an _____.

6. A flat area higher than the land around it is a _____.

7. The breaking down of rocks into smaller pieces is _____.

8. A large amount of water that covers the land is a _____.

Check Understanding

Write the letter of the best choice.

9. Which of these is a low area?
   A. mesa   **C.** plateau
   B. mountain   **D.** valley

10. Which of these words describes a plain?
    F. deep   **H.** hilly
    G. flat   **I.** steep

11. **CAUSE AND EFFECT** Which of these is an effect of weathering?
    A. mountain building
    B. water freezing
    C. volcano erupting
    D. rock splitting

12. Which landform does this illustration show?
    F. mountain
    G. plain
    H. plateau
    I. valley

13. Which of these causes the land to change slowly?

   A. flood   **C.** glacier

   B. earthquake   **D.** volcano

14. Where do most earthquakes happen?

   F. on buttes   **H.** on plains

   G. at faults   **I.** in valleys

15. **COMPARE AND CONTRAST** Which type of landform is a kind of mountain?

   A. volcano   **C.** plateau

   B. plain   **D.** valley

16. How does a flood change the land?

   F. It cracks rock.

   G. It drops soil.

   H. It lifts mountains.

   I. It sends out lava.

Inquiry Skills

17. Why would it be useful to make a model to study erosion caused by glaciers?

18. Compare and contrast the effects of weathering and the effects of erosion.

 Read/Inquire/Explain

19. Which of these rocks have undergone more weathering? Explain your answer.

20. In which of these three areas do you think flooding would most likely happen? Explain your answer.

A.

Plains

B.

Mountains

C.

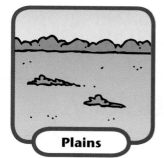

Valleys

253

The Water Cycle

Vocabulary

FCAT-Tested	Other Terms
condensation	fresh water
evaporation	glacier
water cycle	groundwater
atmosphere	precipitation
	oxygen
	weather
	temperature
	anemometer

What do YOU wonder?

Water is just about everywhere on Earth. Where do you think big waves of water like the one in this picture are found?

Where Is Water Found on Earth?

Fast Fact

Water Everywhere!
Almost three-fourths of Earth is covered by water! In the Investigate you will observe this by using a model.

Where in the World Is Water?

Materials
- plastic inflatable globe
- pencil
- sheet of paper
- colored pencils or crayons

Procedure

1. Work in a group of five. Choose one person to be the recorder.

2. The other four persons toss the globe gently to one another.

3. The catcher catches the globe with open hands. The recorder **records the data** of whether the catcher's right index finger touches land or touches water.

4. Continue tossing and recording until the globe has been tossed 20 times.

Step 2

Step 3

Draw Conclusions

1. Total the catches. How many times did the catcher's right index finger touch water? How many times did it touch land?

2. Where did the catcher's finger land more often? Why do you think this happened?

3. **Inquiry Skill** Scientists use **numbers** to **collect data**. Using your data, estimate how much of Earth's surface is covered by water.

Investigate Further

Gather Data The more data you collect, the more accurate your data will be. How would doing the Investigate 10 more times change your data? Try it! **Communicate** your results in a bar graph.

SC.H.1.2.1.3.1 keeping accurate records,
SC.H.1.2.3.3.1 working collaboratively,
SC.H.3.2.2.3.1 collects data

257

VOCABULARY

fresh water p. 259

glacier p. 260

groundwater p. 260

SCIENCE CONCEPTS

▶ why water is important

▶ where water is found on Earth

READING FOCUS SKILL

MAIN IDEA AND DETAILS Look for details about water.

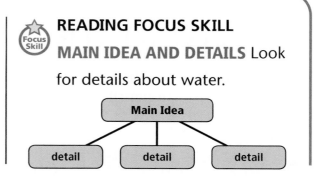

The Importance of Water

You drink water. You use water when you take a bath or a shower. You might even play in water. More than two-thirds of your body is made of water! Animals need water to stay healthy. Plants also need water. Some animals and plants live in water. You and other living things on Earth could not live without water.

Water isn't important only to living things. It's also important to Earth's environment. Water changes Earth's surface. Without water, there would be no rivers, lakes, or oceans. There would be no rain, snow, or clouds.

Deer must drink water to stay alive. ▶

Farmers use a lot of water to grow crops. It takes 11 liters (3 gal) of fresh water to grow a single tomato.

If you look at a picture of Earth taken from space, you will see a lot of blue. Earth looks blue because of the water. Most of the water seen from space is in Earth's seas and oceans. This water is salt water.

Most land plants can't live if salt water is put on them. Many animals, including people, can't drink salt water. Most plants and animals need fresh water to live. **Fresh water** is water that has very little salt in it. Only a small part of Earth's water is fresh. Most of the fresh water on Earth is frozen.

 MAIN IDEA AND DETAILS What are two types of water?

Math in Science
Interpret Data

Water on Earth
Most of the water on Earth is found in the oceans. For every liter of liquid fresh water, there are 2 liters of frozen fresh water and 97 liters of salty ocean water.

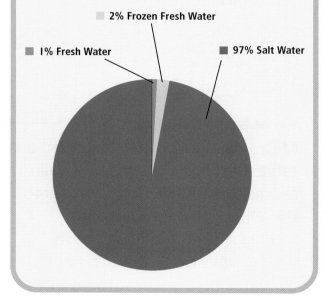

2% Frozen Fresh Water

1% Fresh Water

97% Salt Water

Fresh Water

Almost all the fresh water on Earth is found in one place—Antarctica. Antarctica is the land at the South Pole. Most of the fresh water there is frozen in glaciers. A **glacier** is a huge sheet of moving ice.

Not all fresh water is frozen. Fresh water is also found in the form of rain and melted snow. The water from rain and snow flows into streams, rivers, ponds, and lakes.

Fresh water can also be found under the ground. After a rain, water soaks into the ground. The water moves through the soil until it reaches solid rock. The water collects above the solid rock. This underground supply of water is called **groundwater**. Many people dig wells in the ground and pump up groundwater to supply their homes with water.

 MAIN IDEA AND DETAILS Where is fresh water found on Earth?

How Much Water?

Measure a gallon of water and a tablespoon of water. If the gallon represents all the water on Earth, the water in the tablespoon represents all the liquid fresh water. How does the total amount of water on Earth compare with the amount of water available for people to drink?

Lake Eola in Orlando, Florida, is an example of a freshwater lake.

This is a picture of Lake Powell. You can see how high the water has been by looking at the water lines on the rocks.

Salt Water

Almost all water on Earth is salt water. You can find salt water in oceans, seas, and gulfs. Three major saltwater bodies surround the United States. These are the Atlantic Ocean, the Pacific Ocean, and the Gulf of Mexico. You can also find salt water in some lakes, such as Great Salt Lake, in Utah.

You can't drink salt water, but salt water is very important. When sunlight hits the ocean, the top part of the water becomes warm. Warm ocean water moves around Earth and helps keep some places warm. People use many things from the ocean, such as fish.

▲ The state of Florida is almost completely surrounded by salt water.

MAIN IDEA AND DETAILS Where is salt water found?

1. MAIN IDEA AND DETAILS Draw and complete this graphic organizer.

Main Idea: About three-fourths of Earth's surface is covered by water.

Salt water	Frozen fresh water	Fresh water
Where it is found: **A** _____	Where it is found: **B** _____	Where it is found: lakes, rivers, and underground

2. SUMMARIZE Use the completed graphic organizer to write a lesson summary.

3. DRAW CONCLUSIONS Why is it important to not litter in fresh water or salt water?

4. VOCABULARY Write a sentence explaining how the terms *fresh water*, *glacier*, and *groundwater* are related.

FCAT Prep

5. Read/Inquire/Explain
Suppose you are digging a hole in the ground. Right after you start digging, you notice that the soil is very damp. Using your observations, explain what might have happened.

Links

Writing

Persuasive
Write a **letter** to your city mayor, explaining that there isn't a lot of fresh water on Earth. Give the mayor reasons people should protect the fresh water.

Art

Animal Mobile
Find out about the kinds of animals that live in water. Make a mobile that shows some of these animals. Hang a label under each animal that says whether the animal lives in salt water or in fresh water.

 For more links and activities, go to **www.hspscience.com**

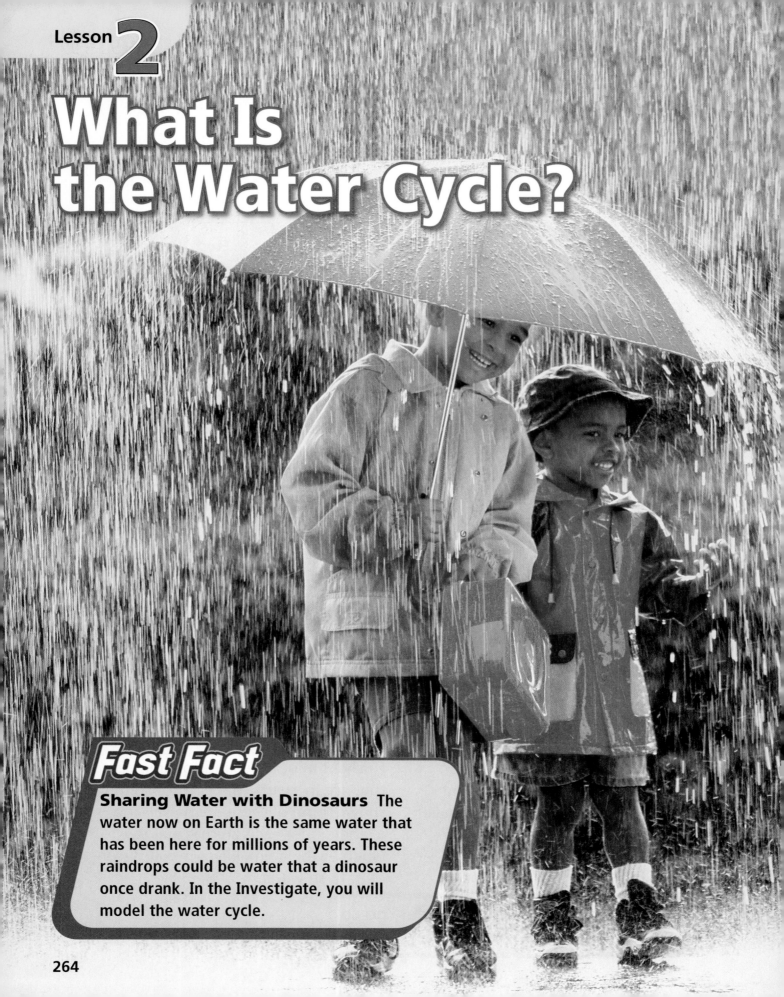

What Is the Water Cycle?

Fast Fact

Sharing Water with Dinosaurs The water now on Earth is the same water that has been here for millions of years. These raindrops could be water that a dinosaur once drank. In the Investigate, you will model the water cycle.

Condensation in a Terrarium

Materials
- clear plastic salad container
- water
- soil
- spray bottle
- packet of seeds

Procedure

1. To build a terrarium, put about 3 cm of soil in a clear plastic salad container.

2. Plant the seeds. Follow the instructions on the seed package.

3. Using a spray bottle, spray the soil until it is moist. Close the lid of the container, and label the container with your name.

4. Place the terrarium next to a sunny window or under a lamp. **Observe** your terrarium for several days. Write down all the changes you see.

Step 2

Potting soil

Step 4

Draw Conclusions

1. What changes happened inside the terrarium?

2. Did anything in the terrarium remind you of weather? If so, what was it?

3. **Inquiry Skill** You watered your terrarium only one time. **Infer** how water may have gotten on the lid of the terrarium.

Investigate Further

Do the same Investigate, but don't close the lid. What do you think will happen? **Compare** your observations with the lid closed and not closed.

SC.H.1.2.1.3.1 keeping accurate records,
SC.H.1.2.4.3.1 comparing/contrasting,
SC.H.2.2.1.3.1 makes predictions

VOCABULARY

condensation p. 268

evaporation p. 269

precipitation p. 270

water cycle p. 270

SCIENCE CONCEPTS

▶ how water changes forms

▶ how water moves from place to place

READING FOCUS SKILL

SEQUENCE

Look for the sequence in which water changes forms.

Different States of Water

Maybe you have watched water boiling in a pot. If the water boils for a long time, no water will be left in the pot. Even though the water seems to disappear, it really doesn't. The water just changes from a liquid to a gas. The water in the pot was a liquid. The rising vapor that you couldn't see was in the form of a gas.

All water on Earth is in one of three states. It is a liquid, a solid, or a gas. Solid water is ice. Water in gas form is *water vapor*.

The water in this canal is in a solid form during the winter.

The state that water is in depends on its temperature. At room temperature, water is a liquid. When water is cold enough, it turns into ice. When water is hot enough, it turns into water vapor, which is a gas.

Look at the picture on the left hand page. You know the temperature in that place is cold because the water is ice. Water becomes ice only when its temperature is 0°C (32°F) or colder. Now, look at the picture on this page. You know the temperature in this place must be above 0°C because the water is liquid. Above 100°C (212°F), water becomes water vapor.

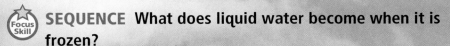 **SEQUENCE** **What does liquid water become when it is frozen?**

In the summer, the water in the canal is liquid.

How Water Changes States

If you have seen liquid on the outside of a glass that has a cold drink inside, you have seen water change its state. You might know that when water gains or loses thermal energy, the temperature of the water changes. Thermal energy gain makes the temperature of water go up. Thermal energy loss makes the temperature of water go down.

When water vapor loses thermal energy, the vapor becomes liquid. The process of a gas turning into a liquid is **condensation**. Clouds are formed from water vapor.

When water vapor condenses on dust particles in the air, clouds form. ▼

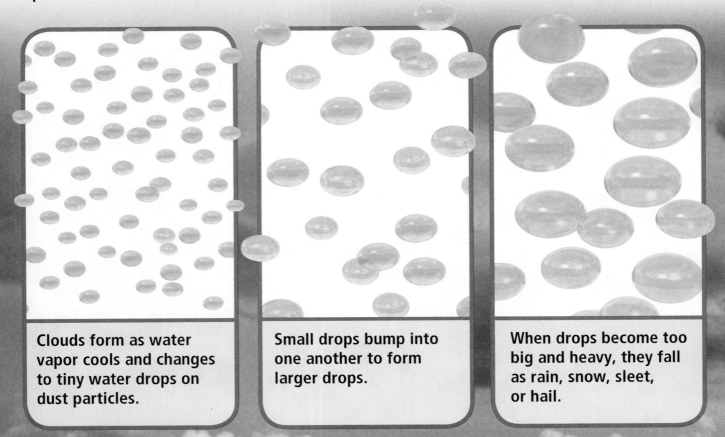

Clouds form as water vapor cools and changes to tiny water drops on dust particles.

Small drops bump into one another to form larger drops.

When drops become too big and heavy, they fall as rain, snow, sleet, or hail.

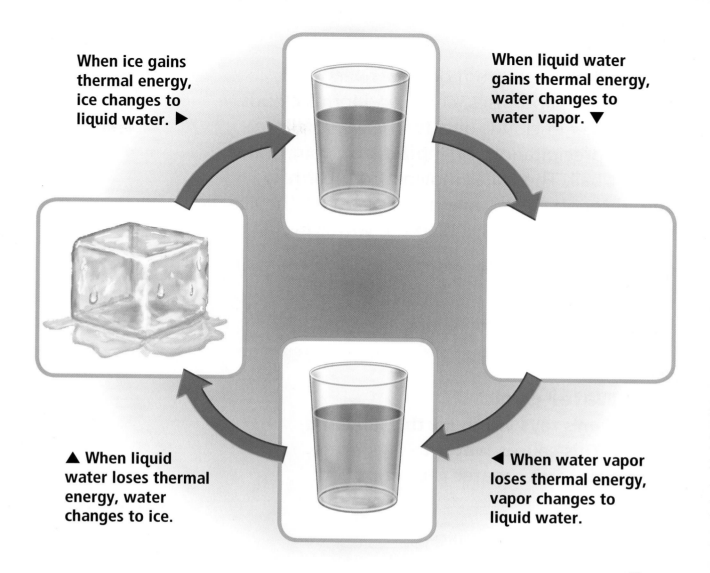

When ice gains thermal energy, ice changes to liquid water. ▶

When liquid water gains thermal energy, water changes to water vapor. ▼

▲ When liquid water loses thermal energy, water changes to ice.

◀ When water vapor loses thermal energy, vapor changes to liquid water.

When liquid water gains thermal energy, the water changes to water vapor. This change is **evaporation**. Think about water boiling in a teakettle. The space just above the spout where you don't see anything is where water has changed state. Here water is a vapor, or a gas. The cloud above the kettle shows condensation. The water has changed to a liquid.

 SEQUENCE What happens to water vapor when it loses thermal energy?

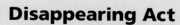

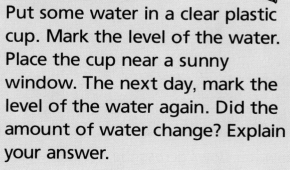

Disappearing Act
Put some water in a clear plastic cup. Mark the level of the water. Place the cup near a sunny window. The next day, mark the level of the water again. Did the amount of water change? Explain your answer.

The Water Cycle

Water evaporates from oceans, rivers, and lakes. Water vapor rises, cools, and forms clouds. When water in clouds gets too heavy, it falls to Earth as precipitation. **Precipitation** is rain, snow, sleet, or hail. The water moving from Earth's land, through rivers toward the ocean, to the air, and then back again is called the **water cycle**.

 SEQUENCE What must happen before precipitation can fall?

Science Up Close

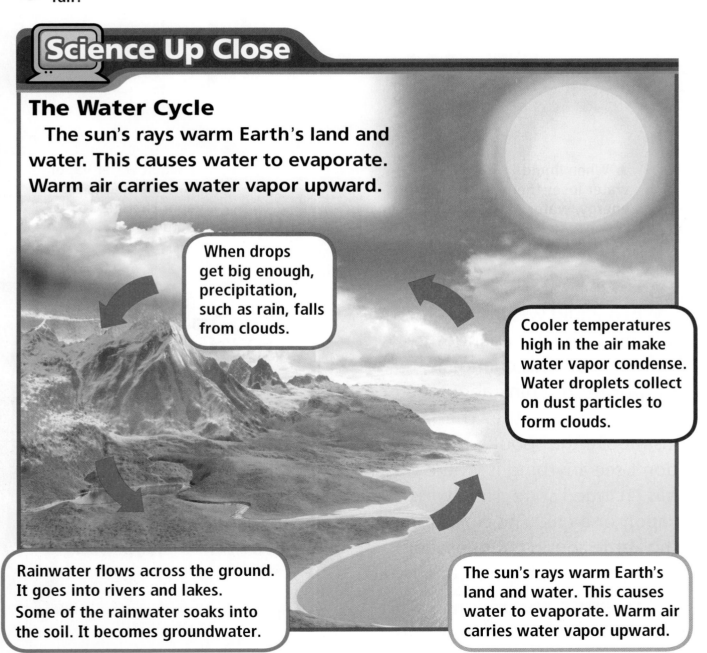

The Water Cycle

The sun's rays warm Earth's land and water. This causes water to evaporate. Warm air carries water vapor upward.

When drops get big enough, precipitation, such as rain, falls from clouds.

Cooler temperatures high in the air make water vapor condense. Water droplets collect on dust particles to form clouds.

Rainwater flows across the ground. It goes into rivers and lakes. Some of the rainwater soaks into the soil. It becomes groundwater.

The sun's rays warm Earth's land and water. This causes water to evaporate. Warm air carries water vapor upward.

1. SEQUENCE Draw and complete this graphic organizer.

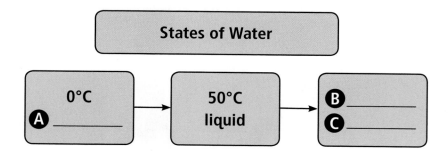

States of Water

A _____ 0°C → 50°C liquid → B _____ C _____

2. SUMMARIZE Write a paragraph summarizing the stages of the water cycle.

3. DRAW CONCLUSIONS Suppose you leave a glass of water outside early in the morning. The temperature is 29°C (84°F). If there is no rain during the day, what might you find that night in the glass?

4. VOCABULARY Write a paragraph about the water cycle. Include the terms *condensation, evaporation, precipitation*, and *water cycle*.

FCAT Prep

5. What form does water take at room temperature?
A. ice
B. liquid
C. snow
D. solid

Links

Writing

Narrative
Many people enjoy watching and listening to rain falling. Write a **poem** about the way you sometimes feel when you listen to rain.

Math

Construct a Bar Graph
Look at the Interpret Data in Lesson 1. Using the same data, construct a bar graph. Which graph do you think is easier to read? Explain your answer.

For more links and activities, go to **www.hspscience.com**

What Is Weather?

Fast Fact

When the Wind Blows Weather vanes show the direction of the wind. Long ago, weather vanes were among the few tools that people used to predict the weather. In the Investigate, you will make a tool to measure the wind.

Measuring Wind

Materials
- 3 small white paper cups
- cap of a ballpoint pen
- wire
- 2 cardboard strips
- red paper cup
- watch
- stapler
- scissors

Procedure

1. Make an X with the cardboard strips. Staple them together.

2. **CAUTION:** Carefully use scissors to make a hole in the middle of the X. Push the pen cap into the hole.

3. Cut a slit in the opposite side of each cup. Attach a cup to the end of each cardboard strip by pushing the cardboard through the slits.

4. Push most of the wire into the ground. Balance the pen cap on the wire.

5. **Observe** the cups for one minute. Count the number of times the red cup spins by. **Record** your data.

6. Repeat your observation at the same time each day for a week.

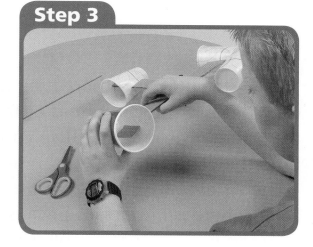

Step 3

Step 5

Draw Conclusions

1. Make a bar graph that shows the number of turns the cup made on each day of the week.

2. **Inquiry Skill** How did making a graph help **communicate** your results?

Investigate Further

Predict what would happen if you added 2 more cups. Try it.

SC.H.1.2.5.3.1 uses models, SC.H.2.2.1.3.1 makes predictions,
SC.H.2.2.1.3.2 uses graphs, SC.H.3.2.2.3.1 collects data,
SC.H.3.2.2.3.2 presents scientific information

VOCABULARY

atmosphere p. 274

oxygen p. 274

weather p. 276

temperature p. 277

anemometer p. 277

SCIENCE CONCEPTS

▶ what weather is

▶ how weather is measured

READING FOCUS SKILL

COMPARE AND CONTRAST

Look for ways that clouds are alike and different.

alike	different

The Air Around You

How do you know there is air around you? You can't see air. You can't hold or taste air. You know that air is all around because you can feel it. Every time the wind blows, you can feel air moving.

The air around Earth is the **atmosphere**. The atmosphere is important because it has oxygen. **Oxygen** is a gas that people need to live. The atmosphere also has gases that plants need to live.

Water vapor is in the atmosphere. Water vapor helps make clouds. Rain, snow, and other kinds of precipitation fall from clouds.

 COMPARE AND CONTRAST How does air compare with a solid object, such as a rock?

One reason this kite can fly is because of the force of the wind on it.

Types of Clouds

Cirrus Clouds
Cirrus clouds are the highest clouds. Cirrus clouds look like wisps of hair.

Cumulus Clouds
Cumulus clouds are lower than cirrus clouds. Cumulus clouds look puffy.

Stratus Clouds
Stratus clouds are the lowest clouds. A stratus cloud looks like a sheet or a layer of clouds.

Weather Patterns

What is today's weather like where you live? Is it sunny? Cloudy? Rainy? Weather both helps and harms people. For example, rain brings water for crops, but too much rain can cause floods that destroy homes.

Weather is what is happening in the atmosphere at a certain place and time. The weather in a place depends on where the place is. In the United States, places in the south are usually warmer than places in the north.

 COMPARE AND CONTRAST How can weather both help and harm people?

Features on Earth's surface, such as a coastline, can change the weather.

Sea Breeze

▲ On the coast, cooler air over the water moves toward land during the day. This makes a sea breeze.

Land Breeze

▲ During the night, air is cooler over land, so a land breeze moves air toward the water.

Gathering Weather Data

You can learn a lot about the weather by looking out a window. Sometimes, you may want to know facts about the weather that you can't see. Weather instruments can help you gather weather data. For example, you can use a thermometer to find the temperature. **Temperature** is the measure of how hot or cold something is. Another weather instrument is an anemometer. An **anemometer** (an•uh•MAHM•uht•er) measures wind speed.

 COMPARE AND CONTRAST Compare a thermometer with an anemometer.

These people are using special instruments to collect weather data at weather stations.

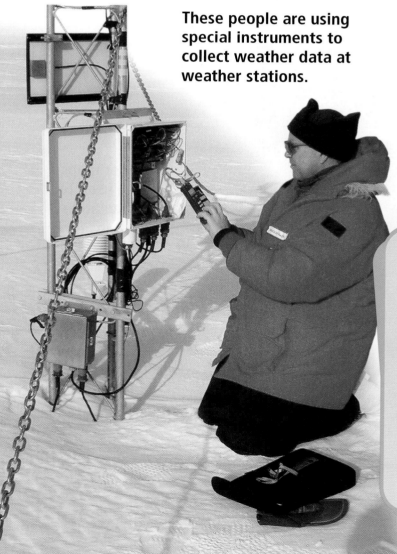

Use a Rain Gauge
Tape a centimeter ruler to the outside of a clear plastic jar. Place your "rain gauge" outside in an open area before a rain. Afterward, use the ruler to measure the amount of rain. How much rain fell?

Predicting Weather

People use weather instruments to predict weather. One instrument that is used to predict weather is a weather satellite. A weather satellite in space may take pictures of clouds. The satellite sends the pictures to Earth. People use the pictures to see how clouds move. People also use the pictures to make weather maps.

Look at the weather map below. You can find maps like this in newspapers. You can also see weather maps on television news shows. Weather maps show information such as temperature and the chance of rain.

 COMPARE AND CONTRAST Look at this weather map. How does Orlando's weather differ from Seattle's weather?

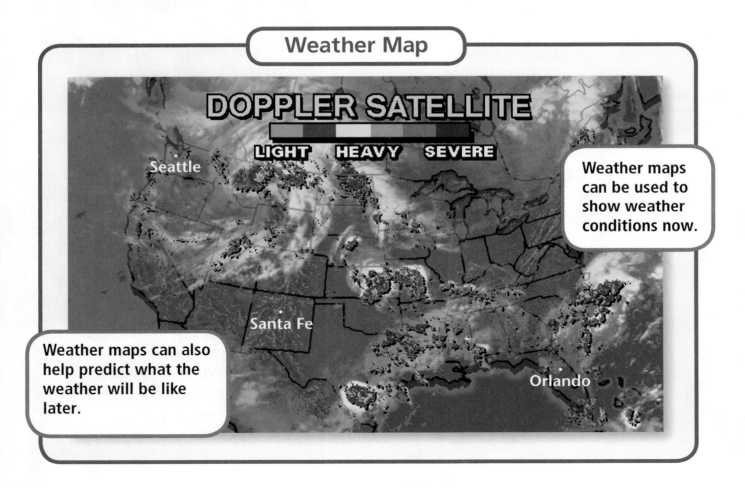

Weather Map

DOPPLER SATELLITE

LIGHT   HEAVY   SEVERE

Seattle

Santa Fe

Orlando

Weather maps can be used to show weather conditions now.

Weather maps can also help predict what the weather will be like later.

1. COMPARE AND CONTRAST Draw and complete this graphic organizer.

Type of Cloud	Where It Is	What It Looks Like
Stratus	low in the atmosphere	a flat sheet
Cumulus	**A** _____	**B** _____
Cirrus	**C** _____	**D** _____

2. SUMMARIZE Write two or three sentences that tell what this lesson is mainly about.

3. DRAW CONCLUSIONS Does the ocean affect weather? Explain your answer.

4. VOCABULARY Write a short story about a weather forecaster. Use all the vocabulary words from this lesson in your story.

FCAT Prep

5. Read/Inquire/Explain Examine the weather map on the left-hand page. Describe the weather in Santa Fe, New Mexico.

Links

Writing

Narrative
Write a personal **story** describing some weather you have seen. Describe what the weather was like and how it affected you or your family.

Health

Weather and Health
Weather affects people's health. Choose a type of weather, and draw a poster showing how to stay healthy in that kind of weather. For example, it is important to wear sunscreen on sunny days.

 For more links and activities, go to **www.hspscience.com**

A TOY STORY

Little rubber ducks, turtles, beavers, and frogs have been on a long journey. Hundreds have washed up on shore in recent years.

In 1992, boxes of the toys fell off a ship in the Pacific Ocean. The floating toys began a journey that would teach scientists about ocean currents. An *ocean current* is a flow of water in the ocean.

Arctic Travelers

The toys were first seen making their way into the Arctic Ocean. The Arctic Ocean is where the North Pole is located. For years, the toys were trapped in ice.

The toys then began to appear in the northern Atlantic Ocean. Recently, some of the toys were found washing up on beaches in eastern Canada and the northeastern United States.

Scientists have been very interested in the toys' travels. The first rubber toys washed up on the shores of Alaska in 1992. Since then, scientists have put into computers any information they know about ocean currents, as well as wind speed and wind direction. The computers then predicted where and when some of the toys would reach shore. As the toys landed, the scientists have seen that some of their theories were correct.

ARCTIC OCEAN

1999 Iceland

1995 Bering Strait

2001 ATLANTIC OCEAN

Alaska (UNITED STATES)

CANADA

1992 Toys fall overboard

UNITED STATES

2003 New England

PACIFIC OCEAN

Computer-Predicted Path

Toys or Trash?

Each year, about 10,000 shipments fall overboard. "When trash goes into the ocean, it doesn't disappear," said one ocean expert. "It just goes somewhere else."

Some trash gets eaten by ocean creatures and birds that mistake it for food. Other trash washes up on shore. The story of the bath toys is helping to make people aware of the ocean trash problem. "You can learn a lot from a [rubber] duck on a beach," said the ocean expert.

THINK ABOUT IT

1. What can the lost toys teach people about Earth's oceans?

2. What else can be done to teach people about pollution in Earth's oceans?

Find out more! Log on to **www.hspscience.com**

Teaching About Change

Bin Wang lives in Hawai`i, where the weather is usually beautiful. In spite of the weather where he lives, Wang studies storms and changes in the weather.

Bin Wang is a meteorologist, or weather expert. He studies the weather and how it changes over time. He can forecast what the weather will be like in the near future.

Wang has studied the weather of the Pacific Ocean for many years. He has written more than 100 research papers on weather. As a result of Wang's work, people can be better prepared for deadly Pacific storms.

Career Meteorologist

Meteorologists don't just predict next week's weather. These scientists use computers and historical records to study weather patterns over many years. Information from weather experts can also help businesses. Farmers, pilots, and ship captains are just some of the people who rely on weather information for their work.

Spin In

Find out more! Log on to
www.hspscience.com

You Can Do It!

Cloud in a Jar

Procedure

1. Put a pan in a freezer for an hour.
2. Just before you take out the pan, have your teacher half-fill a jar with hot water.
3. Remove the pan from the freezer, and fill it with ice cubes. Place the pan on top of the jar. Leave it there for a few minutes.

Materials
- metal pie pan
- freezer
- glass jar without lid
- hot water
- ice cubes

Draw Conclusions

Observe what happens inside the jar. How is this like part of the water cycle?

Weather Station

What is the weather like today where you live? Will the weather be different tomorrow? What will the weather be like at the end of the week? Think about the different ways you can observe the weather to answer these questions. Then design a weather station to help you record the weather. Keep records about your town's weather for at least a week.

Review and FCAT Preparation

Vocabulary Review

Use the terms below to complete the sentences. The page numbers tell you where to look in the chapter if you need help.

fresh water p. 259

groundwater p. 260

condensation p. 268

evaporation p. 269

precipitation p. 270

water cycle p. 270

atmosphere p. 274

weather p. 276

1. The changing of a liquid into a gas is _____.

2. The movement of water between Earth's air and land is part of the _____.

3. Water that has very little salt in it is _____.

4. The air around Earth makes up the _____.

5. The changing of a gas into a liquid is _____.

6. What is happening in the atmosphere at a certain place and time is _____.

7. Earth's underground supply of water is _____.

8. Rain, snow, sleet, and hail are examples of _____.

Check Understanding

Write the letter of the best choice.

9. Where is most of the water on Earth located?
   A. in freshwater lakes
   B. in glaciers
   C. in oceans
   D. underground

10. **MAIN IDEA AND DETAILS** What are glaciers made of?
   F. gas
   G. ice
   H. groundwater
   I. salt water

11. Which of the following is **not** a type of precipitation?
   A. groundwater
   B. hail
   C. sleet
   D. snow

12. What happens to water vapor as it moves upward in the air?

   F. It becomes hot.

   G. It evaporates.

   H. It forms clouds.

   I. It becomes a solid.

13. SEQUENCE Which sequence shows forms of water from the coldest to the hottest temperatures?

   A. ice, liquid water, water vapor

   B. ice, water vapor, liquid water

   C. liquid water, water vapor, ice

   D. water vapor, ice, liquid water

14. If water vapor loses thermal energy, which process will occur?

   F. condensation   **H.** freezing

   G. evaporation   **I.** melting

15. Which instrument would you use to measure wind speed?

   A. anemometer

   B. rain gauge

   C. thermometer

   D. weather vane

16. Which of the following are the lowest clouds in the atmosphere?

   F. cirrus

   G. cumulus

   H. satellite

   I. stratus

Inquiry Skills

17. LaDonne observes and collects data from her rain gauge each day. Compare her drawings from Tuesday and Wednesday.

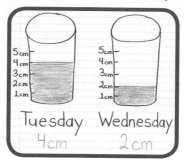

18. Suppose you leave an empty covered jar outside in the evening. When you get up the next morning, there is water in the jar. Infer what happened.

 ## Read/Inquire/Explain

19. Scott is a farmer. Why is it important for him to watch the weather report each day?

20. You know that most of the water on Earth is salt water. Explain why it's important to keep water clean, especially fresh water.

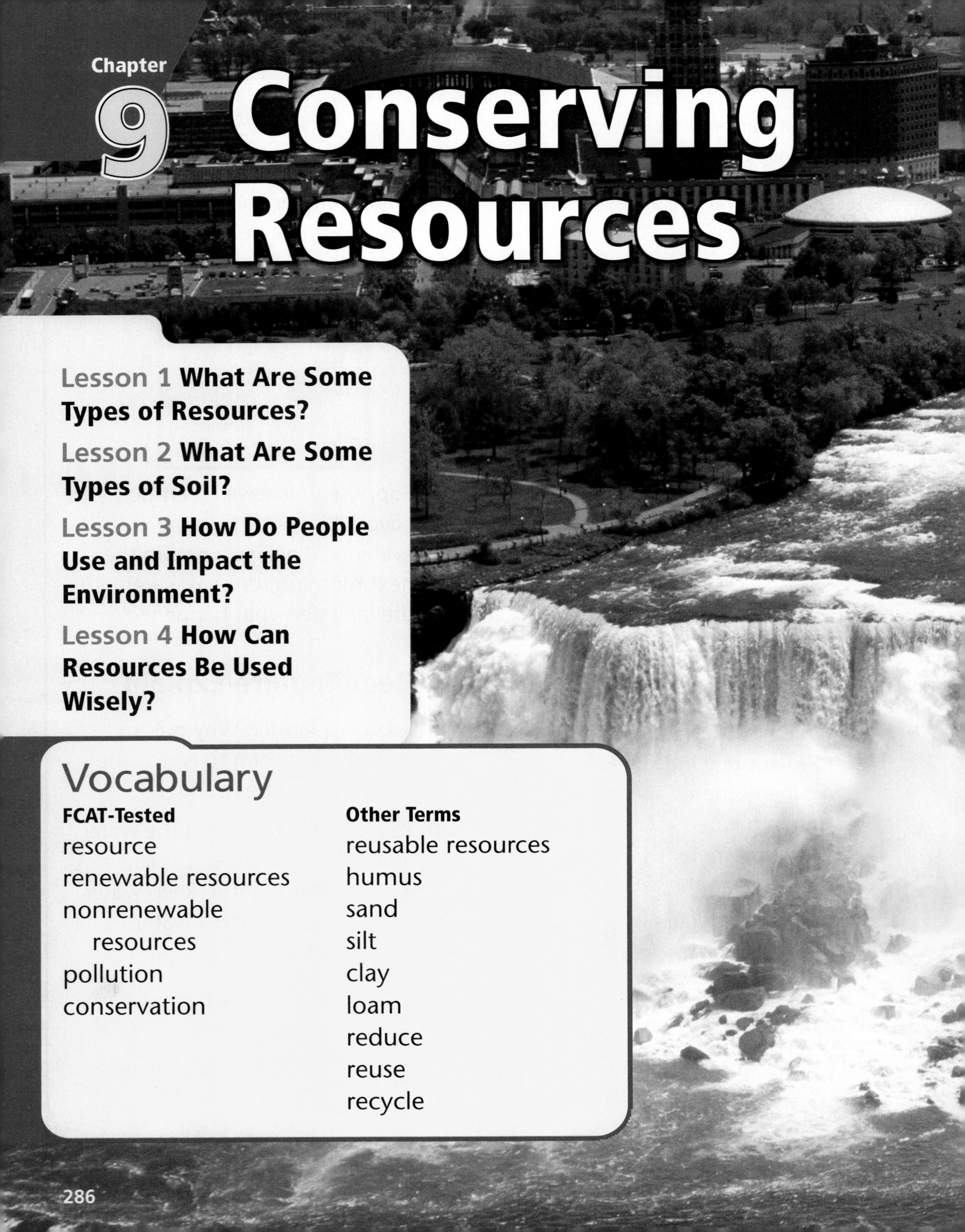

Chapter

9 Conserving Resources

Vocabulary

FCAT-Tested

resource
renewable resources
nonrenewable resources
pollution
conservation

Other Terms

reusable resources
humus
sand
silt
clay
loam
reduce
reuse
recycle

What do **YOU** wonder?

Resources are found almost everywhere. What resources do you see in this picture? How do you use these resources?

What Are Some Types of Resources?

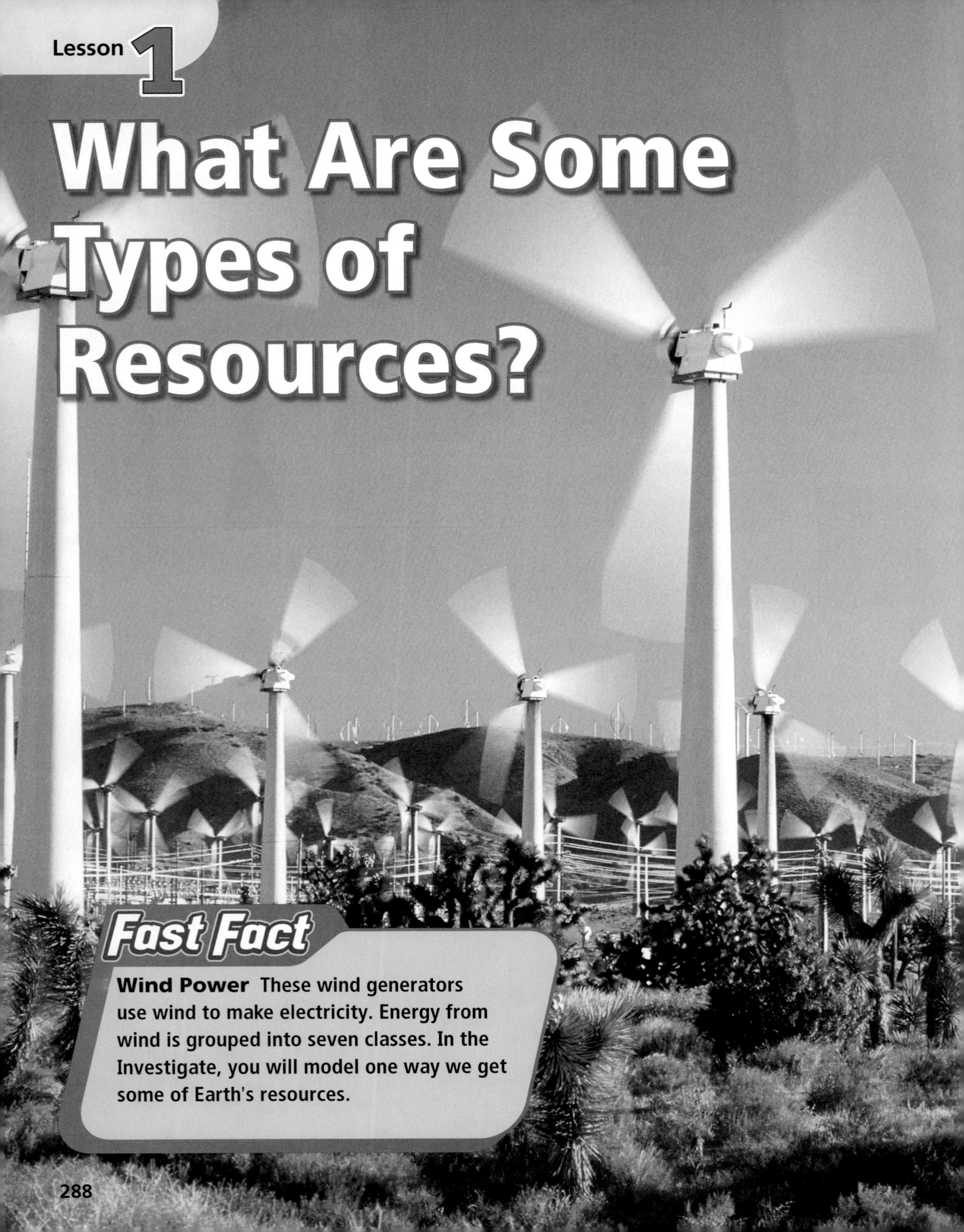

Fast Fact

Wind Power These wind generators use wind to make electricity. Energy from wind is grouped into seven classes. In the Investigate, you will model one way we get some of Earth's resources.

Mining Resources

Materials
- oatmeal-raisin cookie
- dropper
- paper plate
- water
- toothpick

Procedure

1. **Observe** your cookie. **Record** the number of raisins you see.

2. Put a few drops of water around each raisin. The cookie should become moist but not wet.

3. Use the toothpick to "mine" all the raisins from the cookie. If they are hard to get out, put a few more drops of water around them. **Record** the number you removed.

Step 2

Step 3

Draw Conclusions

1. Were there any raisins that you didn't see in the cookie the first time? Why didn't you see them?

2. How did the water help you dig out the raisins? How did the digging affect the cookie?

3. How is mining raisins from a cookie like mining resources from Earth?

4. **Inquiry Skill** Scientists use their observations to infer how similar things work. Use your observations to infer how mining could affect the land around the mine.

Investigate Further

Can the cookie be completely "mined" without tearing it up? **Hypothesize** how this might be done. Test your **hypothesis**.

Reading in Science

SC.B.2.2.2.3.1 natural resources, **SC.B.2.2.2.3.2** renewable/nonrenewable resources, **LA.A.2.2.1** main idea and details

VOCABULARY

resource p. 290

renewable resources
  p. 292

reusable resources
  p. 293

nonrenewable
  resources p. 294

SCIENCE CONCEPTS

▶ what resources are
▶ which resources will not run out and which may run out

READING FOCUS SKILL

MAIN IDEA AND DETAILS Look for details about resources.

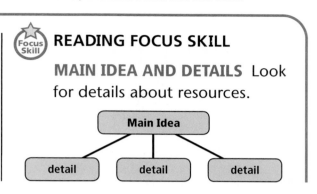

Resources

What materials have you used so far today? You ate food for breakfast. Then you used water to brush your teeth. Now you are using this book. The food, the water, and even this book all came from resources. A **resource** is a material found in nature that is used by living things.

▼ People use fish as a resource.

People use many kinds of animals as resources. For example, cows are used for both meat and milk. ▼

290

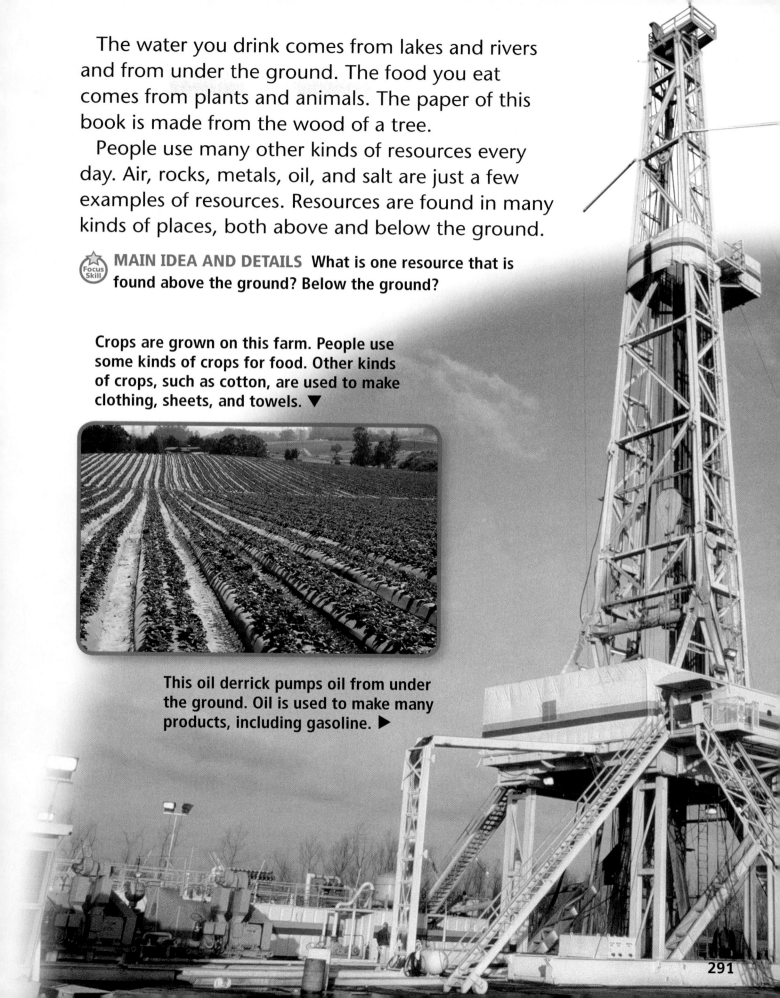

The water you drink comes from lakes and rivers and from under the ground. The food you eat comes from plants and animals. The paper of this book is made from the wood of a tree.

People use many other kinds of resources every day. Air, rocks, metals, oil, and salt are just a few examples of resources. Resources are found in many kinds of places, both above and below the ground.

(Focus Skill) MAIN IDEA AND DETAILS What is one resource that is found above the ground? Below the ground?

Crops are grown on this farm. People use some kinds of crops for food. Other kinds of crops, such as cotton, are used to make clothing, sheets, and towels. ▼

This oil derrick pumps oil from under the ground. Oil is used to make many products, including gasoline. ▶

Renewable Resources

After you cut down a tree to make paper, you can plant another tree. The new tree takes the place of the tree that was cut down. Trees are renewable resources. **Renewable resources** are resources that can be replaced during a human lifetime. Plants and animals are renewable resources. Some kinds of energy are renewable resources, too. For example, energy from the sun is a renewable resource.

 MAIN IDEA AND DETAILS What are some kinds of renewable resources?

This forest is a renewable resource. Its trees can be used to make houses, furniture, pencils, and paper. New trees can be planted to take the place of the ones that are cut down. ▼

▲ Air is a resource you need to breathe. Cars and factories make the air dirty. Plants, wind, and rain help clean the air to make it safe to breathe again.

Reusable Resources

Some kinds of resources can be used again and again. These kinds of resources are called **reusable resources.** Air and water are two kinds of reusable resources. After you take a bath, the water is dirty. When you drain the tub, the water goes to a water treatment plant. There the water is cleaned so it can be reused.

MAIN IDEA AND DETAILS What are some kinds of reusable resources?

Hunting for Resources
Go outside or look out a window. Make a list of the resources you see. Which of those resources are renewable? Which are reusable?

293

Nonrenewable Resources

You probably have watched someone fill up a car's tank with gasoline. Cars burn gasoline for energy. When the gasoline is used up, the tank needs to be filled again.

The oil that is used to make gasoline is not renewable or reusable. One day, it will all be gone. Oil is a nonrenewable resource. **Nonrenewable resources** are resources that cannot be replaced in a human lifetime. When these resources are used up, there will be no more. Some other nonrenewable resources are coal, soil, and metals.

Miners dig coal out of mines deep underground. Coal is burned to make electricity. Coal takes thousands of years to form. ▼

(Focus Skill) **MAIN IDEA AND DETAILS** What are some nonrenewable resources?

There are only certain amounts of metals on Earth. No more can be made. Some of Earth's metal resources, such as copper and iron, are dug up at strip mines like this one. ▼

1. MAIN IDEA AND DETAILS Draw and complete this graphic organizer.

Main Idea: **A** _____ are materials that are found in nature and are used by living things.

Examples of renewable resources: wind

B _____

Examples of reusable resources: air

C _____

Examples of nonrenewable resources: oil

D _____

2. SUMMARIZE Write a summary of this lesson. Begin with the sentence *There are three types of resources.*

3. DRAW CONCLUSIONS How is the sun a renewable resource?

4. VOCABULARY Write a short paragraph that describes the differences between renewable resources, reusable resources, and nonrenewable resources.

FCAT Prep

5. Which of the following resources is nonrenewable?

A. air   **C.** coal
B. animals   **D.** water

Links

 ## Writing

Narrative

Choose a nonrenewable resource that you have used today. Write a **story** that describes how your life would be different without that resource.

 ## Math

Solve a Problem

Suppose your town uses 5 tons of coal a year and has enough coal to produce energy for 20 years. If your town used only 4 tons each year, how long would the coal last?

 For more links and activities, go to www.hspscience.com

What Are Some Types of Soil?

Fast Fact

Slow-Forming Soil It takes between 3,000 and 12,000 years to form soil that is good for farming. In the Investigate, you'll find out about two kinds of soil.

Observing Soil

Materials
- 2 soil samples
- small paper plates
- microscope or hand lens
- toothpick

Procedure

① Get a soil sample from your teacher. Place a few grains of the soil on a paper plate.

② Using the microscope or hand lens, observe the soil. Use the toothpick to move the soil grains around. Notice the colors, shapes, and sizes of the grains. Record what you observe by drawing the soil grains.

③ Pick up some soil from the plate. Rub it between your fingers. How does it feel? Record what you observe.

④ Repeat Steps 1 through 3 with the other soil sample.

Step 2

Step 3

Draw Conclusions

1. What senses did you use to observe the soil?

2. Describe your observations.

3. **Inquiry Skill** Scientists observe things so they can compare them. How were the soil samples alike? How were the soil samples different?

Investigate Further

Which soil holds more water—potting soil or sandy soil? Write a hypothesis. Then plan and conduct an investigation to find out.

SC.A.2.2.1.3.1 tools to see details, **SC.H.1.2.1.3.1** keeping accurate records, **SC.H.1.2.2.3.1** following experimental design, **SC.H.1.2.2.3.2** using scientific instruments, **SC.H.1.2.4.3.1** comparing/contrasting

VOCABULARY

humus p. 298
sand p. 301
silt p. 301
clay p. 301
loam p. 302

SCIENCE CONCEPTS

▶ how soil is layered
▶ how soils are different

READING FOCUS SKILL

COMPARE AND CONTRAST
Compare and contrast layers and types of soil.

| alike | | different |

Layers of Soil

You might not think of soil as a resource, but it is a very important one. Without soil, plants couldn't grow. Many animals wouldn't have places to live.

Soil is a mixture of many different things. Soil is made up of water, air, humus, and tiny pieces of rock. **Humus** is the part of soil that is made up of parts of dead plants and animals. For example, when a tree loses a leaf, the leaf falls to the ground. As the leaf breaks down into smaller parts, it becomes humus.

This plant's roots grow in soil. ▼

The soil close to the surface has a lot of humus. Soil that is deeper down has less humus and more small pieces of rock. If you cut into the soil, you would see different layers at different depths.

 COMPARE AND CONTRAST How is soil close to Earth's surface different from the soil deeper below the surface?

Science Up Close

Topsoil
Soil forms in layers. The top layer is called *topsoil.* Topsoil has a lot of humus. Many small animals, such as ants and earthworms, live in topsoil.

Subsoil
The layer underneath topsoil is called *subsoil.* Subsoil does not have a lot of humus, but it does have small pieces of rock in it.

Bedrock
If you dig deep enough into soil, you will reach solid rock. This solid rock is called *bedrock.* Most of the small pieces of rock in soil come from the bedrock underneath it.

For more links and activities, go to
www.hspscience.com

Different Types of Soil

Not all soil is the same. In the United States alone, there are more than 70,000 different kinds of soil. Soils can have different colors. Some soils can hold more water than other soils.

Another difference among soils is the size of the rocks found in them. The rock sizes make the soils feel different.

This soil is made up mostly of sand. The sand grains are big enough to see without a hand lens. ▼

This clay soil is made up of very tiny grains of rock. You would need a microscope to see the grains. ▼

Soils that have tiny pieces of rock that you can see with your eyes alone are mostly **sand**. Soils with grains of rock that are too small to see with your eyes are called **silt**. Soils with very, very tiny grains of rock are known as **clay** soils.

The main difference between sand, silt, and clay soils is their grain size. These three types of soils can also be made up of different minerals.

 COMPARE AND CONTRAST Compare sand, silt, and clay soils.

Insta-Lab

Make a Soil Model
Put pieces of rock in the bottom of a plastic bottle. Then add a mixture of rock and humus. Finally, put humus and tiny pieces of rock on top. Label the layers. Is the soil in your top layer sand, silt, or clay?

The Importance of Soil

What would the world be like without soil? People couldn't make bricks, pottery, or other items that are made from clay soil. Many animals would have nowhere to live, and plants would not be able to grow.

Soil is very important to people for growing fruits and vegetables. The best kind of soil to use to grow fruits and vegetables is loam. **Loam** is a mixture of humus, clay, silt, and sand. Most soils found on farms are loam.

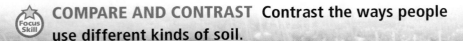 **COMPARE AND CONTRAST** Contrast the ways people use different kinds of soil.

This woman grows flowers and vegetables in loam. Clay soil would stay too wet. Sandy soil would dry out too quickly. ▼

1. **COMPARE AND CONTRAST** Draw and complete this graphic organizer.

Soils

How soils are alike:
All soils have water,
A _____, air,
and **B** _____.

How soils are different:
Soils have different colors,
C _____, **D** _____,
and different abilities to
hold water.

2. **SUMMARIZE** Write three sentences that tell what this lesson is mainly about.

3. **DRAW CONCLUSIONS** Why do you think plants need soil to grow?

4. **VOCABULARY** Draw a graphic organizer that shows how humus, sand, silt, and clay are related to loam.

FCAT Prep

5. **Read/Inquire/Explain** Robin wants to start a vegetable garden in her back yard. The soil in her back yard is mostly clay. What should Robin do before she plants her vegetable seeds?

Links

Writing

Persuasive
Suppose you are selling a type of soil. Write an **advertisement** that will persuade adults to buy your soil. Your advertisement should explain the best uses for the soil.

Physical Education

Take a Hike
Take a walk in your town with an adult family member. Collect small amounts of soil from three places. Compare the soils. Discuss other resources you saw on your walk.

 For more links and activities, go to
www.hspscience.com

How Do People Use and Impact the Environment?

Fast Fact

Florida Orange Groves Orange trees need rich soil, clean water, and warm weather. They get all these things in Florida, the leading state for orange growing. In the Investigate, you'll find out about the importance of clean water to plants.

Pollution and Plants

Materials
- 3 clear plastic cups
- clean water
- potting soil
- salt water
- grass seeds
- oily waters
- measuring cup

Procedure

1. Your teacher will provide you with three containers of water. One will have clean water, one will have water polluted with salt, and one will have water polluted with oil.

2. Fill the three plastic cups with potting soil. Plant three seeds in each cup. **Measure** 10 mL of clean water. Water the seeds in the first cup with the clean water, and label the cup. Repeat with the other two cups and containers of water.

3. Place the cups in a sunny window. Every day, water each cup with the water it was first watered with.

4. **Observe** the cups for 10 days. Each day, **record** your observations.

Step 2

Step 3

Draw Conclusions

1. What did you **observe**?

2. Which plants grew best?

3. **Inquiry Skill** Scientists **compare** things to see how they are alike and how they are different. How are the plants grown with the three kinds of water alike and different?

Investigate Further

Would watering plants with water containing vinegar or dish detergent affect their growth? **Predict** what would happen. Then try it! Make sure to wear goggles.

SC.H.1.2.1.3.1 keeping accurate records, **SC.H.1.2.2.3.2** using scientific instruments, **SC.H.1.2.4.3.1** comparing/contrasting, **SC.H.2.2.1.3.1** makes predictions

305

VOCABULARY

pollution p. 308

SCIENCE CONCEPTS

▶ how land is used
▶ what the different types of pollution are

READING FOCUS SKILL

CAUSE AND EFFECT Look for ways people affect the environment.

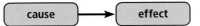

cause ⟶ effect

Uses of the Land

The land people live on is a very important resource. People use land in many different ways. People build on land. They use resources from the land to make buildings. Rocks and wood are building materials that come from the land.

Many other resources that are useful to people also come from the land. Metals, gemstones, and coal are dug up, or mined, from the land. Land is also used for farming. Farmers use the soil to grow plants that are used for food, medicine, cloth, and more.

Big cities like Miami spread out for many miles. There are many uses of land in this picture.

Whenever people use land, they change it in some way. Building, mining, and farming all change the land. Sometimes the effects are good. For example, planting trees helps keep the soil in place. But sometimes the effects are bad. For example, mining can tear up the land. This harms the plants and animals that live in the area.

 CAUSE AND EFFECT **What effects can people's actions have on land?**

It is important for city planners to include open spaces such as parks for people to enjoy. ▶

Land Pollution

People can also change land by polluting it. **Pollution** (puh•LOO•shuhn) is any harmful material in the environment. There are many types of harmful materials, or pollutants. Solid waste, chemicals, noise, and even light can be pollutants.

One kind of pollution is land pollution. Land pollution can happen when people throw trash away in the wrong places. The trash can harm plants and animals. It can also pollute the water under the ground.

 CAUSE AND EFFECT What are some effects of land pollution?

Every year in the United States, more than 100 tons of trash are put into landfills. ▼

Math in Science
Interpret Data

A T-shirt can take 6 months to break down. A rope can take a year. How many years does it take for a tin can to break down? A glass bottle?

How Long It Takes for Materials to Break Down

Material	Months
Newspaper	1
Cotton T-shirt	6
Rope	12
Tin can	1,200
Glass bottle	6,000

▲ After a windy or rainy day, the pollution over the city is cleared away.

▲ If the air over the city does not move, the pollution will stay in place. This makes the air unhealthful to breathe.

Air Pollution

Pollution affects more than just the land. Air can be polluted, too. Smoke, mostly from trucks, cars, and factories, is one cause of air pollution.

Air pollution can make it hard for people to breathe. Air pollution can also change the weather. For example, air polluted by car and factory gases traps heat from sunlight. This makes Earth warmer. Scientists call this *global warming*.

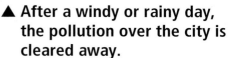 **CAUSE AND EFFECT** What can air pollution do to people?

Insta-Lab

Seeing Air Pollution

Smear a circle of petroleum jelly in the center of a white paper plate. Leave the plate outdoors for a day or two. Observe the plate. How has it changed? What caused the change?

Water Pollution

Pollution in the air and on the land can get into water when there is rain. Rain washes pollutants from the air and land into the water. People who dump trash, oil, and other pollutants into the water also cause water pollution.

Drinking polluted water can make people sick. Animals that live in polluted water can also get sick. Some kinds of water pollution can be cleaned up. Water treatment plants can take pollutants out of water to make it clean again.

 CAUSE AND EFFECT What can cause water to become polluted?

Oil is being cleaned from this bird's feathers. Without this help, the bird would probably die. ▼

Sometimes, oil enters the oceans as a result of an accident. It takes many people to clean up an oil spill.

1. CAUSE AND EFFECT Draw and complete this graphic organizer.

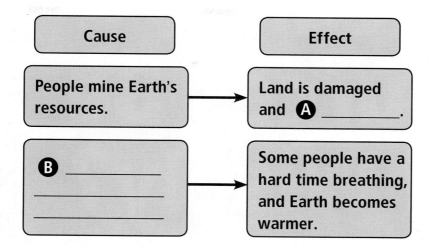

Cause	Effect
People mine Earth's resources.	Land is damaged and **Ⓐ** _____.
Ⓑ _____ _____ _____	Some people have a hard time breathing, and Earth becomes warmer.

2. SUMMARIZE Write a summary of this lesson by explaining the causes and effects of pollution.

3. DRAW CONCLUSIONS Can things other than people cause pollution? Explain.

4. VOCABULARY Describe what pollution is, and list three examples.

FCAT Prep

5. Which of the following resources comes from land?

A. air

B. fish

C. trees

D. water

Links

Writing

Expository

Suppose nobody tries to clean up pollution now. Write a **description** of what you think Earth would look like 100 years from now.

Health

Help Stop Littering!

Litter is a type of land pollution. Make a poster that asks people not to litter. Put up the poster in your school library or in another public place.

 For more links and activities, go to www.hspscience.com

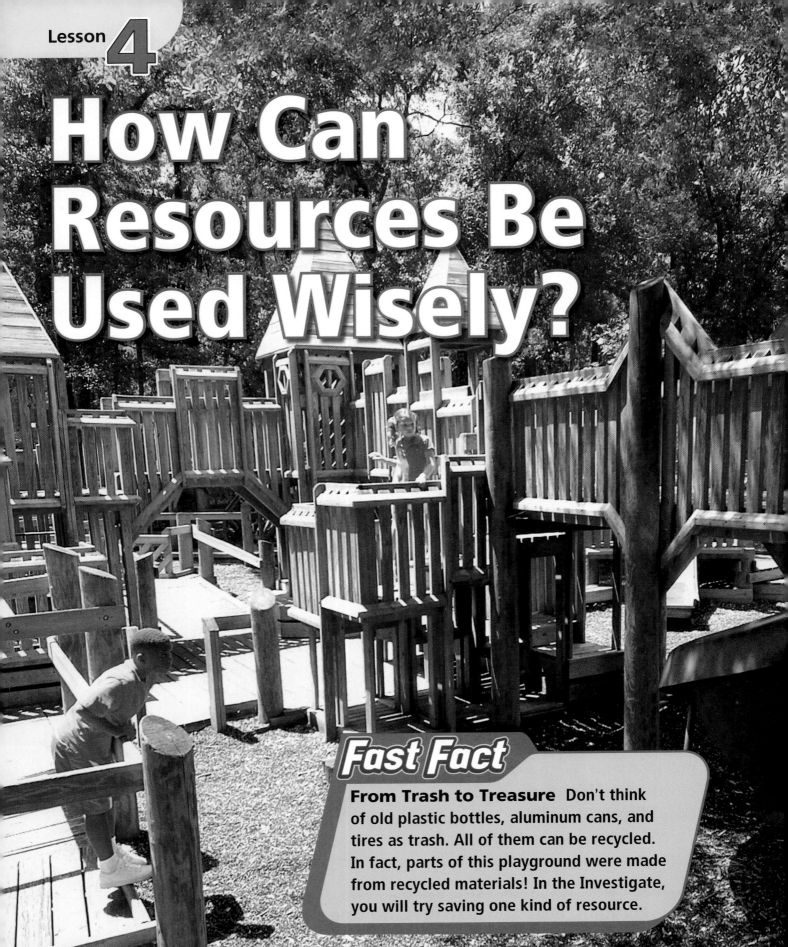

How Can Resources Be Used Wisely?

Fast Fact

From Trash to Treasure Don't think of old plastic bottles, aluminum cans, and tires as trash. All of them can be recycled. In fact, parts of this playground were made from recycled materials! In the Investigate, you will try saving one kind of resource.

Taking a Look at Trash

Materials • large plastic trash bags • bathroom scale • calculator

Procedure

1 With the rest of your class, save all the paper you would normally throw away for one week.

2 At the end of each day, weigh the paper. **Record** the weight.

3 Use your data to make a line graph showing the weight of each day's collection.

4 Add up all the weights shown on your graph. The sum tells how many pounds of paper the class collected in one week.

Step 2

Step 3

Draw Conclusions

1. Suppose that 1 pound of paper takes up 2 cubic feet of space. How much landfill space would your class save by recycling the paper you saved this week?

2. Inquiry Skill There are many ways you can **communicate** an idea. In this investigation, you **used numbers** to describe the weight of the paper collected. How does using numbers help you tell people what you found out?

Investigate Further

Predict how much paper your class could save by using both sides of each sheet. **Plan and conduct an investigation** to find out.

SC.H.1.2.1.3.1 keeping accurate records, **SC.H.1.2.3.3.1** working collaboratively, **SC.H.2.2.1.3.2** uses graphs, **SC.H.3.2.2.3.1** collects data, **SC.H.3.2.2.3.2** presents scientific information

SC.B.2.2.2.3.1 natural resources, **SC.D.2.2.1.3.1** reuse, recycle, reduce, **LA.A.2.2.1** main idea and details

VOCABULARY
conservation p. 314
reduce p. 316
reuse p. 317
recycle p. 318

SCIENCE CONCEPTS
- how conservation saves resources
- how to reduce, reuse, and recycle

READING FOCUS SKILL

MAIN IDEA AND DETAILS Look for details about how to protect the environment.

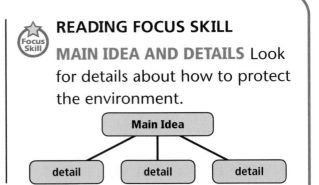

Main Idea
detail | detail | detail

Ways to Protect the Environment

People use a lot of resources. You have read that many resources are nonrenewable. This means that if we use up those resources, we will have none of them left. To protect Earth's resources, it is important to practice conservation. **Conservation** (kahn•ser•VAY•shuhn) is saving resources by using them wisely. Making sure resources do not get used up is one way to protect the environment.

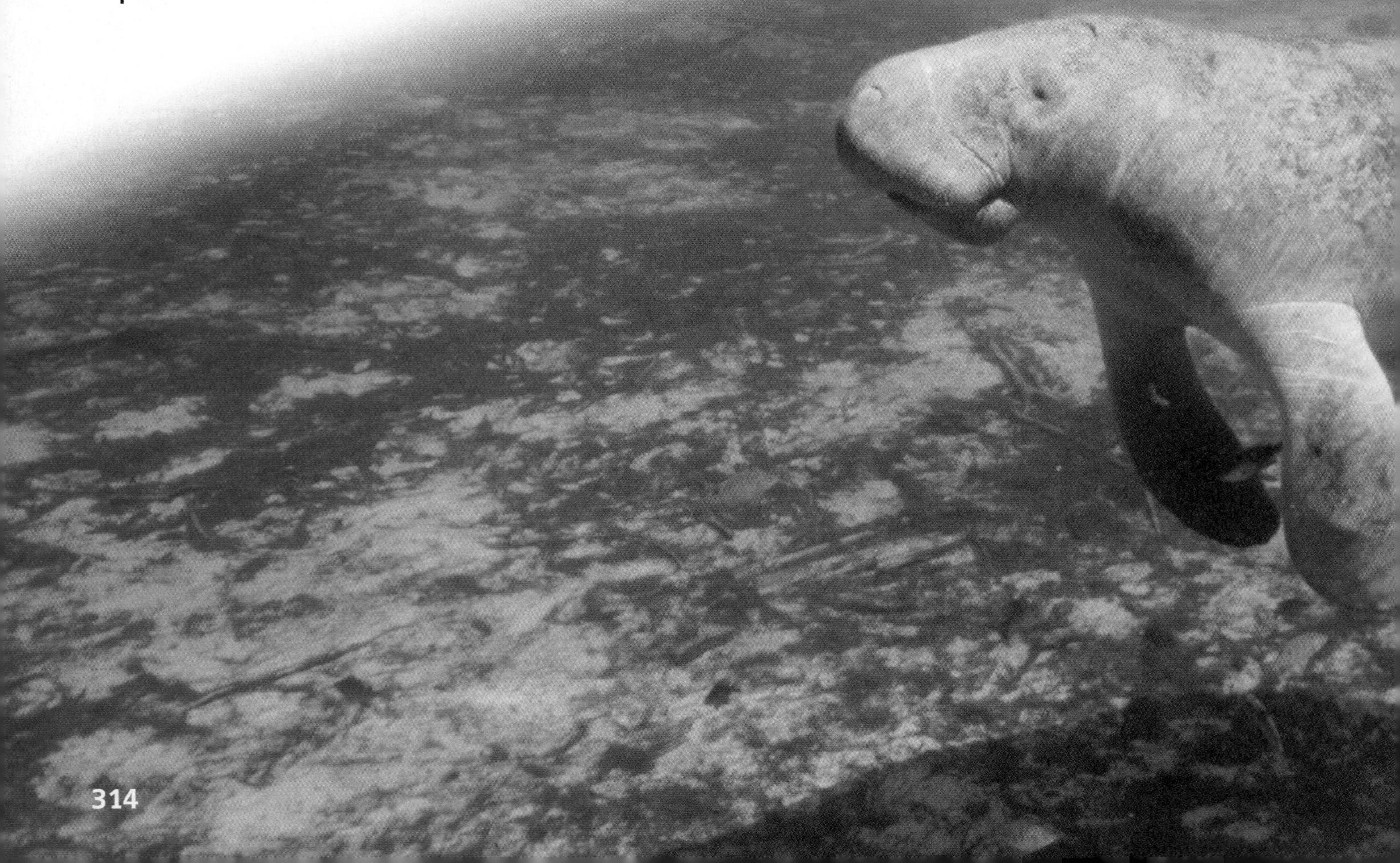

Using certain resources can cause the environment to become polluted. You have read that pollution can harm people, animals, and plants. Because of this, it is important to keep pollution from getting into the environment. It is also important to clean up any pollution that has already gotten into it. In this lesson, you will learn how to conserve resources and cut down on pollution.

 MAIN IDEA AND DETAILS What are two ways to protect the environment?

When people protect the environment, they make it safer and more enjoyable.

Reduce

One of the ways you can protect the environment is to **reduce** the amount of resources you use. To reduce your use of resources means to use less of them. For example, you can use less water by taking showers instead of baths. You can use less electricity if you turn the TV off when you are not watching it. If people use fewer resources, there will be more resources to use in the future.

 MAIN IDEA AND DETAILS What are two ways you can reduce your use of resources?

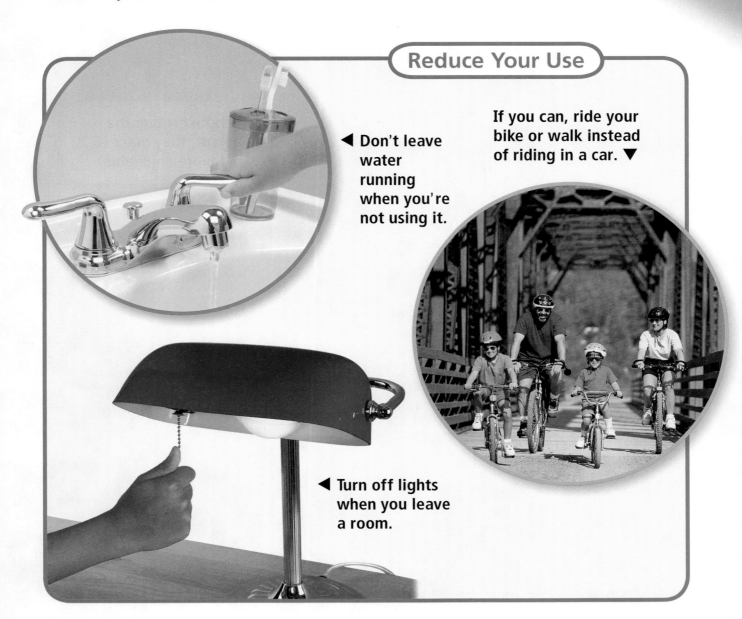

Reduce Your Use

◄ Don't leave water running when you're not using it.

If you can, ride your bike or walk instead of riding in a car. ▼

◄ Turn off lights when you leave a room.

▲ These students are reusing paper bags to make gift wrap.

Reuse

Do you wear clothes that no longer fit your older brother or sister? Do you fix toys when they break, instead of buying new ones? If so, you are reusing resources. When you **reuse** a resource, you use it again and again. Reusing helps reduce the amount of resources that would be needed to make new things. Reusing resources also saves people money.

 MAIN IDEA AND DETAILS Why is it important to reuse resources?

What Can Be Reused?
Take a look at some of the things around you. Which of these things can be reused? How can they be reused? Make a table that lists some of your ideas.

317

Recycle

Another way to save resources is to recycle them. To **recycle** means to break a product down or change it in some way and then use the material to make something new. Many materials, such as paper, glass, the aluminum from cans, and some plastics, can be recycled.

Recycled materials can be used to make many new products. Paper that is recycled can be used to make cards, paper towels, and newspaper. Plastic that is recycled can be used to make park benches, doormats, and much more.

▲ This symbol means that a product can be recycled.

 MAIN IDEA AND DETAILS What are some materials that can be recycled?

When you recycle, you help conserve resources by reusing the same resource. ▼

1. MAIN IDEA AND DETAILS Draw and complete this graphic organizer.

Main Idea: There are three ways to protect the environment and conserve resources.

 A _____

 B _____

C _____

2. SUMMARIZE Use your completed graphic organizer to write a short summary of this lesson.

3. DRAW CONCLUSIONS List all the resources that you save when you reuse a cotton T-shirt instead of buying a new one.

4. VOCABULARY Write a paragraph that correctly uses the terms *reduce, reuse,* and *recycle.*

FCAT Prep

5. Read/Inquire/Explain Miles reads the newspaper every day. What resource would he conserve if he recycled the newspapers?

Links

Writing

Expository
Invent a product that can be made from products that people already have around the house. Write a **how-to paragraph** explaining how to make the new product.

Music

Recycling Rhyme
Write the words to a song that tells people why it's good to recycle. Use a tune you already know. Sing your song in class.

 For more links and activities, go to www.hspscience.com

WIND FARMS

If you listen to the news, you are sure to hear discussions about energy sources. Oil, coal, and nuclear power are all sources of energy for the United States. Yet there's an energy source you do not hear much about: wind energy.

Many energy companies are trying to change that. Many of those companies are turning to wind power as a clean, cheap, renewable source of electricity.

Down on the Farm

According to the U.S. government, wind energy is the fastest-growing energy source in the world. Today, the U.S. has more than 6,300 megawatts of wind generating capacity. Companies are harnessing the wind on wind farms. A wind farm is a place where modern windmills use the power of wind to make electricity.

A wind farm is made up of rows of wind turbines. A wind turbine is a tower with a set of large blades on top. A turbine is like the opposite of a fan. Instead of using electricity to produce wind, wind turbines use wind to produce electricity.

As the wind blows, it turns the blades. The blades then spin a shaft, which is connected to a generator. The generator then produces electricity which is sent out along wires connected to the turbine.

Good Wind Areas

Most wind farms are located in coastal areas or mountains, where winds blow at a steady and fast speed. According to the government, wind farms work best in about 6 out of 100 cities in the United States.

THINK ABOUT IT

1. How can wind energy help conserve natural resources, such as oil?
2. Why is wind energy called "renewable"?

Windfall

Although a wind turbine costs thousands of dollars to build, the government says that wind energy is one of the lowest-priced energy sources around.

Spin-In

Find out more! Log on to
www.hspscience.com

People

Recycling Adventure

Tatiana Perez recently spent the day at the Garbage Museum in Stratford, Connecticut. "I had no idea how much trash people throw out," she said. Tatiana also learned a lot about what can and cannot be recycled.

Tatiana also watched as people sorted different kinds of bottles, paper, and metal to be recycled and reused. As part of her visit, Tatiana was able to make her own notebook from paper recycled at the Garbage Museum. "I'm going to write down all the things I learned about today," she said.

You Can Do It!

Model a Water Treatment Plant

Procedure

1. Put some soil into an empty plastic jug. Fill the jug with water.

2. Close the jug tightly, and shake it until the water and soil are mixed.

3. Hold a coffee filter over a bowl while a partner slowly pours some water from the jug into the filter.

4. Observe what happens.

Materials

- water
- bowl
- soil
- coffee filter
- empty plastic jug

Draw Conclusions

How was the dirty water similar to polluted water? What happened when the water was poured through the filter?

What Can't Be Recycled?

Not everything can be recycled. For example, gasoline and some kinds of plastics cannot be recycled. Do research to find out which materials can be recycled and which cannot. Make a poster that shows what you learned. Include on the poster some tips on how to sort items correctly for recycling. Present your poster to the class.

Review and FCAT Preparation

Vocabulary Review

Use the terms below to complete the sentences. The page numbers tell you where to look in the chapter if you need help.

renewable resource p. 292
reusable resource p. 293
nonrenewable resource p. 294
humus p. 298
clay p. 301
pollution p. 308
conservation p. 314
reduce p. 316

1. Soil that has very, very tiny grains of rock is known as _____.

2. A resource that may be used up one day is a _____.

3. When you use resources wisely, you are practicing _____.

4. When you use less of a resource, you _____ your use of it.

5. A resource that can be replaced in a human lifetime is a _____.

6. A harmful material in the environment is _____.

7. The part of soil that is made up of parts of dead plants and animals is _____.

8. A resource that you can use again and again is a _____.

Check Understanding

Write the letter of the best choice.

9. Which of the following is a reusable resource?
   A. coal
   B. oil
   C. seed
   D. water

10. Which type of resource is the oil that gasoline is made from?
    F. nonrenewable resource
    G. refundable resource
    H. renewable resource
    I. reusable resource

11. Which of these is a type of soil?
    A. bedrock   **C.** mineral
    B. loam   **D.** pebble

12. COMPARE AND CONTRAST
Compare the soils in the picture below. Why is Layer A the topsoil?

   F. It has no humus.
   G. It has smaller rocks.
   H. It has humus.
   I. It has large rocks.

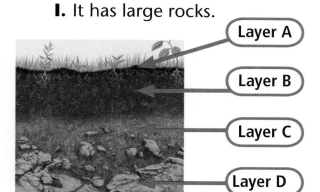

Layer A

Layer B

Layer C

Layer D

13. MAIN IDEA AND DETAILS Which technology can you use to help cut down on air pollution?

   A. a bicycle
   B. a car
   C. a cell phone
   D. a water bottle

14. Which technology is used to clean polluted water?

   F. a car engine
   G. an oil tanker
   H. a tire-recycling plant
   I. a water treatment plant

15. Which of these resources can you conserve by recycling paper?

   A. aluminum   **C.** gasoline
   B. coal   **D.** trees

16. Look at the symbol below. What does it represent?

   F. conservation
   G. recycling
   H. renewing
   I. soil formation

Inquiry Skills

17. List the resources you observe on your way to school. Be sure to list at least one of each kind of resource—renewable, reusable, and nonrenewable.

18. Compare recycling resources with reducing the use of resources.

Read/Inquire/Explain

19. Many minerals found in Earth's crust are mined as resources. What kind of resource do you think minerals are? Explain.

20. This graph shows a sample of loam. Why do you think water is an important part of loam?

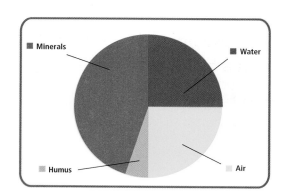

Earth and Space

The chapters in this unit address these Grade Level Expectations from the Florida Sunshine State Standards.

EARTH SCIENCE

Chapter 10 Earth's Place in the Solar System

SC.E.1.2.1.3.1	knows that days and nights change in length throughout the year.
SC.E.1.2.1.3.2	knows the patterns of average temperatures throughout the year.
SC.E.1.2.2.3.1	knows the frequency of the lunar cycle is approximately 28 days.
SC.E.1.2.3.3.1	knows the sun is a star that is much nearer to the Earth than the other stars.
SC.E.1.2.4.3.1	knows the characteristics of Mercury, Venus, Earth, and Mars.
SC.E.1.2.5.3.1	knows the relative positions of all the planets.
SC.E.2.2.1.3.1	knows that, in addition to the sun, there are many other stars that are far away.

The investigations and experiences in this unit also address many of the Grade Level Expectations in Strand H, The Nature of Science.

Science in Florida

Cape Canaveral

The Sunshine State

USA

Dear Juan,

Today I saw a rocket launched from the Kennedy Space Center in Cape Canaveral. It was carrying a probe that will explore the solar system. The rocket lit up the sky and left a trail of smoke.

I would love to be an astronaut when I grow up. I think it would be neat to go places where nobody has ever been before. There is so much that we still don't know about space.

See you soon,

Jennifer

FCAT Writing

Writing Situation
Think about traveling in space. Write a story about your adventures in space.

Experiment!

Space Suits Scientists at NASA have designed special spacesuits for astronauts to wear in space. The suits need to be thick to protect the astronauts. How does a thick spacesuit affect how easily an astronaut can move around in space? For example, can an astronaut make repairs quickly while wearing a spacesuit? Plan and conduct an experiment to find out.

Chapter 10

Earth's Place in the Solar System

Lesson 1 **What Causes Earth's Seasons?**

Lesson 2 **How Do Earth and the Moon Interact?**

Lesson 3 **What Is the Solar System?**

Vocabulary

FCAT-Tested	Other Terms
axis	rotation
moon phases	revolution
planet	lunar cycle
solar system	lunar eclipse
star	solar eclipse
constellation	orbit

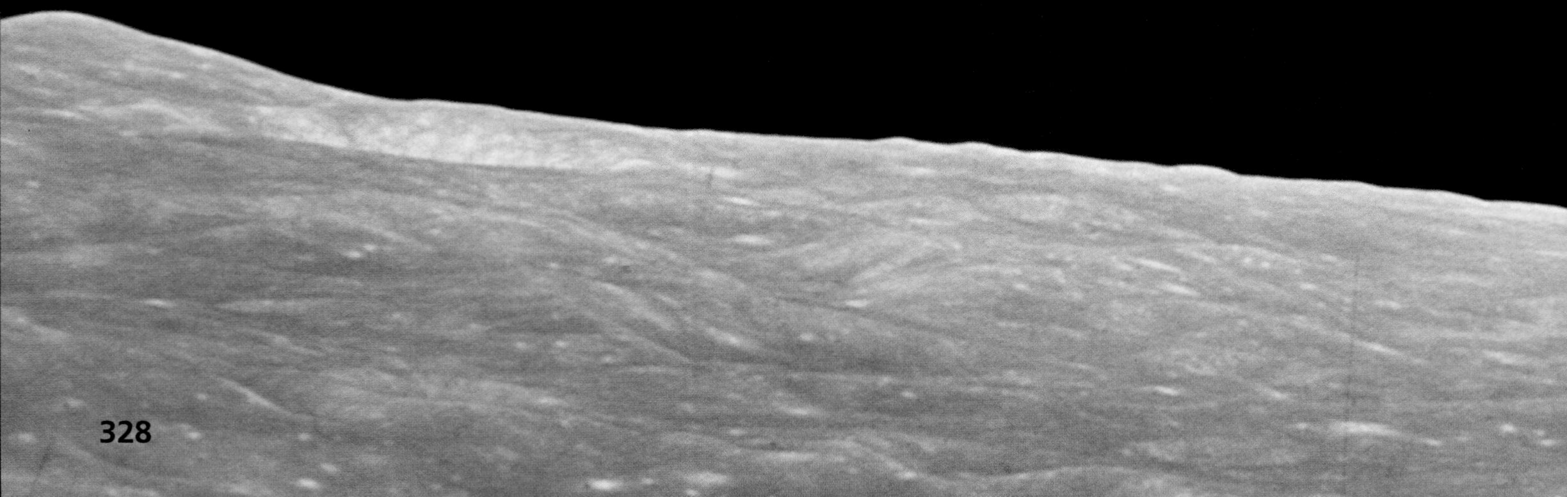

The moon moves in a path around Earth. It takes about 28 days for the moon to complete this journey. How long does it take for Earth to complete its journey around the sun?

Lesson 1

What Causes Earth's Seasons?

Fast Fact

Weather Mystery Earth is farthest from the sun in July and closest to it in January. Yet it is colder in the United States in January than it is in July! In the Investigate, you will learn the reason.

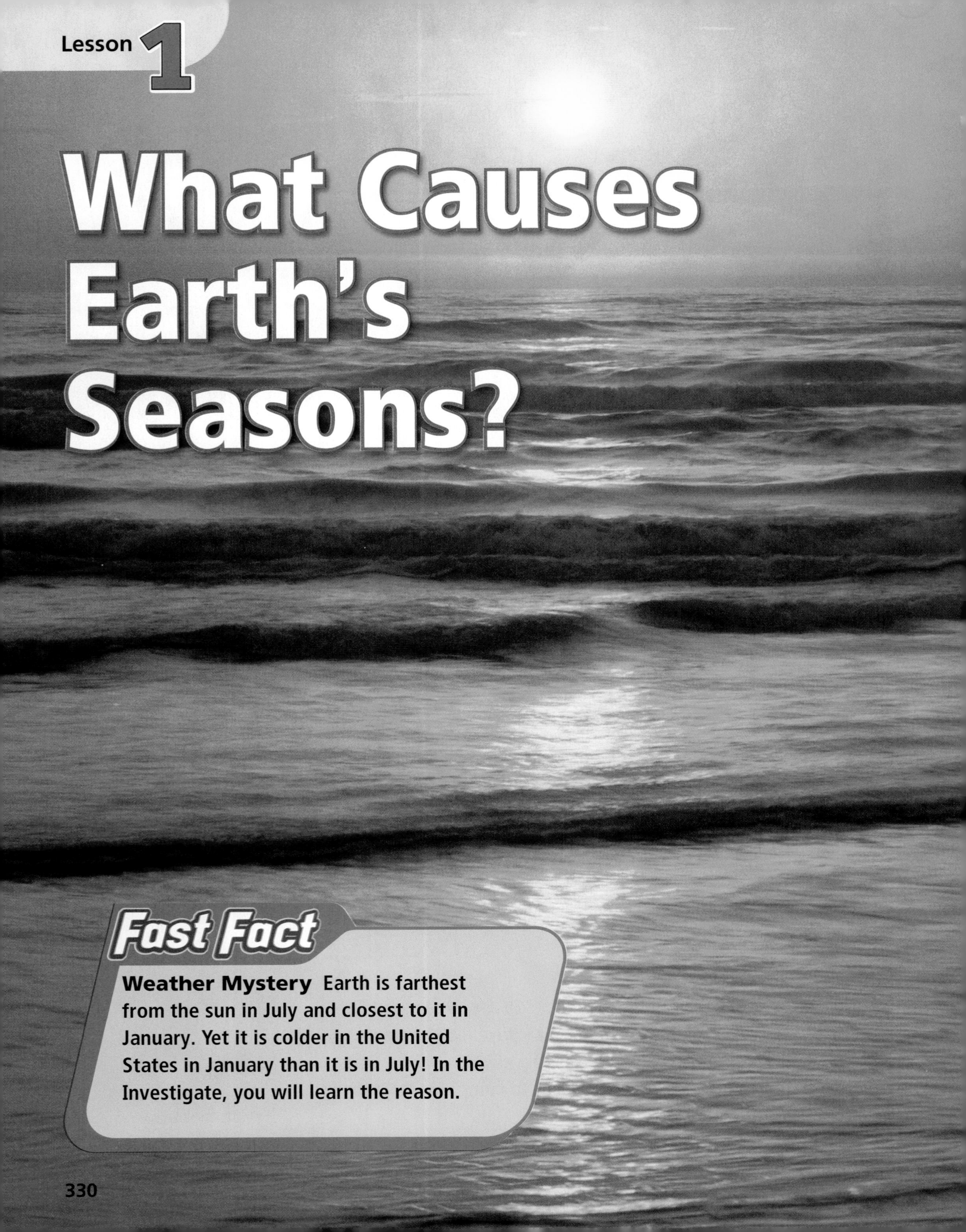

How Sunlight Strikes Earth

Materials
- clear tape
- meterstick
- graph paper
- black marker
- large book
- wooden block
- flashlight
- red marker

Procedure

1. Tape graph paper to a book. Hold a flashlight about 50 cm above the paper. Shine the light straight down. You will see a circle of light.

2. Have a partner use the black marker to trace the circle of light. **Observe** the light on the paper. **Record** the number of squares inside the black line.

3. Keep the flashlight in the same position. Have a partner put a block under one end of the book. This time, use the red marker to trace the light on the paper. **Observe** the light on the paper, and **record** the number of squares inside the red line.

Step 2

Step 3

Draw Conclusions

1. Inside which line was the light brighter? Inside which line are there more squares?

2. **Inquiry Skill** **Compare** the ways the light rays struck the straight and tilted surfaces. At which time would you **infer** that Earth has warmer weather—when the sun's rays strike it directly or at a slant? Explain.

Investigate Further

Form a **hypothesis** about what will happen if the book is tilted even more. **Plan and conduct an experiment** to test your idea.

SC.H.1.2.2.3.1 following experimental design, **SC.H.1.2.2.3.2** using scientific instruments, **SC.H.1.2.3.3.1** working collaboratively, **SC.H.1.2.4.3.1** comparing/contrasting, **SC.H.3.2.2.3.1** collects data

VOCABULARY

axis p. 332
rotation p. 332
revolution p. 333

SCIENCE CONCEPTS

▶ what causes the seasons

▶ what causes day and night

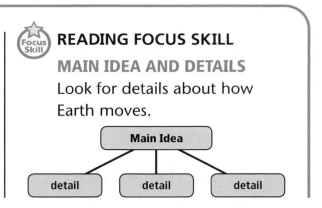

READING FOCUS SKILL

MAIN IDEA AND DETAILS

Look for details about how Earth moves.

How Earth Moves

As you read this book, it may seem as if you're sitting still. In fact, you're moving through space at about 107,000 kilometers (about 66,000 mi) per hour! Although you don't feel the motion, Earth is both traveling and spinning.

Earth spins just the way a top does. Picture a line going through Earth from the North Pole to the South Pole. This imaginary line through Earth is called Earth's **axis**. Look at the picture on this page. As you can see, Earth's axis is not straight up and down. Instead, the axis is tilted a little. The spinning of Earth on its axis is called **rotation**.

Earth rotates on its axis once every day.

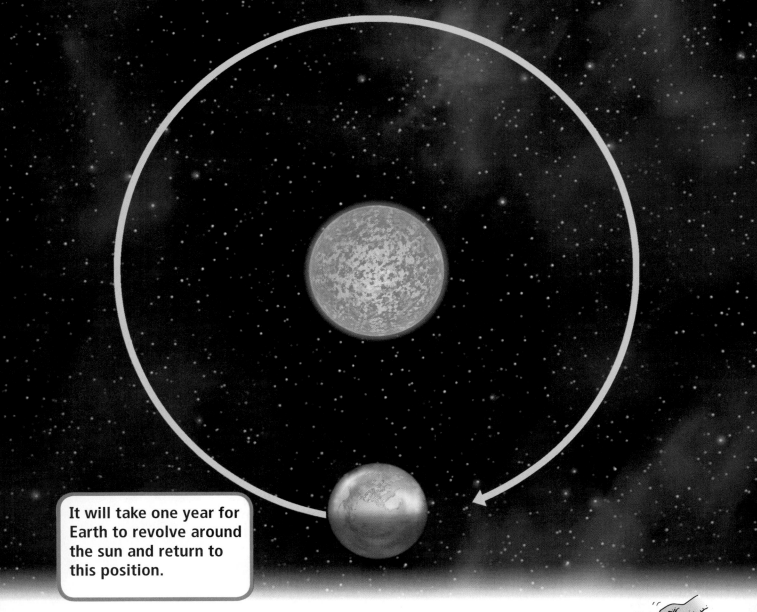

It will take one year for Earth to revolve around the sun and return to this position.

Rotation isn't the only way Earth moves. Earth also revolves around the sun. One trip around the sun is one **revolution**. Each revolution takes about 365 days. People use Earth's movements to measure time. One rotation of Earth takes one day. One revolution of Earth takes one year.

 MAIN IDEA AND DETAILS What are the two ways in which Earth moves?

Modeling Motion
Crumple a piece of yellow paper into a ball to model the sun. Then crumple a piece of blue paper into a ball to model Earth. Use the models to show the two ways Earth moves. As Earth turns and travels, is the same part always facing the sun? Explain.

Seasons

During the year, some parts of Earth have four seasons—winter, spring, summer, and fall—with different weather. One weather difference is temperature. You might wonder what causes these temperature differences.

In the Investigate, you learned that when light rays strike directly, the light is brighter than when they strike at a slant. That's because light rays that strike at a slant spread out more.

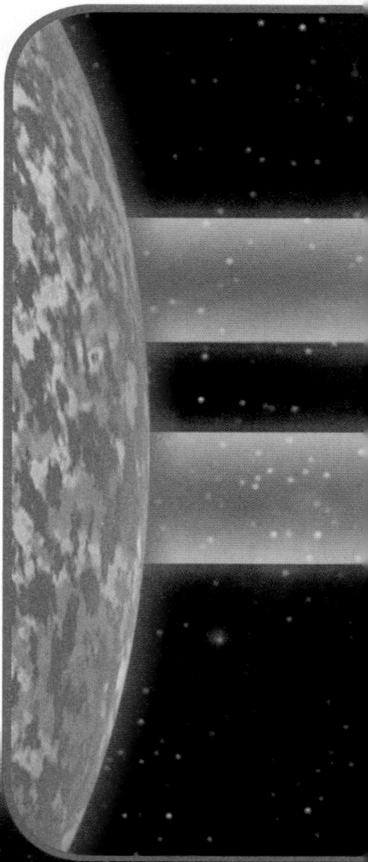

When light rays strike Earth's northern half at their greatest slant, we have winter. At the same time, light rays strike part of Earth's southern half directly. Summer starts in December there! When light rays strike part of Earth's northern half directly, we have summer. At the same time, light rays strike Earth's southern half at their greatest slant. There, winter starts in June!

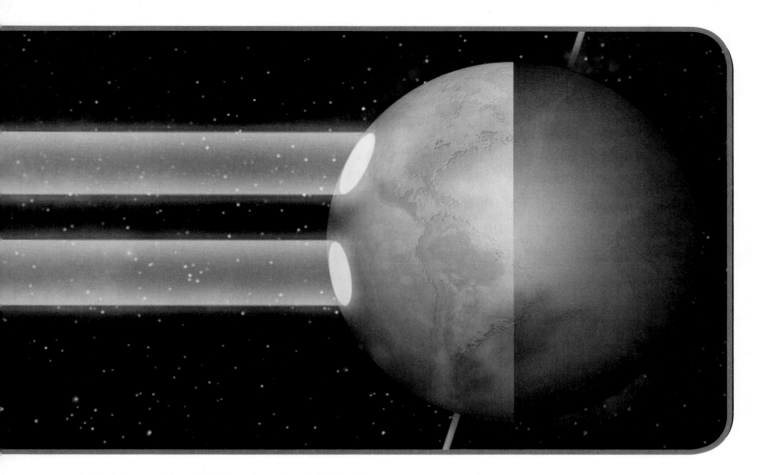

▲Light rays that strike at a slant have the same amount of energy as light rays that strike directly. Their energy is just spread out over a larger area.

Earth is tilted on its axis as it revolves. This causes the same part of Earth that is tilted toward the sun at one time to be tilted away from it at another. Places where the sun's rays strike directly are warmer than places where the rays strike at a slant.

Where the sun's rays strike Earth directly, the season is summer. Where they strike Earth at the greatest slant, the season is winter.

 MAIN IDEA AND DETAILS What causes seasons?

Day and Night

Earth takes one year to revolve around the sun, but only one day to rotate. As it rotates, half of Earth faces the sun and has daytime. The other half of Earth faces away from the sun and has nighttime.

Since some places have day while others have night, it can't be the same time everywhere. People have divided the world into time zones so that places near one another have the same time. When it's 12 noon in Orlando, Florida, it's 6 o'clock in the evening in Madrid, Spain.

 MAIN IDEA AND DETAILS What causes day and night?

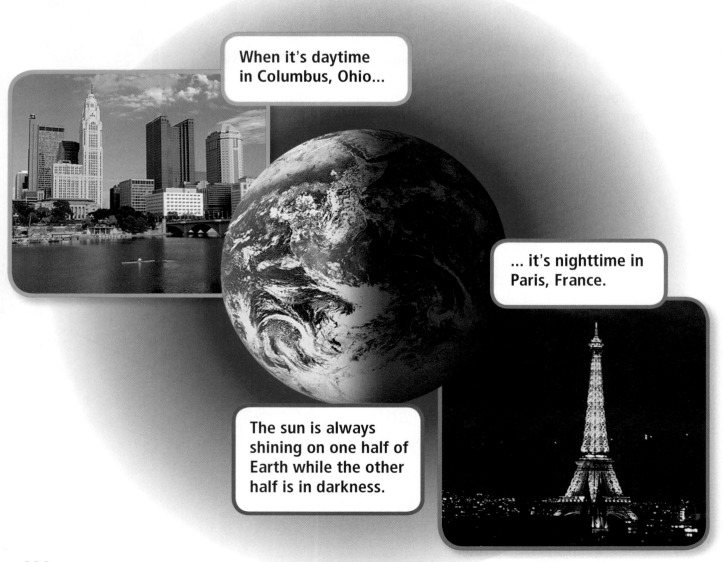

When it's daytime in Columbus, Ohio...

... it's nighttime in Paris, France.

The sun is always shining on one half of Earth while the other half is in darkness.

1. MAIN IDEA AND DETAILS Draw and complete this graphic organizer.

> **Main Idea:** Earth moves in two different ways—rotation and **A** _____.

> Earth's **B** _____ causes the seasons.

> Earth's **C** _____ causes day and night.

2. SUMMARIZE Write a summary of this lesson. Begin with the sentence *Earth moves in two ways*.

3. DRAW CONCLUSIONS What might happen to seasons if Earth did not tilt on its axis?

4. VOCABULARY Draw and label a diagram that shows Earth's revolution, rotation, and axis.

FCAT Prep

5. Read/Inquire/Explain Mike lives in Chicago. At 8:00 A.M., Mike calls a friend in Australia. He finds out his friend and the family are sleeping. Why would Mike's friend be asleep?

Links

Writing

Expository

A day always has 24 hours, but the lengths of daytime and nighttime change during the year. Do research to find out why this happens. Then write a **report** about your findings.

Math

Construct a Graph

As the seasons change, so does the weather, including the temperature. Find out the average temperature for each month in your town. Make a bar graph that shows this information.

 For more links and activities, go to **www.hspscience.com**

How Do Earth and the Moon Interact?

The Moon's Phases

Materials   • flashlight   • volleyball

Procedure

1. Work in groups of three. Use the picture in step 1 to set up the area. Your teacher will darken the room. One classmate will hold a volleyball at position 1. Another classmate will shine a flashlight on it. The third group member will stand in the middle and observe the ball and make a drawing of the ball's lighted side.

2. The classmate holding the volleyball will move to positions 2, 3, and 4. Keep rotating to face the classmate with the volleyball. Observe and record the light at each position.

3. Switch roles so that everyone can observe the pattern.

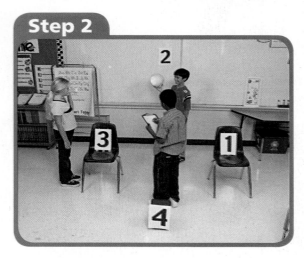

Draw Conclusions

1. What part of the ball was lighted at each position?

2. What does the ball represent? The flashlight? The person recording?

3. **Inquiry Skill** If the ball represents the moon, what can you infer that the different parts of the lighted ball represent?

Investigate Further

The moon's phases occur in a regular pattern. **Predict** how long it will take the moon to go through all its phases. Test your prediction.

SC.H.1.2.3.3.1 working collaboratively, **SC.H.1.2.5.3.1** uses models, **SC.H.2.2.1.3.1** makes predictions, **SC.H.3.2.2.3.1** collects data, **SC.H.3.2.2.3.2** ways to present scientific information

SC.E.1.2.2.3.1 lunar cycle,
LA.A.2.2.1 sequence

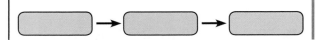

VOCABULARY
moon phases p. 340
lunar cycle p. 341
lunar eclipse p. 342
solar eclipse p. 344

SCIENCE CONCEPTS
▶ what the moon's phases are
▶ what causes eclipses

Focus Skill
READING FOCUS SKILL
SEQUENCE Look for the sequences of lunar phases and eclipses.

Phases of the Moon

You may have noticed that over a period of time, the moon doesn't always look the same. It may look like a circle, a half-circle, or just a thin sliver. The different shapes we see are called **moon phases**.

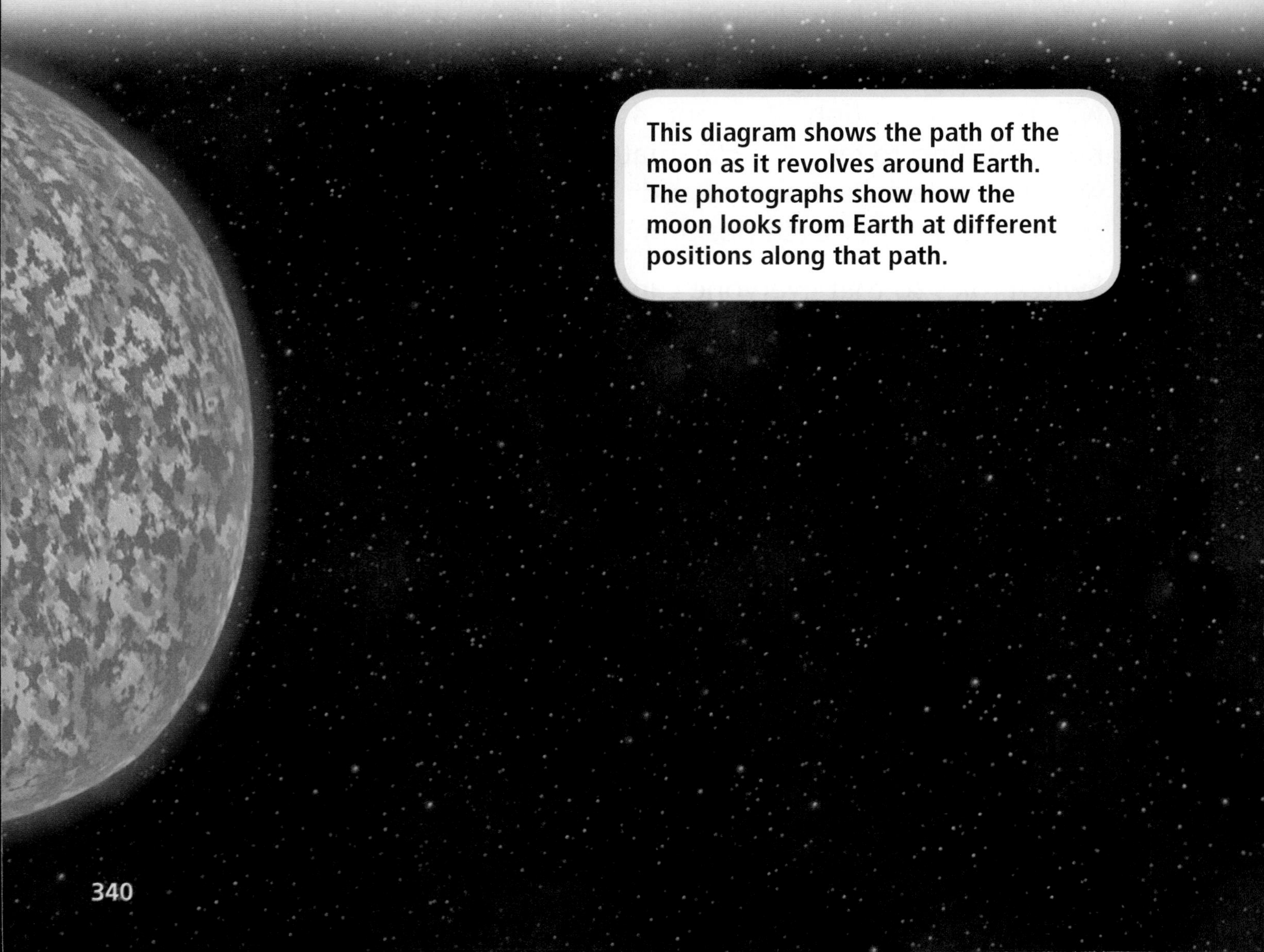

This diagram shows the path of the moon as it revolves around Earth. The photographs show how the moon looks from Earth at different positions along that path.

The moon does not really change. As with Earth, half of the moon is always lit by the sun. Just as Earth revolves around the sun, the moon revolves around Earth. It takes the moon about 29 days to go through its phases in order. This pattern of phases is called the **lunar cycle**. The phase you see at a certain point in the cycle depends on how much of the sunlit side of the moon is facing Earth at that time.

 SEQUENCE Which phase comes after the new moon phase?

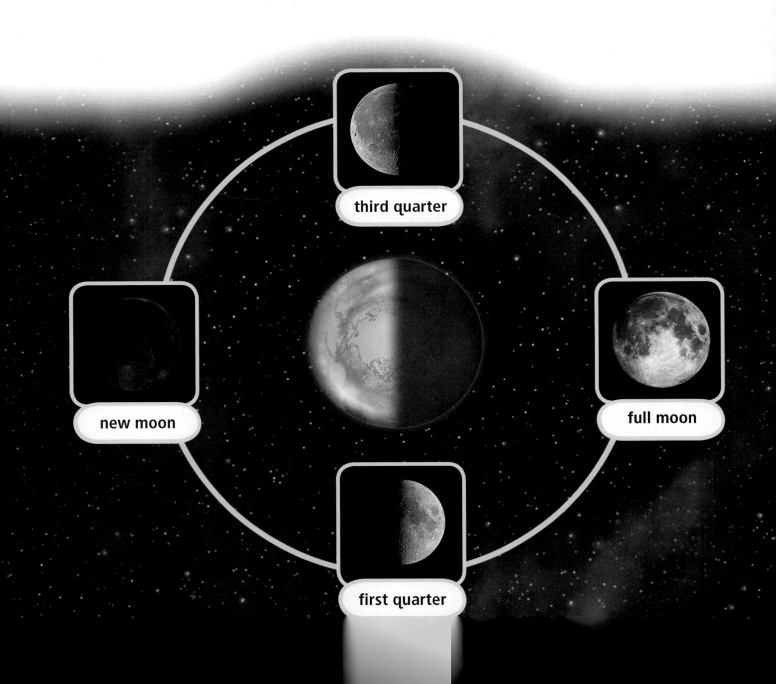

third quarter

new moon

full moon

first quarter

During a total lunar eclipse, the moon can appear to be red.

Eclipses of the Moon

Have you ever made shadow figures with your hands? When you hold your hands in front of a light, the light can't pass through them, so they make shadows. In the same way, Earth makes a shadow because the sun's light can't pass through it.

Sometimes the moon moves into Earth's shadow. This causes a lunar eclipse. A **lunar eclipse** happens when Earth blocks sunlight from reaching the moon. In a lunar eclipse, the moon first gets dark as it moves into Earth's shadow. Then the moon moves out of the shadow and becomes bright again.

 SEQUENCE How does a lunar eclipse happen?

Modeling an Eclipse Make a medium-size ball and a small ball out of clay. Turn off the lights, and hold the medium-size ball in front of a flashlight. Have a partner pass the small ball behind the medium-size ball. What happens? What does this show?

Science Up Close

Lunar Eclipses

Lunar eclipses can happen only during the full moon phase. Sometimes the full moon passes through only part of Earth's shadow. This causes a partial lunar eclipse. At other times, the moon passes through all of Earth's shadow. This causes a total lunar eclipse. The steps of a total lunar eclipse are shown below.

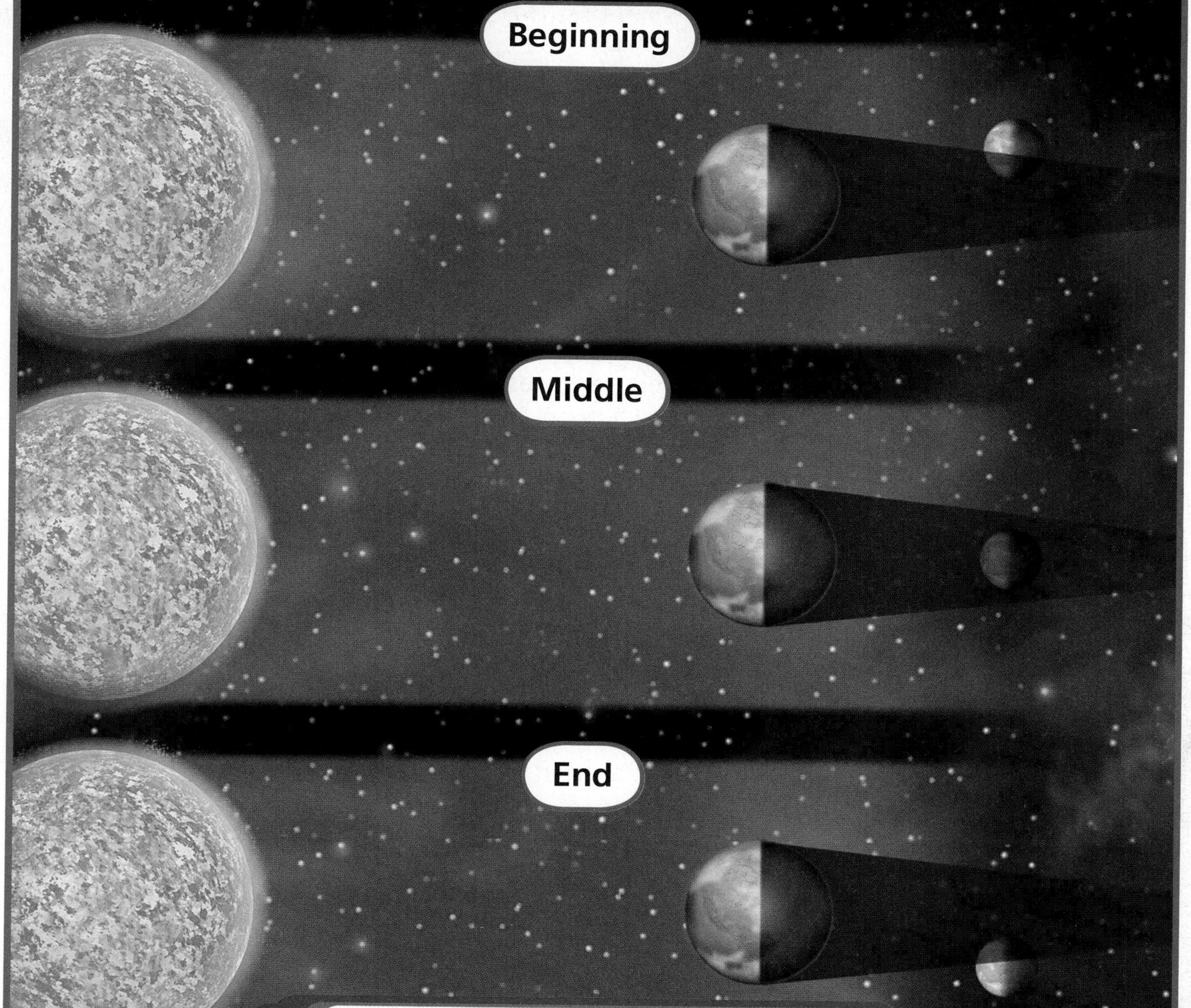

Beginning
Middle
End

For more links and activities, go to **www.hspscience.com**

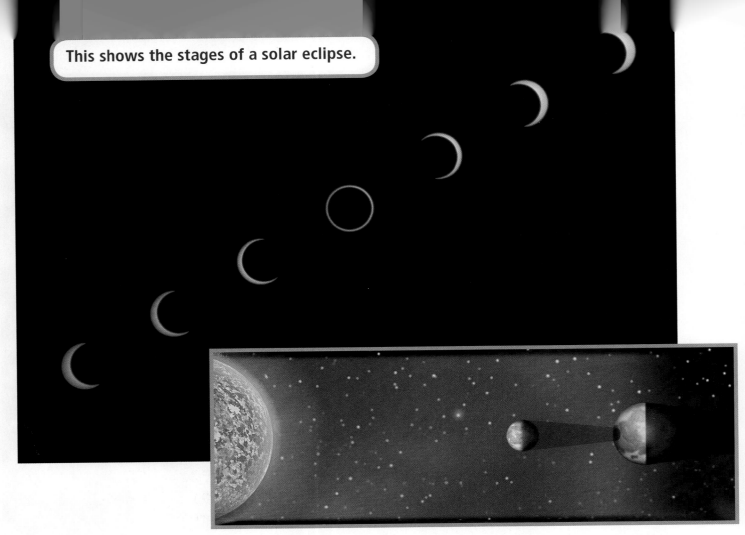

This shows the stages of a solar eclipse.

▲ During a solar eclipse, the moon passes between Earth and the sun. Solar eclipses can happen only during the new moon phase.

Eclipses of the Sun

Just as Earth can block sunlight from the moon, the moon can block sunlight from Earth. When the moon's shadow falls on Earth, a **solar eclipse** happens.

When the moon moves between the sun and Earth, the sky gets dark for a few minutes. Then the moon moves on, and daylight returns. Since the shadow of the moon is small, a solar eclipse can be viewed from only a few places on Earth each time.

 SEQUENCE How does a solar eclipse happen?

1. SEQUENCE Draw and complete this graphic organizer.

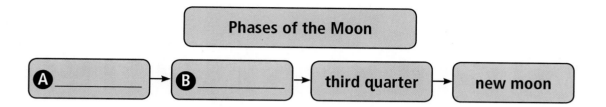

Phases of the Moon

A _____ → **B** _____ → **third quarter** → **new moon**

2. SUMMARIZE Write a lesson summary by using the lesson vocabulary words in a paragraph.

3. DRAW CONCLUSIONS Why does a solar eclipse happen only during the new moon phase?

4. VOCABULARY Make drawings to illustrate the terms *moon phase, lunar eclipse,* and *solar eclipse.* Be sure to label your drawings.

FCAT Prep

5. How often does the lunar cycle repeat itself?

  A. about every day

  B. about every 29 days

  C. about every week

  D. about every year

Links

Writing

Narrative
Astronauts first landed on the moon on July 20, 1969. Do research to learn details about the event. Then write a **story** about the landing from the point of view of one of the astronauts.

Language Arts

Picture Vocabulary
Look up the words *waxing* and *waning.* Write down their definitions. Then draw the phases of the moon and label which phases are *waxing* or *waning.*

 For more links and activities, go to www.hspscience.com

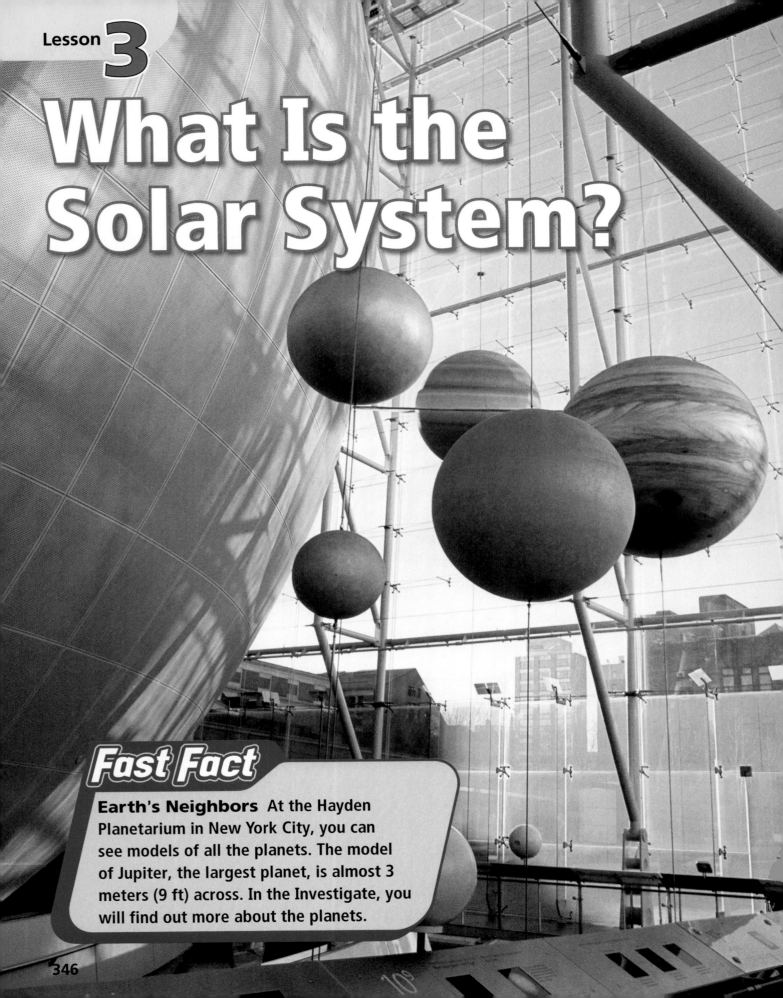

What Is the Solar System?

Fast Fact

Earth's Neighbors At the Hayden Planetarium in New York City, you can see models of all the planets. The model of Jupiter, the largest planet, is almost 3 meters (9 ft) across. In the Investigate, you will find out more about the planets.

The Planets

Materials • pencil • paper

Procedure

1 Use numbers from the Planet Data table to list the planets in order by their distance from the sun, from closest to farthest.

2 Next to the planets' names, record their distances from the sun.

Draw Conclusions

1. Which planet is closest to the sun?

2. Which planet is farthest from the sun?

3. How many planets are between Earth and the sun?

4. Which planets are Earth's nearest neighbors?

5. **Inquiry Skill** Scientists sometimes use numbers to put things in order. List other ways you could order the planets.

Planet Data	
Planet	Distance From Sun (in millions of kilometers)
Earth	150
Jupiter	778
Mars	228
Mercury	58
Neptune	4,505
Pluto	5,890
Saturn	1,427
Uranus	2,869
Venus	108

Step 2

Investigate Further

How could you use numbers to help you plan a model of the solar system? Plan a simple investigation for the model.

SC.H.1.2.2.3.1 following experimental design, SC.H.2.2.1.3.2 uses graphs, SC.H.3.2.2.3.1 collects data, SC.H.3.2.2.3.2 presents scientific information

Reading in Science

SC.E.1.2.3.3.1 sun, a close star, SC.E.1.2.4.3.1 Mercury, Venus, Earth, Mars, SC.E.1.2.5.3.1 planet positions, SC.E.2.2.1.3.1 stars far away, LA.A.2.2.7 compare and contrast

VOCABULARY
planet p. 348
orbit p. 348
solar system p. 348
star p. 349
constellation p. 354

SCIENCE CONCEPTS
▶ what the planets are like
▶ what other kinds of bodies in the solar system are like

READING FOCUS SKILL
COMPARE AND CONTRAST
Look for ways to compare details about bodies in the solar system.

alike ——— different

The Solar System

In Lesson 1, you learned that Earth revolves around the sun. Earth is not the only **planet**, or large body of rock or gases, that does this. Eight other planets revolve around the sun. Each planet revolves in a path called an **orbit**. Many small objects orbit the sun, too. The sun, the planets, and these small objects make up the **solar system**.

 COMPARE AND CONTRAST How are the planets alike? How are they different?

Mercury   Venus   Earth   Mars

The Sun

The sun is the center of the solar system. It is also the biggest object in the solar system. The sun is one of the many, many stars in the universe. **Stars** are hot balls of glowing gases that give off energy.

The sun is the star closest to Earth. Light energy from the sun is very important to life on Earth. The sun's energy helps plants grow and keeps Earth warm. Without the sun, Earth would be too cold for anything to live on it.

 COMPARE AND CONTRAST How are stars different from planets?

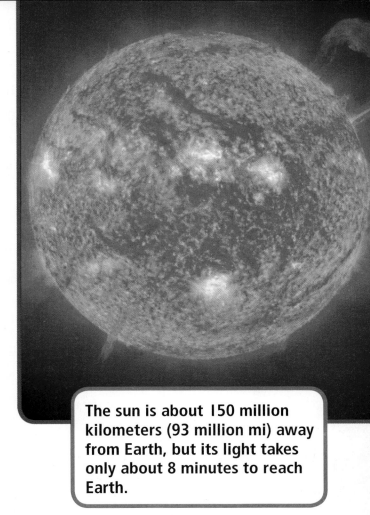

The sun is about 150 million kilometers (93 million mi) away from Earth, but its light takes only about 8 minutes to reach Earth.

Nine planets orbit the sun. The largest planet is Jupiter.

Saturn

Uranus

Neptune

Pluto

The Inner Planets

The four planets closest to the sun are called the inner planets. The inner planets are Mercury, Venus, Earth, and Mars. You can sometimes see Venus and Mars at night. They look like stars, but their light is steady—it does not twinkle. If you use a telescope, you may be able to see Mercury as well.

Venus

Venus
Fun Fact: Venus rotates backward compared with most other planets. Venus may once have had oceans, but they have evaporated.
Length of Day: about 243 Earth days
Length of Year: about 225 Earth days
Moons: none
Surface: rocky, with constant cover of thick clouds
Distance Across: about 12,000 kilometers (7,500 mi)

Mercury

Mercury
Fun Fact: In the daytime, much of Mercury's surface is hot enough to melt lead. Even so, there may be ice at its poles.
Length of Day: about 176 Earth days
Length of Year: 88 Earth days
Moons: none
Surface: rocky, with many craters
Distance Across: about 4,900 kilometers (3,100 mi)

All of the inner planets have rocky surfaces. They are smaller than most of the other planets. The inner planets are also warmer than the other planets because they are closer to the sun.

 COMPARE AND CONTRAST How are the inner planets different from the other planets?

Earth

Earth
Fun Fact: Earth is the only planet known to have water on its surface. Water is necessary to support life.
Length of Day: 24 hours (1 Earth day)
Length of Year: about 365 days (1 Earth year)
Moons: 1
Surface: mostly water, with some land areas
Distance Across: about 12,750 kilometers (7,900 mi)

Mars

Mars
Fun Fact: Mars has the largest volcano in the solar system. Mars also has ice under its surface.
Length of Day: about 25 Earth hours
Length of Year: 687 Earth days (almost 2 Earth years)
Moons: 2
Surface: rocky, with red dust and no water
Distance Across: about 6,800 kilometers (4,200 mi)

The Outer Planets

The five planets farthest from the sun are called the outer planets. They include Jupiter, Saturn, Uranus, Neptune, and Pluto. The outer planets are made mostly of frozen gases. Most of them are very large and have many moons.

 COMPARE AND CONTRAST How are most of the outer planets alike?

Jupiter

Jupiter
Fun Fact: Two Earth-sized circles could fit inside Jupiter's Great Red Spot, a huge storm on Jupiter's surface.
Length of Day: about 10 Earth hours
Length of Year: about 12 Earth years
Moons: at least 61
Surface: no solid surface
Distance Across: about 143,000 kilometers (88,900 mi)

Saturn

Saturn
Fun Fact: Saturn has a large system of rings that reaches about 416,000 kilometers (258,000 mi) from its surface.
Length of Day: about 11 Earth hours
Length of Year: about 29 Earth years
Moons: at least 33
Surface: frozen gases
Distance Across: about 120,000 kilometers (74,600 mi)

Uranus

Uranus
Fun Fact: Uranus rolls on its side as it orbits the sun.
Length of Day: about 17 Earth hours
Length of Year: about 84 Earth years
Moons: at least 26
Surface: frozen gases
Distance Across: about 51,000 kilometers (31,700 mi)

Neptune

Neptune
Fun Fact: Neptune is the farthest planet from the sun for 20-year periods when Pluto crosses its orbit.
Length of Day: about 16 Earth hours
Length of Year: about 164 Earth years
Moons: at least 13
Surface: frozen gases
Distance Across: about 49,500 kilometers (about 30,758 mi)

Pluto

Pluto
Fun Fact: Pluto is made of ice. It has a moon almost as large as itself.
Length of Day: about 6 Earth days
Length of Year: about 248 Earth years
Moons: 1
Surface: frozen gases
Distance Across: about 2,400 kilometers (1,500 mi)

Math in Science
Interpret Data

How many Earth years long is one revolution of the sun on the planets Jupiter, Saturn, Uranus, Neptune, and Pluto?

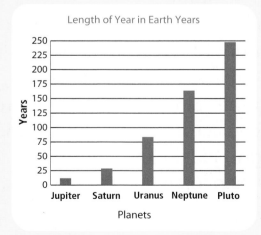

Length of Year in Earth Years

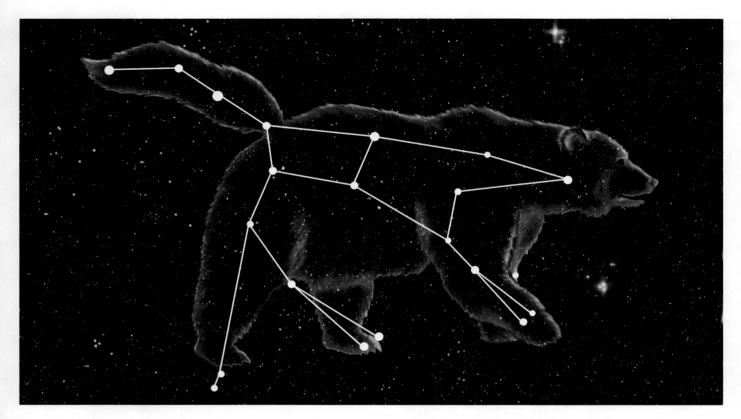

▲ You can see different constellations in different seasons. Some constellations, such as the Big Bear, can be seen all year.

Patterns of Stars

When you look at stars in the sky, you know that no one could ever count them all. Some are very bright, while others are hard to see. How do people tell one star from another? One way is to use constellations. **Constellations** are groups of stars that appear to form the shapes of animals, people, or objects. Since the stars seem to move across the sky during the night, looking for constellations helps people find certain stars.

 COMPARE AND CONTRAST Compare the way people group stars with the way they group the planets.

Finding Constellations
Scatter dried beans on a sheet of paper. Look for shapes made by the beans. Draw them. How might this activity be like what people long ago did when they looked at stars?

1. COMPARE AND CONTRAST Draw and complete this graphic organizer.

	Inner Planets	Outer Planets
Mostly Made of	rock	Ⓐ _____
Number of Moons	Ⓑ _____	most have many
Distance from Sun	near	Ⓒ _____
Size	Ⓓ _____	most are large

2. SUMMARIZE Write a paragraph describing the solar system.

3. DRAW CONCLUSIONS How are Earth and Mars alike? How are they different?

4. VOCABULARY Write a sentence using the vocabulary terms *planets, orbit,* and *solar system.*

FCAT Prep

5. Read/Inquire/Explain Stella likes to look at the stars at night. After several hours, Stella notices that the stars seem to have moved across the night sky. Why do you think the stars seem to move?

Links

Writing

Descriptive
Observe the stars and moon with a parent or guardian. Write a **description** of what you observe, including any constellations you recognize.

Health

Lights at Night
Light pollution, or too many lights in the environment, makes it hard to view stars at night. Light pollution can harm human health. Research ways people can cut down on light pollution. Make a brochure showing what you learned.

 For more links and activities, go to **www.hspscience.com**

Ancient Planet Found

Can you guess what has been around for about 13 billion years? It's a planet that scientists recently discovered. If you think that sounds old, you're correct. The newly discovered planet is more than twice as old as Earth. In fact, the new discovery is the oldest planet known to exist.

However, don't rush out to try to get a peek at the planet. It is too far away to be seen. Scientists found the planet by using the Hubble Space Telescope.

A Special Telescope

The Hubble Space Telescope is a special kind of telescope. Rather than sitting in a dome on Earth, this telescope floats in space about 375 miles above Earth. Since it is in space, it can take pictures of stars and planets no other telescope can take.

Images from Hubble Space Telescope.

Near the End?

Scientists say the Hubble's discovery is important. It means that planets probably began forming much earlier than experts once thought. "This means that 13 billion years ago, life could have arisen and then died out," said one scientist.

The Hubble's discoveries, however, may be coming to an end. The telescope was not designed to stay in space forever. The space agency, NASA, has sent astronauts in the past to repair and upgrade the telescope. Unless another repair mission is sent, the telescope might stop working.

Scientists, however, are working on putting together a repair mission. The repairs and upgrades would be done by robots and would keep the Hubble in space for several more years.

Large in Scope

Hubble is also a lot bigger than many telescopes. It is 13.2 meters (43.5 ft) long and about 4.2 meters (14 ft) around the outside. In other words, it's about the size of a big tractor-trailer truck.

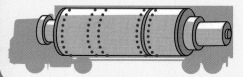

THINK ABOUT IT

1. What can the Hubble Space Telescope teach scientists about the solar system?
2. Why do you think scientists want to discover new planets?

Find out more! Log on to
www.hspscience.com

A Science Groundbreaker

Reva Kay Williams has made a career out of being a groundbreaker. A groundbreaker does not have anything to do with the ground. It means the first person to do something in a particular area. Williams has made amazing discoveries, but she also is the first African American woman in her area of study.

Williams studies a kind of science called astrophysics. *Astrophysics* is the study of astronomy and physics. *Astronomy* is the study of everything in outer space, including stars and

galaxies. *Physics* is the study of how energy and all the material on Earth affect one another. Scientists such as Williams study how energy and all the material in outer space affect one another.

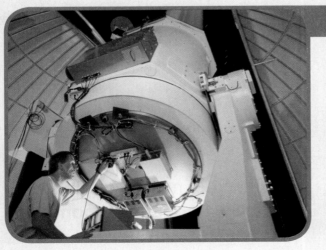

Career   Astronomers

Astronomers spend most of their time looking at planets and galaxies. However, these scientists help solve problems on Earth, too. They can also help astronauts prepare for space flight.

 Find out more! Log on to
www.hspscience.com

You Can Do It!

Materials
- a small self-stick note
- globe
- flashlight

Quick and Easy Project

Sunrise, Sunset

Procedure

1. Write the name of your town on a self-stick note. Stick the note on your state on a globe.

2. Turn off the lights in the room. Shine a flashlight on the globe.

3. Slowly spin the globe counterclockwise.

Draw Conclusions

What happens to the place where you put the note? What does this represent? Describe why the sun appears to move slowly across the sky from east to west during a day.

Design Your Own Investigation

Asteroid Impact

Asteroids are chunks of rock that orbit the sun. What do you think happens when they hit a planet or a moon? Design an investigation to find out. You might drop pebbles into a tray of corn starch and then compare the surface to the surface of the moon. Write a report describing what you found out.

Vocabulary Review

Use the terms below to complete the sentences. The page numbers tell where to look in the chapter if you need help.

axis p. 332
revolution p. 333
moon phases p. 340
lunar cycle p. 341
solar eclipse p. 344
planet p. 348
solar system p. 348
constellation p. 354

1. Each stage of the moon's cycle is called a _____.

2. The movement of Earth once around the sun is called a _____.

3. A group of stars that appears to form a picture is a _____.

4. When the moon's shadow falls on Earth, a _____ happens.

5. The imaginary line Earth rotates around is known as its _____.

6. A large body of rock or gases that orbits the sun is a _____.

7. The pattern of lunar phases is called the _____.

8. The sun, the planets, and the other objects that orbit the sun make up the _____.

Check Understanding

Write the letter of the best choice.

9. Which of the following is responsible for Earth's seasons?
   A. Earth's rotation
   B. Earth's tilt
   C. solar eclipses
   D. the lunar cycle

10. Which of the following is responsible for day and night?
    F. Earth's orbit
    G. Earth's revolution
    H. Earth's rotation
    I. Earth's tilt

11. **COMPARE AND CONTRAST**
    Compare the four areas on the diagram below.

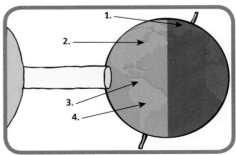

Which area is the warmest?
   A. Area 1   **C.** Area 3
   B. Area 2   **D.** Area 4

12. About how long is the lunar cycle?

   F. 29 days   **H.** 24 hours

   G. 365 days   **I.** 1 week

13. SEQUENCE The steps of a lunar eclipse follow a certain sequence. What happens first?

   A. The moon enters Earth's shadow.

   B. The moon leaves Earth's shadow.

   C. The moon goes dark.

   D. The moon is lighted by the sun again.

14. Which of the following is closest to Earth?

   F. Big Bear   **H.** North Star

   G. Big Dipper   **I.** the sun

15. Which of the following is true about Mercury?

   A. It has plenty of water.

   B. It is far from the sun.

   C. It is made of frozen gases.

   D. It is very hot.

16. Which of the following is true about Venus?

   F. It has two moons.

   G. It is the closest planet to the sun.

   H. Its rotation is in the opposite direction to the rotations of the other planets.

   I. Its day lasts only 11 hours.

Inquiry Skills

17. Infer why animals and plants are found on Earth but not on other planets of the solar system.

18. Order the inner planets from the one closest to the sun to the one farthest from the sun.

Read/Inquire/Explain

19. In what ways is Pluto like an inner planet?

20. The diagram shows Earth's position for each season. Look at the part of Earth where North America is. Explain why daytime is shorter there in winter than in summer.

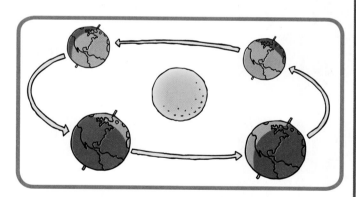

Processes of Life

 The chapters in this unit address these Grade Level Expectations from the Florida Sunshine State Standards.

Chapter 11 **Types of Plants**

SC.F.1.2.3.3.2   understands similarities and differences among plants.

Chapter 12 **Types of Animals**

SC.F.1.2,2.3.1   understands the various ways that animals depend on plants for survival (for example, food, shelter, oxygen).

SC.F.1.2.3.3.1   knows the common and distinguishing characteristics of groups of vertebrate animals (mammals, birds, fish, reptiles, amphibians).

SC.F.1.2.3.3.3   understands that although plants and animals are different, they also share common characteristics (for example, they both have structures for reproduction, respiration, and growth).

The investigations and experiences in this unit also address many of the Grade Level Expectations in Strand H, The Nature of Science.

LIFE SCIENCE

Science in Florida

Gainesville

Dear David,

Today I visited my cousin, who goes to the University of Florida in Gainesville. She took me to the Natural History Museum. I liked the butterfly exhibit the best. There were colorful butterflies flying all around us. We watched a butterfly lay eggs on a leaf. There were also caterpillars eating the leaves, and cocoons hanging all over the place.

Wish you were here,

Kayla

The Sunshine State

USA

FCAT Writing

Writing Situation

Think about living things. Explain how plants and animals are alike and different.

Experiment!

Keeping Warm When it gets cold outside, you probably put on a jacket and a hat. Animals in the wild have to find other ways to stay warm. How do mammals keep warm when the weather turns cold? For example, do mammals with more hair stay warmer than mammals with less hair? Plan and conduct an experiment to find out.

11 Types of Plants

Lesson 1 **What Do Plants Need to Live?**

Lesson 2 **What Are Some Types of Plants?**

Lesson 3 **How Do Plants Make Food?**

Vocabulary

FCAT-Tested

photosynthesis

Other Terms

root

nutrient

stem

leaf

seed

deciduous

evergreen

chlorophyll

What do YOU wonder?

Many people buy flowering plants that attract birds or butterflies to their gardens. How do plants make your life better?

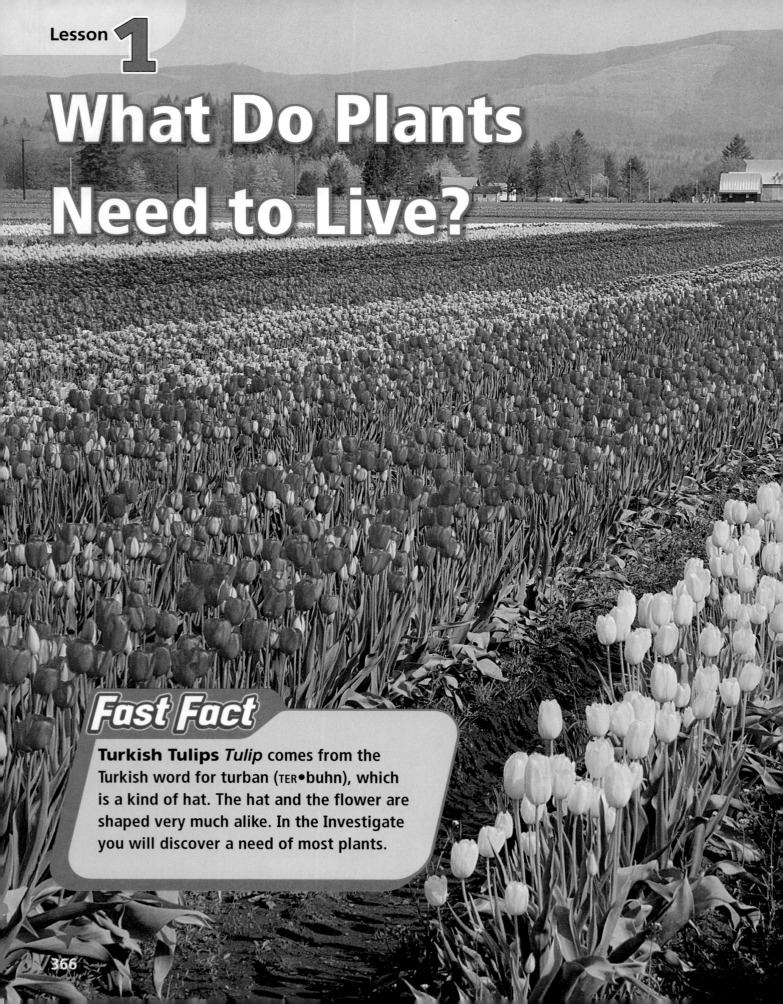

1

What Do Plants Need to Live?

Fast Fact

Turkish Tulips *Tulip* comes from the Turkish word for turban (TER●buhn), which is a kind of hat. The hat and the flower are shaped very much alike. In the Investigate you will discover a need of most plants.

Needs of Plants

Materials
- 3 small plants
- 3 paper cups
- sand
- potting soil
- gravel
- water

Procedure

1. Take 3 plants. Gently shake the soil from each plant. Plant one in a cup of sand. Plant another in a cup of gravel. Plant the third in a cup of soil. Water each plant. Put the cups in a sunny window.

2. **Observe** the plants every other day for two weeks. Water the plants every few days with the same amount of water.

3. **Record** any changes you **observe**. Make sure to look for changes in plant size.

Step 1

Step 2

Draw Conclusions

1. Which plant looked the healthiest after two weeks? Explain why.

2. Which plant looked the least healthy after two weeks? What was different for this plant?

3. **Inquiry Skill** Scientists often **compare** the results they get in their experiments. How could you **compare** your findings?

Investigate Further

Predict how different amounts of water might affect the growth of plants. Try it!

SC.H.1.2.1.3.1 keeping accurate records, **SC.H.1.2.2.3.1** following experimental design, **SC.H.1.2.4.3.1** comparing/contrasting, **SC.H.2.2.1.3.1** makes predictions, **SC.H.3.2.2.3.1** collects data

367

SC.F.1.2.3.3.2 plants/similarities and differences **LA.A.2.2.1** main idea and details

VOCABULARY

roots p. 370

nutrients p. 370

stem p. 370

leaf p. 370

SCIENCE CONCEPTS

▶ what plants need to live

▶ how plants get what they need to live

READING FOCUS SKILL

MAIN IDEA AND DETAILS

Look for details about the things plants need to live.

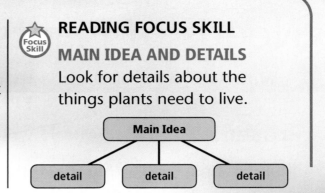

What Plants Need

Plants live and grow in many places. They can grow in a city and in the country. They grow in forests, in fields, and in parks. Some even grow underwater or in deserts! No matter where they grow, most plants need the same things to live.

Every living thing has basic needs. Living things cannot survive unless their basic needs are met. Plants need nutrients from soil, water, air, and light. How are your basic needs the same as and different from a plant's?

◀ This girl is making sure her plants get air, light, water, and soil.

Think about places where plants don't grow. Plants don't grow deep in caves, because there is no light. They don't grow on bare rock, because there is no soil and water. Why do you think there are more plants in a forest than in a desert?

Many people like to garden. They care for plants by giving them water and good soil. However, most plants grow without human care. They get what they need from the sun, the air, the rain, and the soil.

 MAIN IDEA AND DETAILS **What four things do plants need to live?**

Make a Model
Observe how stems carry water to a plant's leaves. Put red food coloring into a cup of water. Add a stalk of celery that has leaves. Let it sit overnight. Measure how far the color traveled up the stalk. Did the color reach the leaves?

Some Plant Parts and What They Do

Compare the ivy on this page to the flower on the page on the right. The plants look very different, but they have the same parts.

The **roots** of most plants grow under the ground. They take in water and nutrients from the soil. **Nutrients** (NOO•tree•uhnts) help plants grow and stay healthy.

The **stem** grows above the ground and holds the plant up. It carries water and nutrients to the leaves. The stem also takes food from the leaves to the roots.

A **leaf** grows out from the stem and is where the plant makes food. Sunlight, air, and water are used inside a leaf to make food that the plant needs, so it can live and grow.

 MAIN IDEA AND DETAILS How does water from the soil travel to the leaves of a plant?

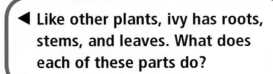

◄ Like other plants, ivy has roots, stems, and leaves. What does each of these parts do?

The stem of the plant helps hold up the leaves. It also carries water and nutrients from the roots to the leaves.

Most plant leaves are green. The green coloring helps leaves collect sunlight. The coloring also helps the plant make its own food so it can live and grow. Some plants are food for animals, too.

The roots of the plant take in water and nutrients from the soil. They also help hold the plant in the ground.

371

How Plants Live in Different Environments

Plants are found almost everywhere on Earth. They even grow in ponds and in deserts. In these places, it can be hard for plants to get what they need.

For example, the desert, where cactus plants grow, is very dry. You might wonder how a cactus gets water. It has a special stem and roots for getting the water it needs. A water lily grows underwater. The roots gather nutrients from the soil and water. A long stem leads to a floating leaf that absorbs sunlight.

 MAIN IDEA AND DETAILS How do plants get what they need from their environments?

Cactus

The roots of the cactus are close to the surface of the soil. They quickly take in rainwater. The cactus's thick stem stores the water.

Math in Science
Interpret Data

How much sunlight do plants need?
Sunlight Needs of Plants

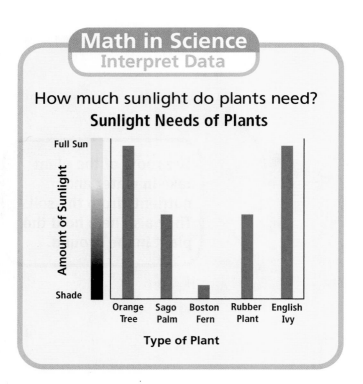

Paperwhites

This plant grows from a bulb. Until its roots grow into the ground, the bulb gives the plant the food it needs.

1. MAIN IDEA AND DETAILS Draw and complete the graphic organizer.

Main Idea: There are many different kinds of plants, but most of them have the same needs.

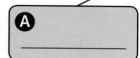 **A** _____

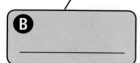 **B** _____

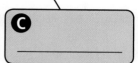 **C** _____

Air

2. SUMMARIZE Use the graphic organizer to write a lesson summary.

3. DRAW CONCLUSIONS Ryan notices that the lettuce plants in the garden are drooping. The soil is dry, and the sun is hot. What should Ryan do? How do you know?

4. VOCABULARY In your own words, write a paragraph explaining how roots and nutrients are related.

FCAT Prep

5. Which is **not** something most plants need to live and grow?

- **A.** nutrients
- **B.** shelter
- **C.** oxygen
- **D.** water

Links

Writing

Expository
Your neighbors want to plant a garden. Write a **friendly letter** to help them choose the best spot to put the garden. Be sure to tell them about the basic needs of plants.

Art

State Symbols
Every state has a state tree and a state flower. What are your state's tree and flower? Draw or paint a picture of each.

 For more links and activities, go to **www.hspscience.com**

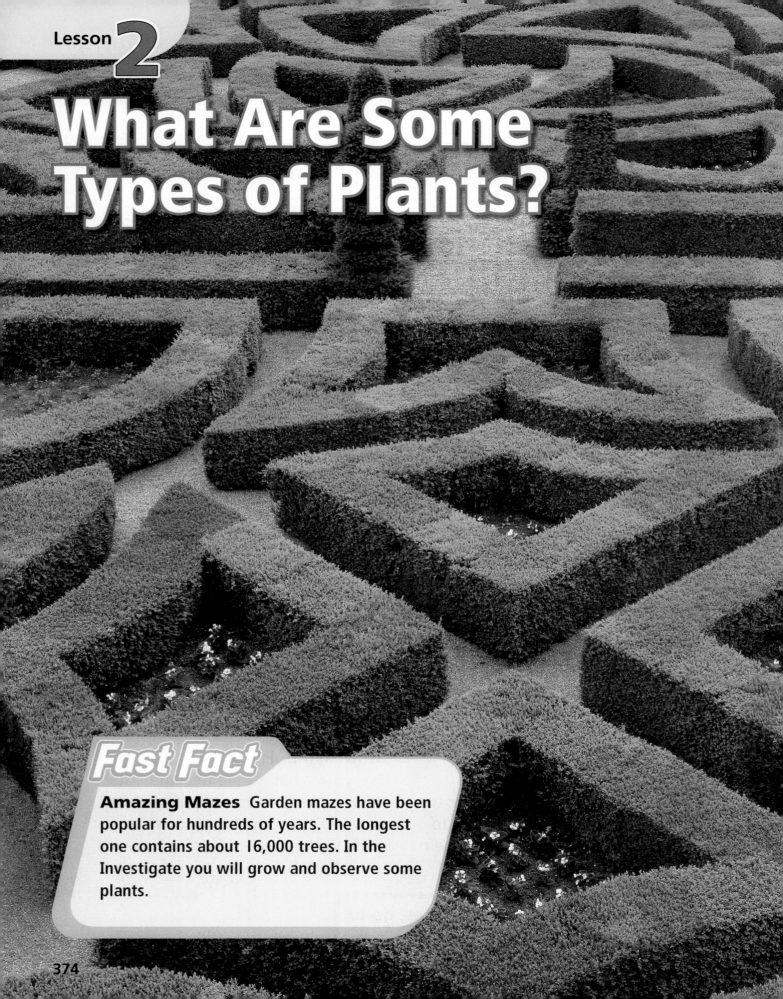

Lesson **2**

What Are Some Types of Plants?

Fast Fact

Amazing Mazes Garden mazes have been popular for hundreds of years. The longest one contains about 16,000 trees. In the Investigate you will grow and observe some plants.

374

Growing Lima Beans

Materials
- 3 lima bean seeds
- 2 zip-top plastic bags
- hand lens
- water
- 2 paper towels

Procedure

1. Split one lima bean seed in half, and use the hand lens to look inside. Identify the new plant inside the seed. After you have finished, put the seed to the side.

2. Fold each paper towel in half. Moisten one of them with water, but don't use too much water. Don't moisten the other towel. Then place each towel inside a plastic bag.

3. Place one seed in each bag. Label the bag with the moistened towel WET, and label the other bag DRY. Seal the bags, and place them where they won't be disturbed.

4. Observe the seeds for 10 school days. Record your observations.

Step 1

Step 3

Draw Conclusions

1. How does a new bean plant grow?

2. **Inquiry Skill** Use what you have observed to draw conclusions about what bean seeds need to grow. Why do you think the seeds didn't need soil to start growing?

Investigate Further

Predict how seeds will grow at different temperatures. Design and conduct an experiment to see if seeds grow faster in warm or cold weather.

SC.H.1.2.1.3.1 keeping accurate records, **SC.H.1.2.2.3.1** following experimental design, **SC.H.1.2.2.3.2** using scientific instruments, **SC.H.2.2.1.3.1** makes predictions, **SC.H.3.2.2.3.1** collects data

VOCABULARY

seed p. 377

deciduous p. 379

evergreen p. 379

SCIENCE CONCEPT

▶ how plants can be grouped

READING FOCUS SKILL

MAIN IDEA AND DETAILS

Look for details about different kinds of plants.

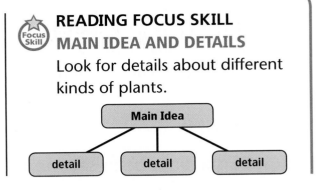

Trees, Shrubs, and Grasses

Suppose your teacher asked you to organize the classroom bookshelves. How would you group the books so that everyone could find what they needed? You might start by putting similar books together. All the science books could go together on one shelf, and all the math books could go on another.

◀ You would have to look closely to see the flowers of the oak tree. The small flowers grow into the tree's seed, the acorn.

There's no way to miss the flowers on the showy azalea. However, the shrub's seeds are tiny.

The flowers of these plants are hard to spot, but the seeds of one kind are easy to see. These palm trees produce large seeds—coconuts.

Just as you had a way to arrange the books, scientists have a way to arrange plants. They group similar plants together. For example, plants that have seeds are put into two groups. One group of plants with seeds has flowers, and the other does not. A **seed** is an early stage of new life for many plants.

The trees, shrubs, and grasses shown on these pages look very different. They may even grow in different places. Yet the trees, shrubs, and grasses are alike in two ways. They all have seeds and they all have flowers.

 MAIN IDEA AND DETAILS How is grouping plants helpful to scientists?

Types of Leaves

You already know that leaves help plants get the light and air they need to make food. Scientists group some plants by the kind of leaves the plants have.

Leaves come in many sizes and shapes. Many leaves, such as the leaves of maple and oak trees, are large and flat. Others, like those from the pine tree, are long and narrow. A leaf may have smooth edges, or it may be jagged. The way a leaf looks can help you identify what plant it came from.

Pine

The long, thin leaves of a pine tree look like needles. Pine trees are grouped as evergreens.

Maple

A maple leaf is broad and flat, with five lobes that have small notches. A maple tree loses its leaves each fall.

Oak

Most oaks are deciduous trees with flat leaves. In the winter, most oak trees have no leaves.

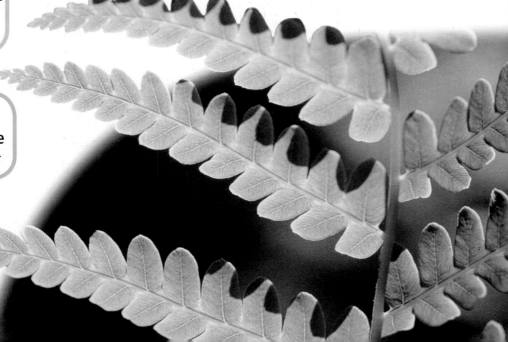

Fern

The fern is a plant with many fronds—the leafy branches are made up of smaller leaflets. ▶

All plants lose leaves and grow new ones. Scientists can group plants based on how they lose their leaves.

Deciduous (dee•sɪj•oo•uhs) plants lose their leaves each year. This usually happens in the fall, when the days get shorter and cooler. During the cold winter months, deciduous plants do not make food.

Evergreen plants stay green and make food all year long. They lose leaves or needles from time to time, but they don't lose them all at once.

MAIN IDEA AND DETAILS How can leaves be used to group plants?

Magnolia

The flat leaves of the magnolia tree are different in shape from pine needles, yet both are evergreen trees.

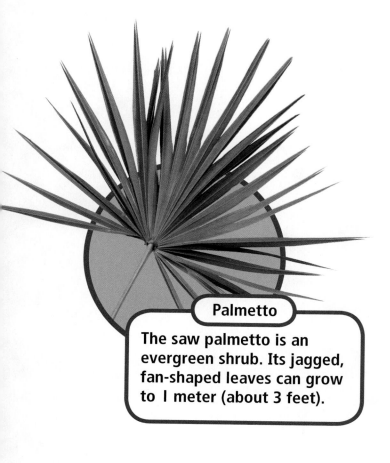

Palmetto

The saw palmetto is an evergreen shrub. Its jagged, fan-shaped leaves can grow to 1 meter (about 3 feet).

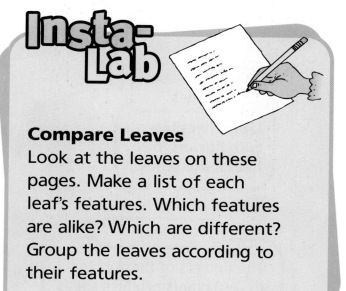

Insta-Lab

Compare Leaves
Look at the leaves on these pages. Make a list of each leaf's features. Which features are alike? Which are different? Group the leaves according to their features.

Plants with Flowers

Think about a garden overflowing with beautiful flowers. Butterflies and bees go from flower blossom to flower blossom. Scientists often group plants by whether they do or don't have flowers.

Some flowers are large and very colorful. Others are small and hard to see. Not all plants even have flowers. In plants that do, the flowers have an important job. Special parts produce seeds.

 MAIN IDEA AND DETAILS What role do flowers play in a plant's life cycle?

Cherry Tree

Flowering cherry trees can be grouped as deciduous, as forming seeds, and as having flowers.

Lilies

Like other plants with flowers, day lilies make seeds.

Phlox

The flowers of these phlox (FLAHKS) plants produce seeds.

Plants Without Flowers

Some plants do not form flowers. They make seeds in their other parts. For example, many evergreen plants make their seeds inside cones. These evergreens are called conifers (KAHN•uh•ferz).

Other plants, such as ferns, make spores (SPOHRZ). Spores are usually brown and can be seen on the underside of a leaf. These spores grow into new fern plants.

Focus Skill **MAIN IDEA AND DETAILS** **How do plants without flowers form new plants?**

Spruce Tree

This evergreen tree forms seeds in its cones.

Dwarf Juniper

The dwarf juniper is an evergreen plant that makes seeds in its cones.

Boston Fern

This Boston fern has spores on the undersides of its lush fronds.

Seeds

Have you ever found seeds inside an apple you were eating? Apple seeds look very different from apple trees. It's hard to believe that a tiny seed can grow into a large tree! But seeds are important. They contain the food to help a new plant grow.

Seeds may be large or small. They may be round, oval, flat, or pointed. Seeds can also be found in many colors. Like an apple seed, all seeds look very different from the plants they become. Yet all seeds grow into plants like the ones they came from.

MAIN IDEA AND DETAILS What does a seed do?

Peas

Each of these tasty peas is a seed that could grow into a new plant.

Sugar Maple

The sugar maple tree has seeds inside a pod that spiral down to the ground.

Oranges

The seeds of this orange can grow into orange trees.

Thistle

Downy fluff covers thistle seeds. The fluff helps the seeds float away in the wind.

1. MAIN IDEA AND DETAILS Draw and complete the graphic organizer.

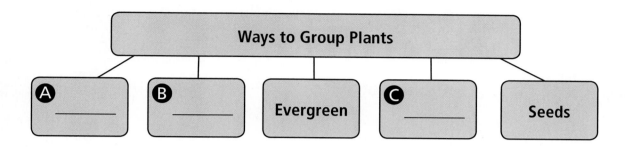

Ways to Group Plants

A _____

B _____

Evergreen

C _____

Seeds

2. SUMMARIZE Write a sentence that tells the most important information in this lesson.

3. DRAW CONCLUSIONS While taking a walk, you find a plant you have never seen before. You observe that it has many small green leaves up and down each branch. You see that there are brown spots under the leaves. What kind of plant might it be?

4. VOCABULARY Use the lesson vocabulary to write a sentence about trees.

FCAT Prep

5. Read/Inquire/Explain What can the shape, color, and size of a leaf help you know?

Links

Writing

Expository
Choose two kinds of plants that you have seen before. Write a paragraph **comparing and contrasting** the two plants.

Language Arts

Generous Plants
Read *The Giving Tree*, by Shel Silverstein. Then write your own story about the things you get from plants.

 For more links and activities, go to **www.hspscience.com**

How Do Plants Make Food?

Fast Fact

Shady Skyscrapers The tall trees in a forest keep much of the sunlight from reaching the plants that grow on the ground. In the Investigate you will see how important light is to a plant.

Light, Plants, Action!

Materials • 2 paper cups • potting soil • 2 small plants • water

Procedure

1 Half-fill each cup with potting soil. Gently place a plant in each cup. Fill the cups with soil. Water each plant lightly. Use just enough water to make the soil damp.

2 Put one cup near a sunny window. Put the other cup in a dark place, such as a cabinet or closet.

3 Observe the cups for two weeks. Water the plants when necessary. Record the changes you observe. Make sure to look for changes in plant size and color.

Step 1

Step 3

Draw Conclusions

1. Which plant looked healthier? How did it look different from the other plant? What do you think made this plant healthy?

2. What was different for the plant that looked less healthy?

3. **Inquiry Skill** Scientists often compare the results they get in their experiments. How would you compare your findings?

Investigate Further

Predict how giving plants different amounts of water might affect them. Now try this!

SC.H.1.2.1.3.1 keeping accurate records, **SC.H.1.2.2.3.1** following experimental design, **SC.H.1.2.4.3.1** comparing/contrasting, **SC.H.2.2.1.3.1** makes predictions, **SC.H.3.2.2.3.1** collects data

Reading in Science

 SC.B.2.2.1.3.1 organisms need energy, **SC.F.1.2.3.3.2** plants/similarities and differences, **LA.E.2.2.1** cause and effect

VOCABULARY

photosynthesis p. 386

chlorophyll p. 387

SCIENCE CONCEPTS

▶ how plants make food

READING FOCUS SKILL

CAUSE AND EFFECT

Look for effects of plants using water and light.

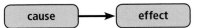

How Plants Get Energy

Suppose you've had a long day at school and you still have a ballgame ahead of you. You need energy, so you eat a healthful snack. To get energy, all animals need to eat food.

Plants are different from animals in that plants can make their own food. The food that plants make is sugar. Plants make sugar by a process called **photosynthesis** (foht•oh•SIN•thuh•sis). The plant uses the sugar it makes for energy.

These plants are part of a roof garden, where they make their own food. ▼

CAUSE AND EFFECT What is the result of photosynthesis?

386

Photosynthesis

During photosynthesis, water and carbon dioxide (dy•AHKS•yd) come together to make sugar. Sunlight provides the energy needed for this to happen. **Chlorophyll** (KLAWR•uh•fihl) is a green substance inside leaves. It helps the plant use light energy.

Plants need light from the sun for photosynthesis. Chlorophyll helps plants use the sunlight.

Air is made up of different gases. One type of gas is called carbon dioxide. Plants need carbon dioxide to make sugar.

Oxygen is another kind of gas. It is made during photosynthesis. You need to breathe oxygen to stay alive.

Water soaks into the soil, where the roots take it in. Stems carry the water to the leaves. Plants also need water to make sugar.

For more links and activities, go to
www.hspscience.com

387

How Plants Are Helpful and Harmful

Plants are helpful to people in many ways. One way we use them is to eat them for food. We get energy and nutrients from eating certain parts of the plants. We get wood and make paper from trees, and we use other plants to make cloth and medicines.

However, some plants can be harmful. They may have poisons in their parts or give people allergy problems.

 CAUSE AND EFFECT Why shouldn't you touch a plant that you have never seen before?

People get energy and nutrients from foods, such as strawberries.

Pollen from plants can cause some people to sniffle, sneeze, cough, and have itchy eyes.

The poison ivy plant can cause some people to have an itchy skin rash.

Grains feed many people around the world.

Insta-Lab

Make a Graph

Make a list of 20 foods that come from plants. Tell whether each food comes from roots, stems, leaves, fruits, or seeds. Make a bar graph from your list.

1. CAUSE AND EFFECT Draw and complete the graphic organizer.

Photosynthesis

Cause

Ⓐ _____ and carbon dioxide come together with the help of **Ⓑ** _____

Effect

Ⓒ _____

2. SUMMARIZE Use your completed graphic organizer to write a summary of photosynthesis.

3. DRAW CONCLUSIONS How does photosynthesis help make the foods that people eat?

4. VOCABULARY Use lesson vocabulary to describe how the green color in leaves helps plants make food.

FCAT Prep

5. What do plants give off during photosynthesis?
- **A.** carbon dioxide
- **B.** oxygen
- **C.** sunlight
- **D.** water

Links

Writing

Expository

List the "ingredients" that are needed for photosynthesis. Then write a **how-to** "recipe" telling the ways the plant uses the ingredients to make its own food.

Health

Natural Health

Use an encyclopedia to learn about a medicine that comes from a plant. Share with your class how the medicine helps people.

 For more links and activities, go to **www.hspscience.com**

389

SCIENCE Spin from WEEKLY READER®

Technology

SC.H.3.2.1.3.1 contributions of scientists, SC.H.3.2.3.3.1 scientific discoveries impact humans, SC.H.3.2.4.3.1 solving problems/new ideas

All Wrapped Up

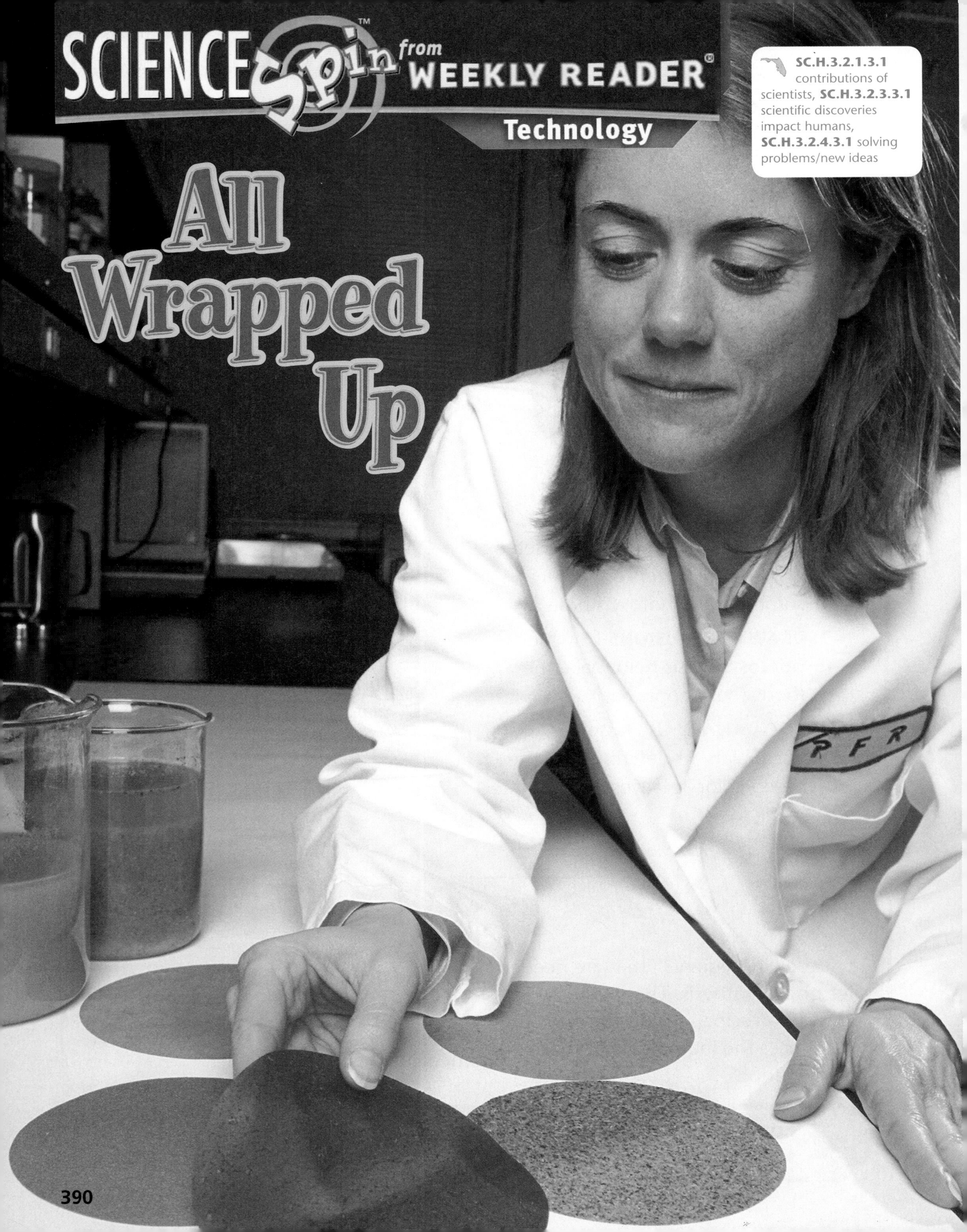

Imagine you sit down to lunch today and your friend pulls a sandwich out of his backpack. Instead of throwing away the wrap the sandwich came in, he rolls it up, pops it into his mouth and says, "Hmmm! Strawberry."

Thanks to Tara McHugh, edible food wraps are now a reality. McHugh, a scientist who studies food, invented a wrap that helps preserve fruits and vegetables.

Lab Wrap

McHugh makes the wraps in her laboratory from dozens of different fruits and vegetables. She may use anything from apricots, guavas, mangos, and papayas to broccoli and carrots.

To make the wraps, the fruits and vegetables are chopped up and mixed with water. McHugh then pours the mixture onto a plate and leaves it out to dry. The wraps are made in different thicknesses and strengths.

Oxygen and Food Don't Mix

The wrap helps protect food by keeping oxygen away from

It's a Wrap

Another benefit is that edible food wraps will reduce the amount of plastic food wrap that ends up in the nation's landfills, said McHugh. According to the U.S. Environmental Protection Agency, nearly two million tons of food wrapping material ends up as waste each year.

it. Oxygen can react with food, causing it to change color or even rot. The film not only protects food, but also adds flavor. For example, an apple could be wrapped in an apple film, or a piece of chicken could be wrapped in an apricot-flavored wrap.

THINK ABOUT IT

1. Why is important to protect foods?
2. How might edible food wraps help protect the environment?

Find out more! Log on to
www.hspscience.com

SC.H.3.2.1.3.1
contributions of scientists

Hunting the Moonseed

Rosa Ortiz is on the hunt for a plant. Ortiz is a botanist. A botanist is a scientist who studies plants. Ortiz travels to study one species, or kind, of plant. This plant is part of the moonseed family.

Moonseed is a vine found in many places. Some types of moonseed can be used as medicines. Ortiz is studying how the plant has changed over time.

Career Nursery Worker

Nursery workers take care of plants. They know how much sun and water plants need. They also know how to protect plants from diseases, insects, and the weather.

Find out more! Log on to
www.hspscience.com

You Can Do It!

Quick and Easy Project

A Fresh Start

Materials
- 1 plant with many stems and leaves
- scissors
- ruler
- 1-L plastic bottle
- water

Procedure

1. **CAUTION:** Be careful when using scissors. Cut off a 15-cm piece of the plant. Make sure a stem and at least one leaf are on the cut piece.

2. Fill the bottle with water. Place the cut stem in the water. The leaf should be sticking out of the water.

3. Place the plant in a sunny spot. Check it every day. Keep the bottle filled with water.

Draw Conclusions

Observe the plant for ten days. Record any changes you observe.

Design Your Own Investigation

Growing Groceries

Think about the plants you eat. How do potatoes, pineapples, and peas grow? What parts do they have that might grow new plants? Choose from the grocery store a plant you eat. Make a prediction about how a new plant could come from it. Then plan and conduct an investigation to see if you were right.

Vocabulary Review

Use the terms below to complete the sentences. The page numbers tell you where to look in the chapter if you need help.

root p. 370

nutrient p. 370

stem p. 370

leaf p. 370

deciduous p. 379

evergreen p. 379

photosynthesis p. 386

chlorophyll p. 387

1. The green substance that helps plants make food is _____.

2. The plant part in which its food is made is the _____.

3. A plant that loses its leaves each fall is said to be _____.

4. A substance that helps plants grow and stay healthy is a _____.

5. An underground plant part that takes in water is the _____.

6. The process that plants use to make food is _____.

7. Plants that do not lose their leaves in the fall are _____.

8. The part that connects a plant's roots to its leaves is the _____.

Check Understanding

Write the letter of the best choice.

9. How are roots like stems?
   A. Both are green.
   B. Both move water.
   C. Both make food.
   D. Both grow under the ground.

10. **CAUSE AND EFFECT** How can plants cause harm?
    F. We get food from them.
    G. We make cloth from them.
    H. They can make us have allergy problems.
    I. They can be used to make medicines.

11. Which are the four things that plants need to live and grow?
    A. water, soil, air, and light
    B. water, soil, air, and warmth
    C. water, soil, oxygen, and warmth
    D. water, soil, oxygen, and light

12. Which things do plants need to make food?

   F. soil, air, water

   G. water, sunlight, oxygen

   H. water, sunlight, carbon dioxide

   I. soil, water, carbon dioxide

13. How does a cactus survive in a very dry environment?

   A. Its roots are deep.

   B. It has no stem or leaves.

   C. Its roots quickly collect rainfall.

   D. It doesn't need water to make food.

14. Which is a way that scientists group plants?

   F. by root length

   G. by plant height

   H. by color

   I. by leaf type

15. MAIN IDEA AND DETAILS Which of the following describes deciduous plants?

   A. They make food in the winter.

   B. They stay green all year long.

   C. They lose their leaves each year.

   D. They have leaves shaped like needles.

16. What do grasses, shrubs, and many trees share?

   F. size and shape

   G. need for oxygen

   H. losing leaves

   I. flowers and seeds

Inquiry Skills

17. Design an experiment to find out if a seed will grow after it has been frozen.

18. Waterlilies can grow under the water. Predict what would happen if you moved a bean plant to the bottom of a deep lake.

READ INQUIRE EXPLAIN Read/Inquire/Explain

19. As Samantha helps her mother plant flower bulbs, she asks why she isn't planting seeds. Do plants that grow from bulbs make seeds? Explain your answer.

20. Zach's younger brother Jake will not eat vegetables. Zach jokes that Jake still eats green plants. How could this be true?

Lesson 1 What Do Animals Need to Live?

Lesson 2 What Are Vertebrates?

Lesson 3 What Are Invertebrates?

Vocabulary

oxygen
vertebrate
mammal
bird
reptile
amphibian
fish
invertebrate

What do YOU wonder?

A flamingo has an interesting way of
eating. Its beak is upside down when
it collects food from the water. What
characteristics make a flamingo a bird?

What Do Animals Need to Live?

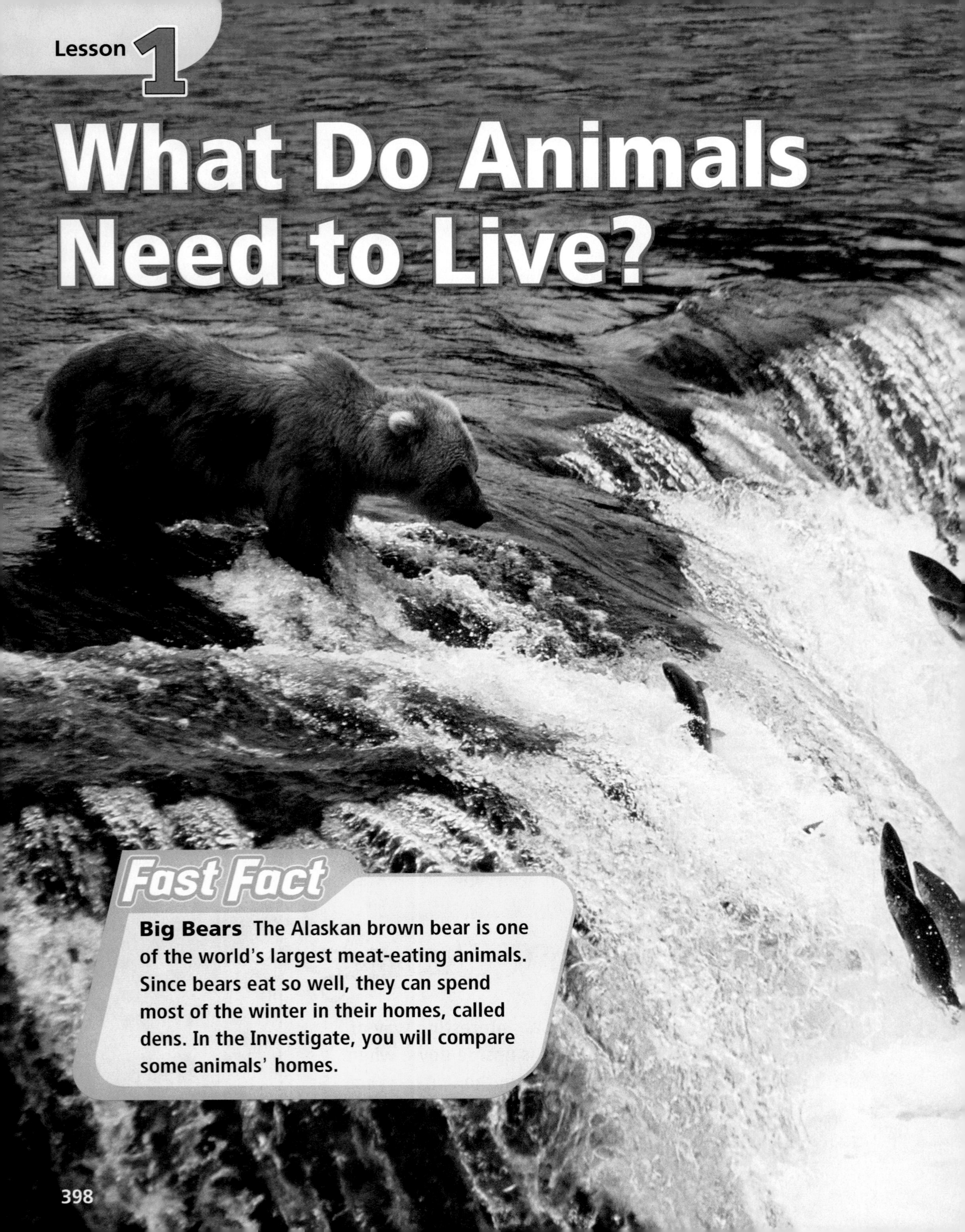

Fast Fact

Big Bears The Alaskan brown bear is one of the world's largest meat-eating animals. Since bears eat so well, they can spend most of the winter in their homes, called dens. In the Investigate, you will compare some animals' homes.

Animal Homes

Materials • **picture cards** • **index cards** • **reference books** • **markers**

Procedure

1 Look at the picture cards your teacher has given you.

2 As you **observe** each picture, notice the animal's home.

3 With a partner, make a matching game. On separate index cards, write the name or draw a picture of each animal. Name or draw its home on another card. Use the picture cards or reference books if you need help.

4 Play your matching game. As you match the animals to their homes, discuss the different types of homes. Talk about the ways the homes are alike and the ways they are different. Then **classify** the animals by the types of homes they live in.

Step 3

Step 4

Draw Conclusions

1. Describe the homes of the foxes and the owl. How are the homes alike? How are they different?

2. **Inquiry Skill Compare** two of the animal homes you **observed**. Explain how each home protects the animal that lives there.

Investigate Further

Study the animal pictures again. **Draw conclusions** about why each animal uses the type of home it does.

Reading in Science

SC.F.1.2.2.3.1 animals depend on plants,
SC.F.1.2.3.3.3 common characteristics of plants
and animals, LA.A.2.2.1 main idea and details

VOCABULARY

oxygen p. 401

SCIENCE CONCEPTS

▶ what animals need in order to live and grow

READING FOCUS SKILL

MAIN IDEA AND DETAILS

Look for details about what animals need in order to live.

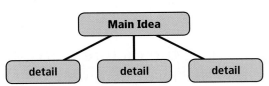

Animals and Their Needs

Have you ever cared for a cat or a dog or had a hamster or a parakeet? These animals are good pets. They are fun to play with and to watch. Just like plants, pets also have needs. They need food, water, and places to live. People give pets these things.

Wild animals have the same needs as pets. However, they must find their own food, water, and shelter.

MAIN IDEA AND DETAILS What do all animals need?

This elf owl finds shelter in a saguaro (suh•GWAR•oh) cactus. How is the owl different from a pet parakeet? ▼

◀ **Pandas look cuddly, but they are not pets. They must find their own food, water, and shelter. They eat bamboo leaves.**

 These hippos rise above the water's surface to breathe air.

Animals Need Oxygen

Animals and plants share many of the same needs. Both have the structures to take in the air they need to live and grow. However, unlike plants, animals take in oxygen. **Oxygen** is a gas that plants give off into the air.

Many animals that live on land get oxygen by breathing air. Some animals get oxygen in other ways. Insects, for example, get oxygen through tiny holes in their bodies. Many water animals, such as fish, get oxygen from the water. Other water animals, like whales, rise to the surface of the water to breathe air.

MAIN IDEA AND DETAILS Name two ways animals get oxygen.

Insta-Lab

Make a Model
Use clay, sticks, and other natural materials to make a model of the home of one of the animals shown in this lesson. What need does the animal's home meet?

Animals Need Water

Did you know that more than half of your body is water? Every day, water leaves your body in your breath, in your sweat, and in your urine. To be healthy, you must drink to replace lost water.

Just like plants, animals also need water. Look at the graph on this page. It's hard to imagine drinking so much water. Just like people, elephants must replace water that leaves their bodies. Most animals get the water they need by drinking it. Other animals get water mainly from the foods they eat.

MAIN IDEA AND DETAILS Name two ways animals get water.

How many times as much water does an elephant need compared with a horse?

Daily Water Needs of Animals

Amount (gallons): 50, 45, 40, 35, 30, 25, 20, 15, 10, 5, 0

Animal: Elephant, Adult human, Horse

▲ This dog gets the water it needs from the people who care for it.

On the plains of Africa, animals must find their own drinking water. ▼

Animals Need Food

Like plants, animals need food to live and grow. However, animals can't make their own food. They must get food by eating plants or other animals.

Animals have body parts that help them get food. For example, an elephant uses its trunk to pull leaves from trees. How do you think the body parts of the animals shown on these pages help them get food?

 **MAIN IDEA AND DETAILS** Why do animals need food?

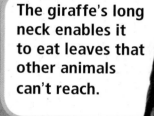
The giraffe's long neck enables it to eat leaves that other animals can't reach.

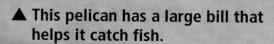
▲ This pelican has a large bill that helps it catch fish.

Animals Need Shelter

Think about yourself on a stormy day. How do you stay warm and dry? Like other animals, you seek shelter—at home or in another safe place. Shelters aren't just homes. Shelters help protect animals from the weather and from other animals. Some animals use different parts of plants for shelter.

There are many kinds of animal shelters. Some birds build nests from twigs, grass, and mud. Beavers build shelters called lodges from mud and wood. Other animals, such as rabbits and moles, make burrows in the ground.

MAIN IDEA AND DETAILS Why do animals need shelter?

These white tent bats find shelter in an odd place— under a leaf! ▼

◄ This robin's nest is high above the ground, where other animals can't bother the young birds.

1. MAIN IDEA AND DETAILS Draw and complete this graphic organizer. List needs of animals.

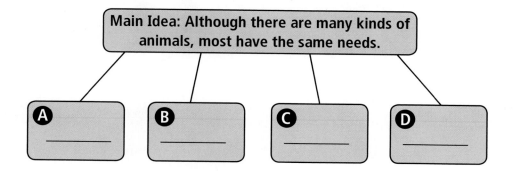

Main Idea: Although there are many kinds of animals, most have the same needs.

Ⓐ _____

Ⓑ _____

Ⓒ _____

Ⓓ _____

2. SUMMARIZE Use the graphic organizer to write a lesson summary.

3. DRAW CONCLUSIONS After a walk, Jacob notices that his pet dog is panting. What should Jacob do? How do you know?

4. VOCABULARY Use your own words to describe how oxygen and air are related.

FCAT Prep

5. What kind of shelters do beavers build?
- **A.** burrows
- **B.** dens
- **C.** lodges
- **D.** nests

Links

Writing

Expository
Write an essay **comparing** your main body parts with the body parts of another animal.

Social Studies

Human Shelters
Early humans used caves as one form of shelter. Use encyclopedias and other references to learn about other early human shelters. Report your findings to your class.

 For more links and activities, go to www.hspscience.com

What Are Vertebrates?

Fast Fact

Going Batty These fruit bats keep
warm by wrapping their wings around
their bodies. Bats can also keep warm by
crowding together in groups called colonies.
In the Investigate, you will make a model of
another way animals keep warm.

Keeping Warm

Materials
- large plastic bowl
- large zip-top plastic bag
- disposable plastic gloves
- water
- ice
- solid vegetable shortening
- large spoon

Procedure

1. Fill the bowl with water and ice. Use the spoon to half-fill the bag with vegetable shortening.

2. Put a glove on each of your hands.

3. Put one of your gloved hands in the zip-top bag. Mold the vegetable shortening so that it evenly covers your hand.

4. Take your hand out of the zip-top bag, and put both hands in the water. **Compare** the ways your hands feel. **Record** your **observations**.

Draw Conclusions

1. Which hand felt warmer in the ice water? Why?

2. **Inquiry Skill** Scientists use models to study something they can't easily observe. In this Investigate, you made a model of a mammal with a layer of blubber, or fat. Why was making a model easier than observing the animal?

Step 3

Step 4

Investigate Further

How does fur protect animals from cold? Write a hypothesis. Conduct a simple investigation to find out.

SC.H.1.2.2.3.1 following experimental design, SC.H.1.2.4.3.1 comparing/contrasting, SC.H.1.2.5.3.1 uses models

Reading in Science

SC.F.1.2.3.3.1 vertebrate characteristics, SC.F.1.2.3.3.3 common characteristics of plants and animals, LA.A.2.2.1 main idea and details

VOCABULARY

vertebrate p. 409
mammal p. 410
bird p. 411
reptile p. 412
amphibian p. 413
fish p. 414

SCIENCE CONCEPTS

▶ that animals with a backbone are grouped by traits

READING FOCUS SKILL

MAIN IDEA AND DETAILS Look for details about different kinds of vertebrates.

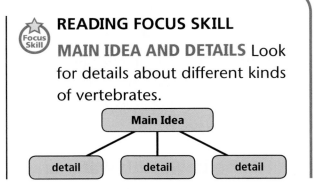

Vertebrates

You have probably seen animals like these in a zoo, in a pet store, or in books. They don't look very much alike, do they? However, the monkeys, bird, snake, frog, and fish all share an important trait. Each of these animals has a backbone. You have a backbone, too. You can feel it in the center of your back.

These monkeys are mammals. They have fur, and they make milk for their young.

Toucans (TOO•kanz) are birds—vertebrates that have feathers and lay eggs.

Animals with a backbone are called **vertebrates** (VER•tuh•brits). Most vertebrates have large brains and sharp senses. These traits help the vertebrates survive. Vertebrates, like most plants and other animals, also have structures that enable them to reproduce.

Scientists classify vertebrates into groups based on their traits. The five major groups of vertebrates are mammals, birds, reptiles, amphibians (am•FIB•ee•uhnz), and fish. Compare and contrast the animals on these pages. What traits does the fish have that the monkeys don't?

MAIN IDEA AND DETAILS What trait do all vertebrates have?

The tree frog started its life as an egg in water. But this amphibian lives on land now.

The snake's long, slithery body may make it seem to have no backbone. But this reptile does have a backbone—a very flexible one.

This scaly fish is a vertebrate that spends its entire life in water.

Mammals

Mice, horses, and bats all have something in common with you. Just like you, these animals are mammals. **Mammals** are vertebrates that have hair or fur.

Mammals also use lungs to breathe. Even mammals that live in the water, such as whales, have lungs. Whales must rise to the top of the water to get oxygen from the air.

Most mother mammals give birth to live young. The young mammals drink milk made by the mother.

MAIN IDEA AND DETAILS What are three traits that all kinds of mammals share?

▲ Pigs aren't furry, but they do have hair—one of the traits of mammals.

Like other mammals, this tiger has fur and makes milk for its young. ▼

▲ The kangaroo is one of just a few kinds of mammals that carry their young in a pouch.

410

These birds look very different from one another. But they all are vertebrates with two legs, feathers, wings, and beaks.

Birds

Birds share some traits, such as a backbone and lungs, with mammals. Yet their body covering is different. **Birds** are vertebrates that have feathers. Some feathers keep birds warm. Others help them fly. Some birds, such as penguins, can't fly, but they still have feathers and wings that are like flippers.

Unlike most kinds of mammals, birds don't give birth to live young. Instead, they lay eggs. The young birds hatch from the eggs. Mother birds don't feed milk to their young.

 MAIN IDEA AND DETAILS What are some traits of birds?

Reptiles

When you think of a snake, do you think of something slimy? Many people do. However, snakes aren't slimy. They are reptiles. **Reptiles** are vertebrates that have dry skin covered with scales.

Like mammals and birds, reptiles breathe with lungs. Some reptiles, like crocodiles, spend a lot of time underwater. These animals must go to the surface to get the oxygen they need. Most reptiles, like the ones shown here, hatch from eggs laid on land.

 MAIN IDEA AND DETAILS What are three traits of reptiles?

This iguana (ih•GWAH•nuh) hatched from an egg laid on land. Like other reptiles, it is dry and scaly.

The alligator breathes with lungs. It must come to the surface to get the oxygen it needs.

This sea turtle lives in the water, but it will lay its eggs on land.

This frog hatched from an egg laid in water. It hatched into a tadpole and then grew into a frog. Tadpoles live in water. Even though it stays near water, the frog lives on land and breathes with lungs.

▲ A salamander's speed and colors help it survive.

Amphibians

Have you ever watched a frog grow? Frogs are amphibians. Young frogs, called tadpoles, hatch from eggs laid in water. Tadpoles don't get oxygen from air. They have gills that get oxygen from water. As tadpoles grow, they develop lungs. Then they can live on land.

Amphibians are vertebrates that have moist skin and legs as adults. Most adult amphibians usually stay close to water so they can keep their skin moist. Most of them also lay their eggs in water.

(Focus Skill) **MAIN IDEA AND DETAILS** Name three traits of amphibians.

Classify Animals
Your teacher will give you picture cards of different vertebrates. Look at the body coverings of the animals on the picture cards. Classify each animal into the vertebrate group it belongs in.

Fish

Have you ever watched a goldfish swim? If so, you might have noticed a flap of skin moving on each side of the fish's head. These flaps cover the gills. Gills take in oxygen from water. **Fish** are vertebrates that take in oxygen through gills and spend their whole life in water.

Most fish lay eggs and have scales. Scales help protect the fish. They are made of a thin, strong material. It is much like the material of your fingernails. Fish don't have arms and legs to help them swim. Instead, they have fins.

 MAIN IDEA AND DETAILS What are some traits of fish?

All the fish shown here may look very different, but they all have scales and gills, and they all live in water. ▶

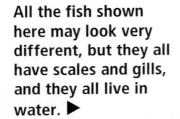

1. MAIN IDEA AND DETAILS Draw and complete this graphic organizer. List traits of each group of vertebrates.

Main Idea: Vertebrates are grouped by their traits.

Mammals	Birds	Reptiles	Amphibians	Fish
A _____	**B** _____	**C** _____	**D** _____	**E** _____
_____	_____	_____	_____	_____
_____	_____	_____	_____	_____

2. SUMMARIZE Write a sentence that tells the most important information in this lesson.

3. DRAW CONCLUSIONS While on a nature hike, Rosita finds an animal she has never seen before. She wonders if it is an amphibian or a reptile. How might she tell the difference?

4. VOCABULARY Use the lesson vocabulary to write a paragraph about vertebrates.

FCAT Prep

5. Read/Inquire/Explain Animals need oxygen to live. Explain how the way a mammal takes in oxygen is different from the way a fish takes in oxygen.

Links

Writing

Narrative
Suppose you have no backbone. Write a funny **story** describing what might happen while you do your daily activities.

Literature

Comparing Animals
Read *Stellaluna*, by Janell Cannon. As you read, make two lists. In one, list the ways in which the animals are alike. In the other, list the ways in which they are different.

 For more links and activities, go to www.hspscience.com

What Are Invertebrates?

Fast Fact

Butterfly Travelers In the fall, monarch butterflies travel very long distances to warmer places. In the Investigate, you will draw conclusions about the travels of another animal.

A Worm Farm

Materials
- large canning jar with ring lid
- sand
- soil
- earthworms
- uncooked oatmeal
- square of dark fabric

Procedure

1. Put 2 cm of moist soil into the jar. Sprinkle a very thin layer of oatmeal over the soil. Add 2 cm of moist sand.

2. Repeat the layers of soil, oatmeal, and sand until the jar is almost full. About 5 cm from the top, add a last layer of soil. Don't sprinkle any oatmeal on top of the last layer. Put several worms on top of the soil.

3. Place the fabric square over the opening of the jar. Screw the ring lid onto the jar. Put the jar in a dark place.

4. After one week, observe the jar. Compare the way it looks now with the way it looked when you set it up.

Step 1

Step 4

Draw Conclusions

1. What changes did you observe?

2. **Inquiry Skill** Draw a conclusion about why these changes occurred.

Investigate Further

Predict some ways worms will affect soil in a garden. Plan and conduct a simple investigation to test your prediction.

VOCABULARY
invertebrate p. 418

SCIENCE CONCEPTS
▶ that animals without a backbone are grouped by traits

 READING FOCUS SKILL

COMPARE AND CONTRAST
Look for ways the groups of invertebrates are alike.

| alike | | different |

Invertebrates

When you hear the word *animal,* do you think of a mammal? Many people do. However, most animals aren't mammals. Most aren't even vertebrates. Most animals are **invertebrates** (in•VER•tuh•britz), or animals without a backbone. There are many more types of invertebrates than there are types of vertebrates.

All the animals shown here are invertebrates. They don't have a backbone.

▲ Unlike the corals, the jellyfish moves in water.

▲ The corals in this colony do not move around. Each is an invertebrate that has its skeleton on the outside.

This scallop's shell has two halves. ▶

Insects, such as this firefly, are invertebrates. Insects have six legs.

Spiders aren't insects. They are in a group of invertebrates that have eight legs. ▼

Like all other invertebrates, the horseshoe crab has no backbone. Unlike the firefly or the spider, it has 10 legs. ▼

There are more than a million kinds of invertebrates. Scientists group invertebrates by ways they are alike. Look at the pictures on these pages. Why might scientists place the firefly, the horseshoe crab, and the spider in different groups?

Invertebrates may have simple or complex bodies. They may have a lot of legs—or no legs at all! Even though there are many different invertebrates, they all have one common trait. None of them has a backbone.

COMPARE AND CONTRAST How are invertebrates like vertebrates? How are they different?

▲ The bumblebee, luna moth, and dragonfly are part of the largest group of invertebrates—the insects.

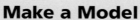
Insects

There are more kinds of insects than of other invertebrates. In fact, there are more kinds of insects than of all other animals put together. Insects live everywhere on Earth. Even cold arctic areas have many insects during the summer.

Insects have three body parts and six legs. They have no backbone, but they have a hard outer covering. Many insects, such as those shown on this page, have wings.

 COMPARE AND CONTRAST How are the animals on this page alike?

Spiders and Ticks

Spiders and ticks look like insects, but they aren't insects. They belong to another group, because they have traits different from those of insects. Spiders and ticks have eight legs and only two body parts. Like insects, spiders and ticks have an outer body covering. The covering helps protect them.

The banana spider and the deer tick are grouped together. They both have two body parts, eight legs, and an outer body covering. ▶

Focus Skill **COMPARE AND CONTRAST** How are spiders and ticks like insects? How are they different from insects?

Science Up Close

Spider Webs

1 The orb spider's body makes silky thread from protein. The web begins with a sticky thread called the bridge.

The spider anchors the next thread to the ends of the bridge. This is the first frame thread, or support for the web. **2**

3 From the first frame thread, the spider anchors more frame threads. The spider spins nonsticky radial threads from the center to the frames.

The spider walks on radial threads when walking on the web. Finally, the spider forms a spiral of sticky silk from the edges of the web to its middle. **4**

 For more links and activities, go to **www.hspscience.com**

421

Snails, Clams, and Squids

Snails, clams, and squids are in the same group. They all have soft bodies. Also, most animals in this group have a head.

Some of these animals, like the squid, have tentacles. Some, like the clam and the snail, have hard shells to protect their soft bodies. They also have a kind of "foot." The foot pokes out of the shell and helps the animal move.

 COMPARE AND CONTRAST How is the coquina clam like the squid? How is it different?

This land snail has a shell that protects its soft body. Its muscular "foot" helps it move. ▶

The Atlantic long-finned squid has no shell. It swims freely, using its tentacles for movement and for getting food. ▶

The sea slug has no shell. It swims or crawls along surfaces to get food. ▼

▲ The Florida coquina (koh•KEE•nuh) clam's shell has two halves that protect the animal's soft body. Like the snail, the clam has a muscular "foot" that helps it move.

The starfish is covered with spines that protect it. ▶

When the sea anemone (uh•NEM•uh•nee) opens its "mouth," its tentacles make it look like a beautiful flower. ▼

▲ Like insects and spiders, this blue crab has a hard outer covering.

Other Kinds of Invertebrates

All the animals shown on this page are invertebrates. The worms you observed in the Investigate are another kind of invertebrate. Worms have no shells, legs, or eyes.

Scientists have not yet found or grouped all of Earth's animals. When a new animal is found, the first thing scientists ask is likely to be, "Does it have a backbone?"

COMPARE AND CONTRAST How is the starfish like the blue crab?

Invertebrates Are Important

Invertebrates are important to other living things. Bees and butterflies, for example, move pollen from one flower to another. This helps the flowers make seeds. Other animals, such as earthworms, improve the soil. Plants grow better in soil that has earthworms than in soil that doesn't.

Many invertebrates are important foods for other animals. People can eat clams and crabs. People also eat the honey and use the wax made by bees.

(Focus Skill) **COMPARE AND CONTRAST** How are earthworms like bees?

▲ Honeybees provide more than just their famous treat, honey. They also make beeswax. One way people use beeswax is to make candles.

◄ The movement of earthworms mixes air into the soil.

1. COMPARE AND CONTRAST Draw and complete this graphic organizer.

Invertebrates	Traits
Insects	**A** _____
Spiders and Ticks	**B** _____
Snails, Clams, Squids	**C** _____

2. SUMMARIZE Write a sentence that summarizes the lesson.

3. DRAW CONCLUSIONS While looking for seashells at the beach, Alex finds an animal with no backbone and no shell. How can he tell if it belongs in the same group of invertebrates as the clams?

4. VOCABULARY Use the lesson vocabulary to write a sentence.

FCAT Prep

5. Which animal is **not** an invertebrate?
   A. clam
   B. earthworm
   C. goldfish
   D. snail

Links

Writing

Persuasive
Everyone has an **opinion** on what is the best. Choose one of your favorite invertebrates. Write at least two paragraphs explaining why you think this animal is the best invertebrate.

Math

Make a Graph
With a classmate, brainstorm a list of the types of invertebrates you might find in a backyard, park, or garden. How many are insects? How many live in water? What other invertebrates are there? Make a bar graph to show your results.

 For more links and activities, go to **www.hspscience.com**

SC.H.3.2.1.3.1 contributions of scientists, SC.H.3.2.3.3.1 scientific discoveries impact humans

The Secret of Silk

Spider webs may look weak, but don't be fooled. They are actually super strong! Spider webs are made of silk. Silk is nature's strongest fiber, or thread. Believe it or not, silk is stronger than a steel wire of the same size.

Scientists have been making silk for years. However, they have not been able to produce silk as strong as a spider's silk. Now some scientists say they have figured out the secret to making strong silk.

Silk from Gel

Scientist David Kaplan told Weekly Reader what his team learned. He said that a spider's body has a little sac where it stores tiny blobs of silk in water. When the spider releases water, the blobs turn into a gel. The spider squeezes the gel from its body, and the silk hardens.

Scientists are now using what they learned to make a strong silk in the lab. Kaplan and another scientist created a gel similar to what a spider might produce. Then they smeared the gel between sheets of glass. By putting pressure on the glass, the scientists were able to create strong, silk-like fibers.

Helpful in Many Ways

The scientists believe the silk will help people in many ways. It may be used for making clothes that protect police officers and soldiers. Scientists say that the silk may also be used to repair bones and ligaments in people's bodies.

Kaplan is very excited about his work. "I hope this discovery will help get kids excited about science," he said. "There is so much to be learned from nature."

THINK ABOUT IT

1. Besides silk, what other things in nature are useful to people? How are those things useful?

Find out more! Log on to
www.hspscience.com

Girl Protects Police Dogs

Stacey Hillman is an amazing 12-year-old. She is the president of her own charity, Pennies to Protect Police Dogs. She raises money to buy bulletproof vests to protect police dogs. "Police dogs are often the ones to go in first to dangerous situations," Stacey said.

Stacey and her charity have received many awards for their work. "I don't do this for the awards. I do it so that the police dogs get vested," said Stacey. So far, Stacey has raised hundreds of thousands of dollars. The money has been used to buy vests for more than 200 dogs across the United States.

K-9 SHERIFF

You Can Do It!

Quick and Easy Project

Goldfish Gills

Procedure

1. Study the goldfish. Locate its gill coverings.

2. Use a stopwatch to count the number of times the gill coverings open and close in 15 seconds.

3. How could you use this number to find out how many times the goldfish opens the gill coverings in one minute?

Materials
- goldfish in bowl with water and water plants
- stopwatch

Draw Conclusions

Observe the goldfish for ten days. Record its gill opening rate once each day. Did the rate change? Record your data in a bar graph.

Design Your Own Investigation

Ready, Set, Breathe

Think about your own breathing. Predict how activity will affect your breathing rate. Then design an investigation to see if your prediction is correct.

Vocabulary Review

Use the terms below to complete the sentences. The page numbers tell you where to look in the chapter if you need help.

oxygen p. 401

vertebrate p. 409

mammal p. 410

bird p. 411

reptile p. 412

amphibian p. 413

fish p. 414

invertebrate p. 418

1. An animal with hair or fur that feeds its young milk is a _____.

2. An animal without a backbone is an _____.

3. A dry, scaly animal that lays eggs and lives on land is a _____.

4. An animal with a backbone is a _____.

5. A vertebrate with two legs, wings, and feathers is a _____.

6. A gas, found in air or water, that animals need is _____.

7. A moist-skinned animal that lives near water is an _____.

8. A vertebrate that lives its whole life in water is a _____.

Check Understanding

Write the letter of the best choice.

9. **MAIN IDEA AND DETAILS** Which detail given below is **not** a basic need of animals?
   A. color
   B. food
   C. shelter
   D. water

10. Why do animals need shelter?
    F. for food
    G. for protection
    H. for quiet
    I. for water

11. Which animals are grouped together?
    A. snails and squids
    B. spiders and ants
    C. goldfish and whales
    D. frogs and snakes

12. How do mammals that live in water get oxygen?
    F. They take it in through gills.
    G. Their skin absorbs it.
    H. They come to the top of the water to breathe air.
    I. They don't need oxygen.

13. Which is **not** a trait of mammals?
  A. fur
  B. giving birth to live young
  C. feathers
  D. feeding milk to their young

14. COMPARE AND CONTRAST
  In what way are birds and mammals alike?
  F. They both have feathers.
  G. They both have fur.
  H. They both breathe with lungs.
  I. They both give birth to live young.

15. Which vertebrate group does the animal below belong to?

  A. amphibians
  B. birds
  C. mammals
  D. reptiles

16. What is one important way scientists group animals?
  F. by their ages
  G. by their lengths
  H. by their colors
  I. by whether they have a backbone

Inquiry Skills

17. Compare amphibians with reptiles.

18. Use body coverings to classify vertebrates.

Read/Inquire/Explain

19. Why do many amphibians stay near water for their entire lives?

20. A bat can fly, but it is not a bird. A bat is a mammal. Use what you know about mammals to identify some traits of bats.

How Living Things Interact with Their Environments

 The chapters in this unit address these Grade Level Expectations from the Florida Sunshine State Standards.

LIFE SCIENCE

Chapter 13 Where Living Things Are Found

SC.G.1.2.2.3.1	knows how organisms with similar needs in a climatic region compete with one another for resources such as food, water, oxygen, or space.
SC.G.1.2.2.3.2	knows behavioral and structural adaptations that allow plants and animals to survive in an environment.
SC.G.2.2.1.3.1	understands that plants and animals share and compete for limited resources such as oxygen, water, food, and space.
SC.G.2.2.2.3.1	knows that the size of a population is dependent upon the available resources within its community.

Chapter 14 Living Things Depend on One Another

SC.G.1.2.5.3.1	understands that energy is transferred to living organisms through the food they eat.
SC.G.1.2.5.3.2	knows examples of living things that are classified as producers, consumers, carnivores, herbivores, and omnivores.

The investigations and experiences in this unit also address many of the Grade Level Expectations in Strand H, The Nature of Science.

Science in Florida

Orlando

Dear Mom and Dad,
 You'll never guess what happened today at Aunt Jessica's. I looked out the window and saw an alligator in the back yard! Aunt Jessica said the alligator wouldn't bother us if we left it alone. She said that it was lying in the sun to warm its body. It was the first time I had ever seen an alligator. It was cool to look at from inside the house, but I'm glad there was a window between us.

Love,

Harrison

The Sunshine State

USA

FCAT Writing

Writing Situation
Suppose you see an alligator at a park. Explain what you would do.

Experiment!

Changing Environments

Throughout the year the weather changes. Most plants and animals are adapted to live in a certain climate. What happens to living things when an environment changes? For example, if a lake dries up, how do the plants living there change? Plan and conduct an experiment to find out.

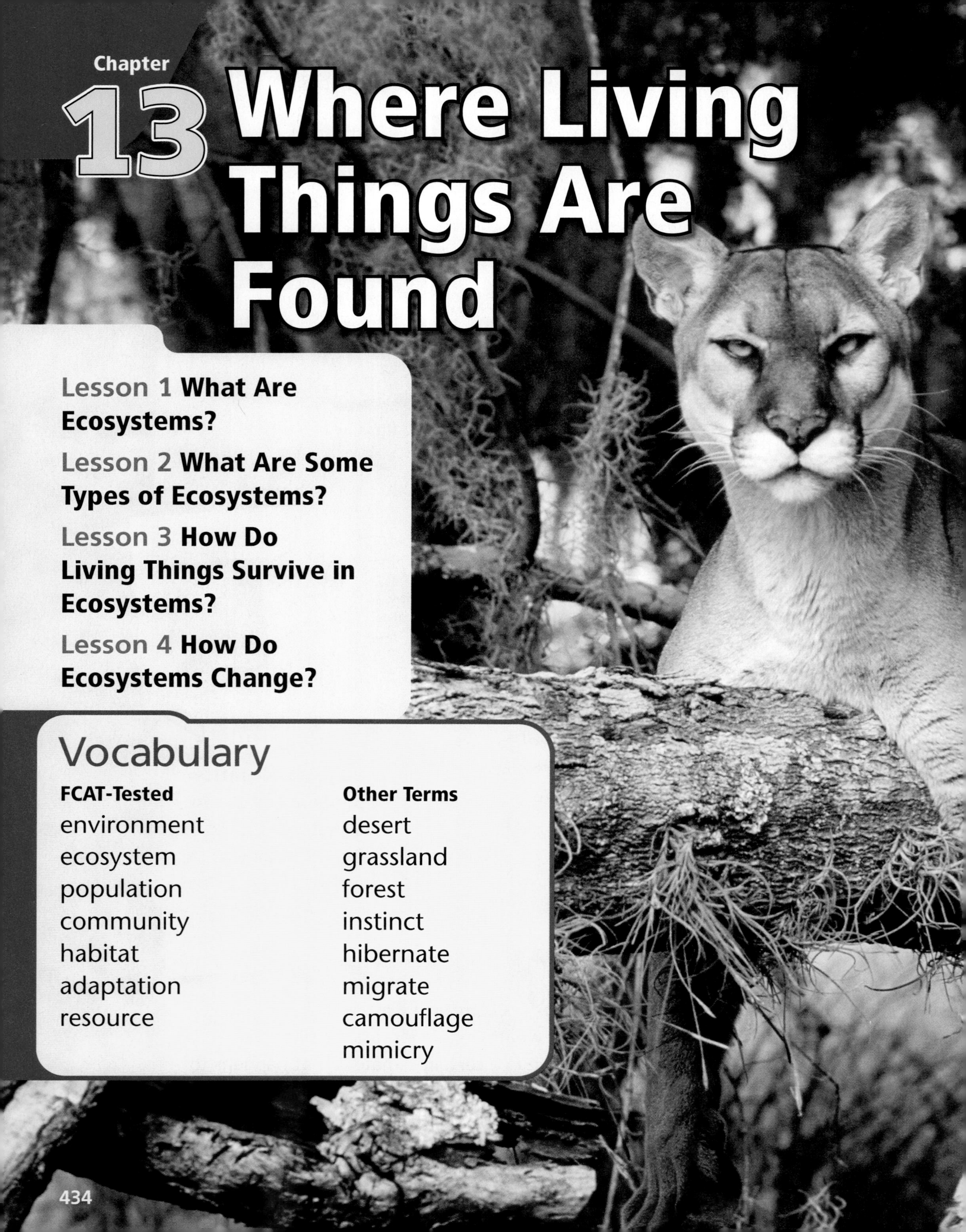

13 Where Living Things Are Found

Vocabulary

FCAT-Tested	Other Terms
environment	desert
ecosystem	grassland
population	forest
community	instinct
habitat	hibernate
adaptation	migrate
resource	camouflage
	mimicry

Everglades National Park, in southern Florida, is one of the largest wilderness areas in the United States. Florida panthers, like the one in this picture, herons, and alligators are just a few of the animals that call the Everglades their home. How do you think the environment helps the animals that live there?

435

What Are Ecosystems?

Fast Fact

Using Ecosystems Every day, the average adult horse needs about one gallon of water for each 100 pounds it weighs. Most horses get their water from the environment in which they live. In the Investigate, you will observe one type of environment.

Observe an Environment

Materials • safety goggles • wire coat hanger

Procedure

❶ CAUTION: **Put on safety goggles.** Bend the coat hanger into a square. Ask your teacher for help if necessary.

❷ Go outside. Place the square on the ground. Closely observe the ground inside the square. This square of ground is an environment.

❸ Copy the table. Record all the living things you observe and how many there are of each. Then record all the nonliving things you observe and how many there are of each.

❹ Share your table with a classmate. Compare the environments you observed. How are they alike? How are they different?

Step 2

Things in My Environment			
Living Things	Number	Nonliving Things	Number

Draw Conclusions

1. Compare the things you found in your environment with the things a classmate found. Why do you think you found different things?

2. **Inquiry Skill** How did you infer which things were living and which things were nonliving?

Investigate Further

Compare the environment you observed at school with an environment you observe at or near your home.

SC.H.1.2.3.3.1 working collaboratively, SC.H.1.2.4.3.1 comparing/contrasting

Reading in Science

SC.G.1.2.2.3.1 organisms compete for resources, **SC.G.2.2.1.3.1** competition for resources, **LA.A.2.2.1** main idea and details

VOCABULARY

environment p. 439
ecosystem p. 440
population p. 440
community p. 440
habitat p. 441

SCIENCE CONCEPTS

▶ what an environment is
▶ what an ecosystem is

READING FOCUS SKILL

Focus Skill

MAIN IDEA AND DETAILS Look for details about environments and ecosystems.

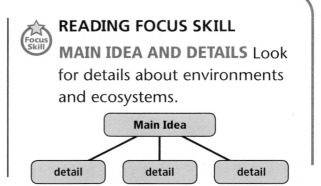

Where Things Live

Living things need a place to live and grow. Fish live in water. Many birds live in trees and fly through the air. Plants grow where there is soil, water, and sun.

Living things can be found almost everywhere on Earth. Some fish can live in the deepest parts of the oceans. Some plants can live on the tops of high mountains. Scorpions can survive in dry deserts. Cattails can grow in swamps.

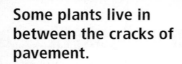

Some plants live in between the cracks of pavement.

The living and nonliving things that surround a living thing make up its **environment**. Plants and animals use things from their environments to meet their needs. What is your environment like?

Many living things may share an environment and its resources—food, water, oxygen, and space. If the environment has too little of any of these things, the living things compete with one another to get what they need.

▲ Koalas in Australia live in eucalyptus trees, whose leaves are their only food.

 MAIN IDEA AND DETAILS What do living things get from their environments?

These prairie dogs can survive and grow in a grassy environment. ▼

This bird makes its nest on a chimney high above the ground. ▼

Parts of an Ecosystem

The organisms living in and around a pond interact with one another. A fish might eat an insect. A frog might sit on a lily pad. Together, the living things and the nonliving things they interact with form an ecosystem. An **ecosystem** (EE•koh•sis•tuhm) is made up of all the living and nonliving things in an environment.

Different types of organisms live in an ecosystem. A group of organisms of the same kind living in the same place is a **population** (pahp•yuh•LAY•shuhn). For example, the frogs in a pond make up one population. The lily pads in the pond make up another population.

All of the populations that live in an ecosystem at the same time form a **community** (kuh•MYOO•nuh•tee).

Science Up Close

Pond Ecosystem

Ponds are rich ecosystems. They are filled with living and nonliving things that interact with one another.

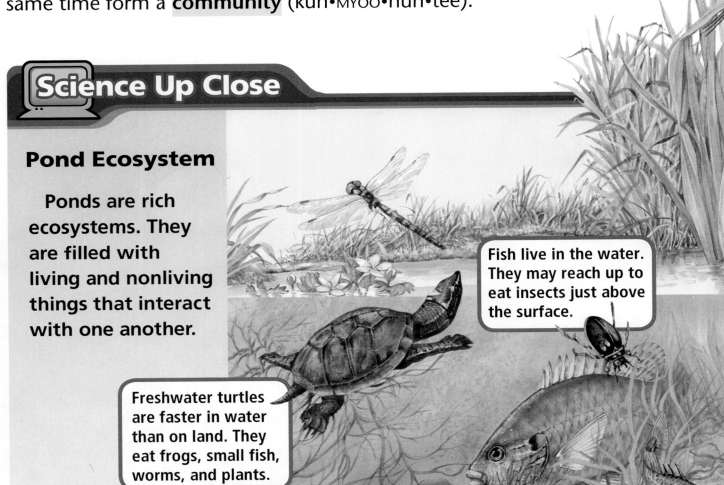

Fish live in the water. They may reach up to eat insects just above the surface.

Freshwater turtles are faster in water than on land. They eat frogs, small fish, worms, and plants.

For more links and activities, go to www.hspscience.com

Each organism in this picture is a part of the pond's community.

All members of a community live in the same ecosystem. However, they don't all live in the same part of the ecosystem. Fish swim in water, but birds build nests in trees. The place in its ecosystem where a population lives is its **habitat**. The habitat includes both living and nonliving things.

MAIN IDEA AND DETAILS What is the difference between a population and a community?

Insta-Lab

Ecosystems Around You
Find out about an ecosystem that is close to where you live. Research what types of plants and animals live there. Draw and color the ecosystem. Label the animals and plants.

Birds such as this kingfisher hunt for fish and frogs near the pond's edge.

Waterlilies float on the surface of the pond. Frogs often rest on their leaves.

Snails crawl on plants that live in shallow water near the pond's edge.

Organisms and Their Habitats

Some organisms can survive only in certain habitats. A polar bear, for example, could not find the water it needs in a desert. A rain forest would be too wet for a desert owl.

An organism's habitat gives it everything it needs to survive. For example, a pond has the water, food, and oxygen that a fish needs. The fish could not survive without these things. What does your habitat provide you with?

 MAIN IDEA AND DETAILS What does a living thing's habitat provide for it?

▲ The scarlet macaw lives high in the trees of the rain forest. It feeds on the fruits and large nuts that grow there.

◄ Mountain goats live on rocky cliffs, where they feed on plants growing among the rocks.

1. MAIN IDEA AND DETAILS Draw and complete the graphic organizer.

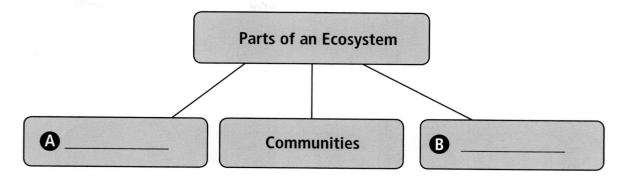

Parts of an Ecosystem

A _____

Communities

B _____

2. SUMMARIZE Use the completed graphic organizer to write a lesson summary.

3. DRAW CONCLUSIONS Nonliving things are part of an ecosystem. Why is this important?

4. VOCABULARY Write two sentences that explain how an environment and an ecosystem are different.

FCAT Prep

5. Which is a nonliving part of an ecosystem?

A. bird
B. water
C. snail
D. cattail

Links

Writing

Narrative

Find an ecosystem near your home or school. Write two paragraphs that **describe** the living and nonliving things in the ecosystem.

Math

Organize Data

In your state, there are many kinds of animals that are endangered. Choose one of these animals, and research its population. How many are there now? How many have there been in each of the last 10 years? Organize your findings in a bar graph.

 For more links and activities, go to www.hspscience.com

What Are Some Types of Ecosystems?

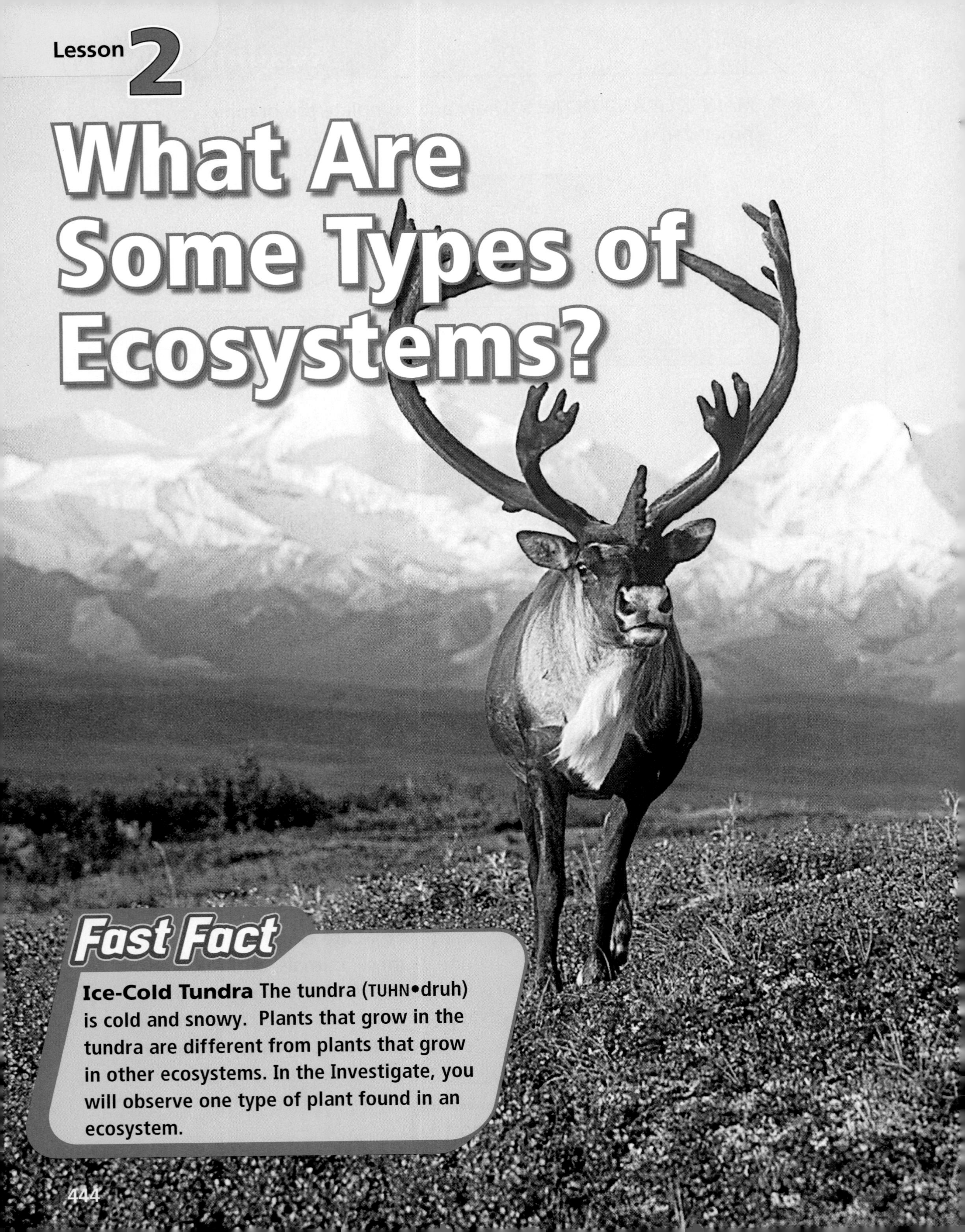

Fast Fact

Ice-Cold Tundra The tundra (TUHN•druh) is cold and snowy. Plants that grow in the tundra are different from plants that grow in other ecosystems. In the Investigate, you will observe one type of plant found in an ecosystem.

Grass Roots

Materials
- plastic gloves
- hand lens
- grass plants
- ruler
- sheet of white paper

Procedure

① Put on the plastic gloves. **Observe** the different types of grass plants your teacher has for you.

② The leaves of a grass plant are called blades. Carefully hold up one grass plant by its blades. Gently shake the plant. **Observe** what happens to the soil.

③ Very carefully remove the soil from around the roots.

④ Place the grass plant on a sheet of white paper. **Observe** it with the hand lens.

⑤ **Measure** the height of the tallest blade and the length of the longest root.

Draw Conclusions

1. **Compare** the height of the tallest blade with the length of the longest root.

2. **Inquiry Skill Infer** how the roots of a tree might be different from the roots of a grass plant.

Step 3

Step 5

Investigate Further

Carefully remove a plant from a pot or the ground. Compare the roots of a grass plant the roots of the plant you chosen.

SC.A.2.2.1.3.1 tools to see details, SC using scientific instruments, SC.H.1.2 comparing/contrasting

VOCABULARY

desert p. 446
grassland p. 447
forest p. 450

SCIENCE CONCEPTS

► how ecosystems are different
► how ecosystems support plants and animals

READING FOCUS SKILL

MAIN IDEA AND DETAILS

Look for details about different ecosystems.

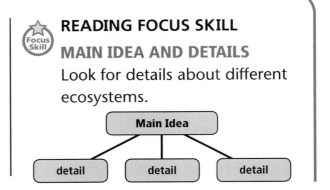

Desert Ecosystems

Deserts are very dry ecosystems. You might think that a desert is just sand. However, there is life in the desert. Desert plants and animals can survive with very little water.

Desert plants, such as the cactus, have thick stems that store water. The roots of a cactus lie just below the soil and spread far from the plant. This lets them take in a lot of water quickly when it rains.

Temperatures in some deserts rise very high by day. Most animals find a shady place to sleep and come out only after sunset. Some animals, such as kangaroo rats, drink hardly any water. They get all the water they need from the plants they eat. Toads keep moist by staying under the soil.

Arches National Park, in Utah, is located in a desert ecosystem. ▼

 MAIN IDEA AND DETAILS How do animals in a desert stay cool?

Grassland Ecosystems

Another kind of ecosystem is the grassland. **Grasslands** are dry, often flat areas of land that are hot in the summer and cold in the winter. They get more rain or snow than deserts but less than most other ecosystems. Food crops grow well there.

As you may have guessed, the main plant in a grassland ecosystem is grass. A few small bushes and wildflowers also grow. Since grasslands are dry, few trees are able to grow there except along rivers and streams.

A grassland ecosystem includes both large animals, such as bison and coyotes, and small animals, such as mice, rabbits, and snakes.

▲ During the 1800s, as many as 60 million bison lived on the grasslands of North America.

MAIN IDEA AND DETAILS Why would a grassland be a good place to start a farm?

▲ The shape of a bottlenose dolphin's body helps it glide through the water.

Saltwater Ecosystems

If you have ever tasted ocean water, you know that it is salty. Oceans cover about three-fourths of Earth's surface, so there are more saltwater ecosystems than any other kind.

Sharks, sea turtles, corals, and octopods are all ocean animals. So are whales and seals. Plantlike organisms, such as kelp and seaweed, are also part of some saltwater ecosystems. Organisms that live in the oceans need salt water. They would not survive in a freshwater environment, such as a pond.

MAIN IDEA AND DETAILS About how much of Earth is NOT covered by oceans?

Freshwater Ecosystems

Rivers, ponds, and streams have fresh water. They make up freshwater ecosystems. Unlike ocean water, fresh water does not have much salt.

Ducks and some kinds of insects live in freshwater ecosystems. So do trout and turtles. Deer and foxes may visit there, too. Many kinds of plants live in freshwater ecosystems.

 MAIN IDEA AND DETAILS Where might you find a freshwater ecosystem?

Float Levels
Half-fill two clear cups with water. Then pour salt into only one of the cups. Label the cups. Float a tennis ball in each cup. How does the salt change the level of the tennis ball?

A river is one type of freshwater ecosystem. ▼

Forest Ecosystems

Forests are ecosystems in which many trees grow. There are different kinds of forests. A tropical rain forest grows where it is hot and wet all year. Animals such as jaguars and monkeys live there.

Most of the trees in a deciduous (dee•SIJ•oo•uhs) forest lose their leaves in the fall. These forests grow where it is warm in summer and cold in winter. Many animals make their homes there.

Evergreen trees, such as pines and firs, grow in a coniferous (koh•NIF•er•uhs) forest. Most trees in coniferous forests have cones. These forests have cool summers and cold winters.

 MAIN IDEA AND DETAILS What kind of forest ecosystem grows where it is hot and wet?

▲ A long-eared owl searches for food in the forest.

Squirrels eat nuts and fruits that grow in the forest. ▼

▼ Deciduous forests provide habitats for rabbits, bears, deer, and foxes.

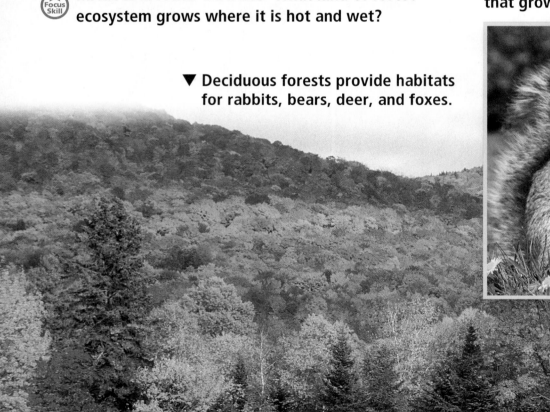

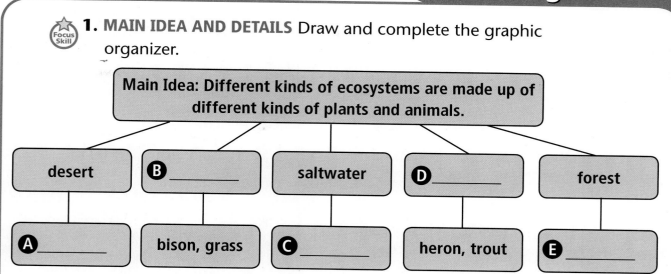

1. MAIN IDEA AND DETAILS Draw and complete the graphic organizer.

Main Idea: Different kinds of ecosystems are made up of different kinds of plants and animals.

- desert
- **B** _____
- saltwater
- **D** _____
- forest

- **A** _____
- bison, grass
- **C** _____
- heron, trout
- **E** _____

2. SUMMARIZE Write a summary of this lesson. Begin with the sentence *Different environments have different ecosystems.*

3. DRAW CONCLUSIONS Suppose all the plants in one ecosystem died. What do you think would happen to that ecosystem? Why?

4. VOCABULARY Write a paragraph comparing the animals and plants in a desert with those in a grassland ecosystem.

FCAT Prep

5. Read/Inquire/Explain

A friend asks for your help in identifying the ecosystem to which a plant belongs. The plant has wide, spreading roots and a thick stem that stores water. Which kind of ecosystem would this plant probably live in?

Links

Writing

Persuasive

Write an **opinion** article for the school newspaper. Explain how cutting down trees for lumber affects the forest ecosystem.

Math

Collect Data

Research an ecosystem you learned about in this lesson. Use reference sources to find out the ecosystem's average monthly temperature and rainfall. Make two bar graphs to show the information you collected.

 For more links and activities, go to www.hspscience.com

How Do Living Things Survive in Ecosystems?

Fast Fact

Chew on This Beavers use their sharp teeth to chew through the trunks and branches of small trees and shrubs. Their brown color helps them blend in with their surroundings. In the Investigate, you'll infer how color helps other living things hide.

How Insects Hide

Materials
- construction paper
- crayons or markers
- scissors
- watch or clock
- ruler
- chenille sticks
- tape

Procedure

Step 2

1. Look around the classroom for a "habitat" for a model insect you will make. **Observe** the colors and shapes of things in the habitat.

2. Draw a construction-paper rectangle 5 cm long and 3 cm wide. This will be the size of your insect.

3. Color the body so your insect blends into its habitat. Make legs and wings.

4. Tape your insect in its habitat. Don't hide it behind anything.

Step 4

5. Ask a classmate to be a "bird." Ask the bird to look for the insect and other classmates' insects for one minute. **Record** results in a table. Continue until the bird finds all the insects.

Draw Conclusions

1. Which insects did the bird find first? Why were they easy to find?

2. **Inquiry Skill** **Infer** why some insects were hard to find.

Investigate Further

Draw conclusions about why the fur of some animals, such as foxes and rabbits, changes color with the seasons.

SC.H.1.2.3.3.1 working collaboratively, **SC.H.1.2.5.3.1** uses models, **SC.H.3.2.2.3.1** collects data, **SC.H.3.2.2.3.2** presents scientific information

VOCABULARY

adaptation p. 454
instinct p. 454
hibernate p. 456
migrate p. 457
camouflage p. 458
mimicry p. 458

SCIENCE CONCEPTS

▶ how organisms adapt to their environments

READING FOCUS SKILL

MAIN IDEA AND DETAILS Look for details about how organisms survive in their environments.

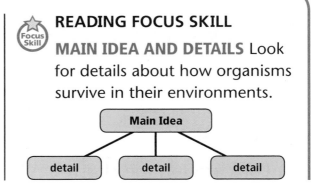

How Living Things Survive

All living things have ways to survive. Any trait that helps an animal survive is an **adaptation**. An adaptation can be physical. For example, the arctic hare in the picture changes color in summer and winter. An adaptation can also be a behavior. A snake hides in the shade when it is hot. Animals learn some behaviors. Other behaviors are instincts. An **instinct** is a behavior an animal knows without being taught.

In the winter this hare has white fur. Its fur changes color to blend in with the environment.

454

Plant Structure

The leaves of a bromeliad (broh•MEE•lee•ad) collect rainwater because of their shape. The stems, roots, and leaves of plants are adaptations that help the plants survive.

Roots with this special shape are called prop roots. These roots help support tall, thin plants, such as corn, and plants that live in swampy areas.

The stem of this vine forms tendrils that hold its leaves up to gather sunlight.

Plants also have adaptations that help them survive. Plant parts are physical adaptations. Remember that the stems of some desert plants store water. Some rain-forest plants have very large leaves. These leaves help them take in more sunlight for making food in the shady forest. Even roots have physical adaptations. Some roots grow deep into the ground to get water from far below the surface.

 MAIN IDEA AND DETAILS What is an example of an adaptation?

Insta-Lab

Thumbs Down

Tuck your thumb into the palm of your hand. Without moving your thumb, try to pick up objects. Now try to write your name without moving your thumb. Share your observations with a classmate. How is the thumb a useful adaptation for humans?

Hibernation

In the fall when the weather gets colder, some animals start eating more food than normal. Then they **hibernate** (HY•ber•nayt), or go into a sleeplike state for the winter. A hibernating animal doesn't move. Its body temperature drops, and its heart rate slows down. The animal might breathe only once in a half hour.

Animals lose more body heat during winter. To stay warm and be active, they would need to eat more, but food is harder to find in winter. A hibernating animal is not active, so it saves energy. It lives off the fat stored in its body, so it doesn't need to find food.

MAIN IDEA AND DETAILS What are two things that happen to an animal's body when it hibernates?

This chipmunk spends time hibernating during the winter. It curls into a ball to stay warm. ▼

Math in Science
Interpret Data

Find the difference between each animal's active and hibernating heart rates.

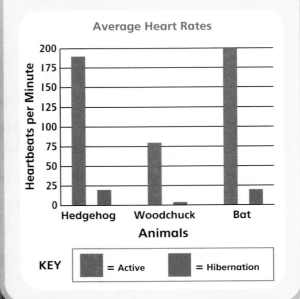

Average Heart Rates

Heartbeats per Minute

200
175
150
125
100
75
50
25
0

Hedgehog   Woodchuck   Bat

Animals

KEY   ■ = Active   ■ = Hibernation

456

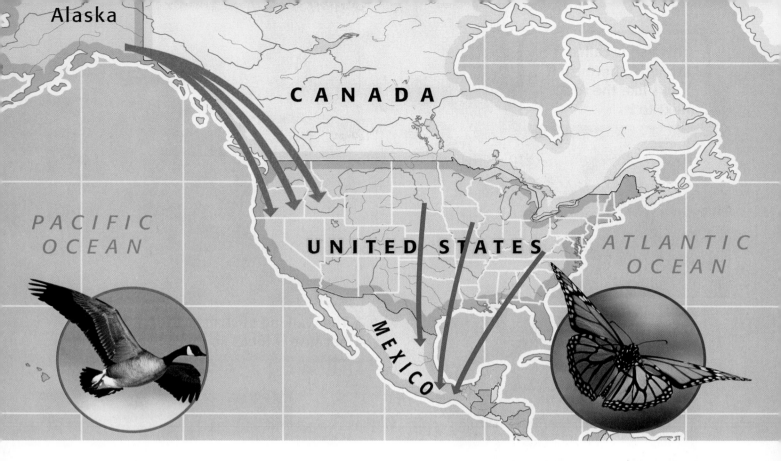

Alaska

CANADA

PACIFIC OCEAN

UNITED STATES

ATLANTIC OCEAN

MEXICO

▲ In fall, Canada geese fly south from northern Canada and Alaska. Groups fly in two lines that form a V shape in the sky.

▲ Millions of monarch butterflies fly from the United States to Mexico each fall. When spring comes, they fly north again to lay their eggs.

Migration

Many animals **migrate** (MY•grayt), or travel from one place to another and back again. Most birds in the Northern Hemisphere fly south in the fall. Southern areas usually have warmer climates and more food. These birds return north in the spring to raise their young.

In the fall, gray whales migrate from the cold waters near Alaska. They spend the winter in the warm waters near California. Female whales stay there to give birth to their young. In the spring, they return to Alaska.

 MAIN IDEA AND DETAILS Why do animals migrate?

This fish is called a stonefish because it looks like the rock next to it.

The walking stick insect is hard to see because it looks so much like the twig.

A chameleon can change its color to look like what is next to it.

The "eyes" on the wings of this moth confuse a bird that tries to eat it. The bird thinks that another animal, much larger than the moth, is looking at it.

Hide and Seek

Some animals can hide without trying. These animals are hidden by their shapes, colors, or patterns. Such a disguise is called **camouflage**. For example, many female birds are brown. These birds blend in with their nests as they sit on their eggs.

Some animals look very much like other animals. Some snakes that are not harmful look just like a harmful kind of snake. Since animals don't know which is harmful, neither snake gets eaten. Imitating the look of another animal is called **mimicry**.

 MAIN IDEA AND DETAILS What is camouflage?

1. MAIN IDEA AND DETAILS Draw and complete this graphic organizer.

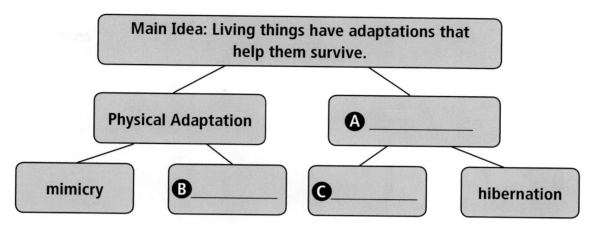

2. SUMMARIZE Write two sentences to tell what this lesson is mainly about.

3. DRAW CONCLUSIONS How do camouflage and mimicry help animals survive?

4. VOCABULARY Write a sentence that explains how the terms *adaptation, hibernation*, and *migration* are related.

FCAT Prep

5. Which of the following is a physical adaptation?
   A. camouflage
   B. hibernation
   C. instinct
   D. migration

Links

Writing

Narrative
Choose an animal that hibernates. Write a **story** about how that animal gets ready for hibernation.

Drama

Migration Play
Research an animal that migrates during the winter. With five other classmates, write a play that tells about the animal's migration path. Perform your play for the class.

 For more links and activities, go to www.hspscience.com

How Do Ecosystems Change?

Fast Fact

Hoover Dam Hoover Dam is on the Colorado River, on the border between Nevada and Arizona. The reservoir, or human-made lake, that formed behind it changed the land forever. In the Investigate, you will observe how an environment can change.

Changing the Environment

Materials
- moist sand
- leaves and twigs
- small stones
- wooden block
- water
- shallow cardboard box
- watering can

Procedure

1 With a partner, pack the sand into the box. Use your fingers to make hills, valleys, and a streambed. Push the leaves and twigs into the sand to represent plants.

2 Carefully lift one end of the box off the table. Place the wooden block beneath that end.

3 Slowly pour a little water from the watering can into the streambed you made. **Observe** what happens to the sand, water, and plants.

4 Pour the water more quickly into the streambed, and **observe** again.

Draw Conclusions

1. What happens to the sand, water, and plants when only a little water is poured into the streambed?

2. Inquiry Skill Add several stones along the streambed. **Predict** what will happen if you pour a lot of water into the streambed. Try it. Was your **prediction** correct?

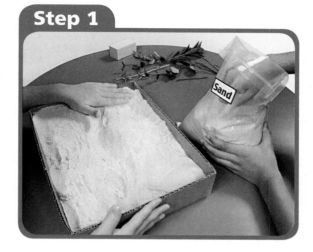

Step 1

Step 3

Investigate Further

Predict what will happen to the sand, plants, and water if you make a dam across your streambed. Try it.

Reading in Science

 **SC.G.2.2.1.3.1** competition for resources, **SC.G.2.2.2.3.1** populations and resources, **LA.E.2.2.1** cause and effect

VOCABULARY

resource p. 463

SCIENCE CONCEPTS

▶ how ecosystems change over time

 READING FOCUS SKILL

CAUSE AND EFFECT Look for the causes of changes in ecosystems.

| cause | → | effect |

How Ecosystems Change

Ecosystems change over time. Sometimes the changes are natural. Fires and floods cause changes. They may destroy habitats and kill many living things. Yet other living things survive. Seeds that survive grow into plants. Animals move back into the area to eat the plants.

Living things change an ecosystem, too. When beavers cut down trees to build a dam, they change the forest. Their dam changes the way the stream flows.

The eruption caused a landslide that took off the top of the mountain.

CAUSE AND EFFECT When beavers build a dam, what are the effects on the ecosystem?

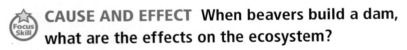

Mount Saint Helens, a volcano in Washington State, was 2,950 meters (9,680 ft) high before it erupted in May 1980.

▲ After the eruption, an area of 180 square kilometers (70 sq mi) was covered with ash. Many habitats were destroyed.

Notice how the area has changed after construction. There are now even a lake and a pond that weren't there before. ▼

▲ This is what the area looked like before construction.

How People Change Ecosystems

People change ecosystems when they use the materials, or **resources**, from them. They cut down trees to build houses. They dig up rocks and stones to make roads. They use water that animals and plants depend on. Some of these changes harm the ecosystem. Car exhaust pollutes the air. Trash pollutes rivers and fields.

People also can help ecosystems. Planting trees after a fire helps develop a new habitat. Bringing water to dry areas helps more plants grow.

 CAUSE AND EFFECT How are ecosystems affected by people?

Trashy Items
Make a list of five things you threw into the trash today. Compare your list with those of two classmates. Together, decide how much of the trash you threw away could have been recycled.

Effects of Changes in Ecosystems

When one part of an ecosystem changes, it can affect the whole ecosystem. Changes such as fires cause some animals to run away. Those that stay must compete for the resources that are left. If there are not enough resources, populations get smaller. Some members die, and some others leave. If a change brings more resources, populations grow.

Some organisms are able to adapt to changes in an ecosystem. People build homes in the habitats of bears, deer, and other animals. The people and animals then have to learn to share the habitats.

 CAUSE AND EFFECT What happens to organisms when an ecosystem changes?

▲ People often see moose in Alaska.

▲ Many ducks live near people.

Deer often dart out in front of cars. Drivers must watch for them. ▼

▲ On some roads in Florida, drivers must stop their cars to let alligators cross.

1. CAUSE AND EFFECT Draw and complete the graphic organizer.

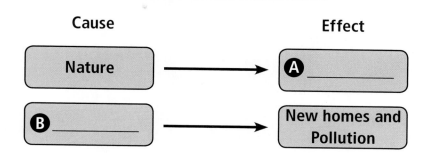

Changes to an Ecosystem

Cause		Effect
Nature	→	**A** _____
B _____	→	New homes and Pollution

2. SUMMARIZE Write a summary of this lesson. Begin with the sentence *Changes in ecosystems have two main causes.*

3. DRAW CONCLUSIONS What are some ways in which people can change an ecosystem for the better?

4. VOCABULARY Write a sentence that identifies three resources in an ecosystem.

FCAT Prep

5. Read/Inquire/Explain Explain how living things can change an ecosystem.

Links

Writing

Narrative
Suppose people are building a neighborhood where a family of bears lives. Write a **story** about what the bears do. You may make your story funny or serious.

Health

Make a Poster
Interview a nurse or doctor. Ask him or her how air pollution changes a person's health. Make a poster of your findings. Share your poster with your class.

 For more links and activities, go to **www.hspscience.com**

SCIENCE Spin™ from WEEKLY READER®

Technology

SC.H.3.2.3.3.1 Scientific discoveries impact humans

HIDING IN PLAIN SIGHT

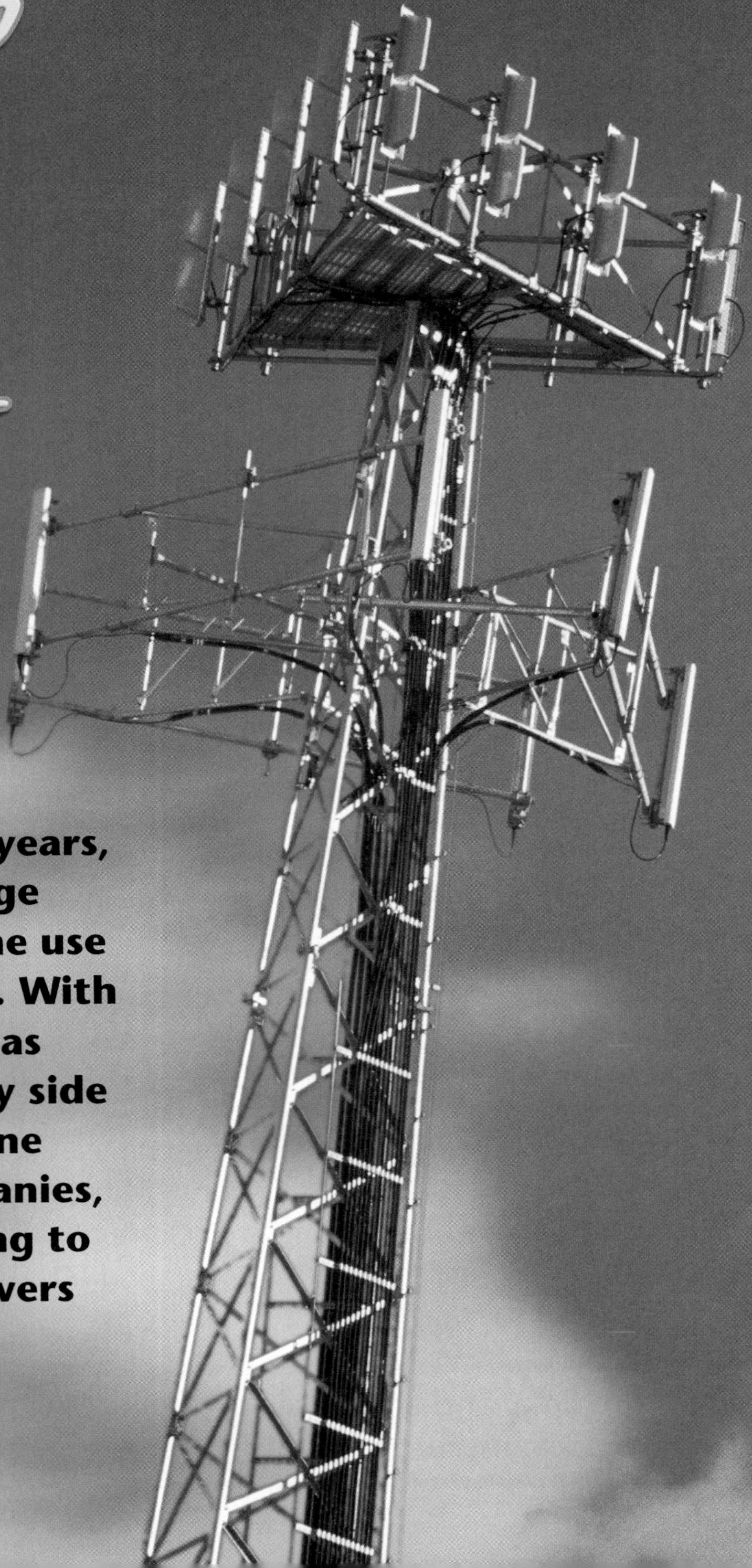

Over the past few years, there has been a huge increase in cell phone use in the United States. With that increased use has come a not-so-pretty side effect: ugly cell phone towers. Some companies, however, are working to make cell phone towers blend in with their surroundings.

Faster, Better, Uglier?

Cell phone companies are working to make cell phone technology faster and better than ever. Cell phone companies divide areas of a state into cells, or areas. Each cell has a base station with a tower and other equipment. Base stations send calls from one cell phone to another.

The problem is that not many people like seeing the tall, metal towers. A company in Arizona has one way to solve that problem, however, and the idea came from observing nature!

The company makes trees, plants, leaves, and bushes from special materials that camouflage, or hide, cell towers. Because the United States has many types of environments—forests, deserts, and wetlands, for example— these hidden towers must be adapted to each environment.

THINK ABOUT IT

1. How would you camouflage a cell tower in the area where you live?

A Tree, or Not a Tree

In most cases, the items look so real that most people don't see any differences. For example, the company made a cactus from a special plastic. The cactus fits with its desert environment and hides a cell phone tower. The company has made pine trees for mountain environments and palm trees for warmer areas.

Find out more! Log on to **www.hspscience.com**

POET of NATURE

When she was a girl, Rachel Carson loved nature, especially birds. As an adult, Carson worked for the U.S. Fish and Wildlife Service.

While there, Carson learned that farmers used chemicals to keep insects from eating crops. She believed that those chemicals also harmed nearby animals and people.

Later, Carson wrote a book called *Silent Spring*. The book told a story of how pesticides harmed animals, especially birds. Rachel Carson's book helped people make laws. Those laws make sure that pesticides that might harm ecosystems won't be used.

Career Environmental Scientist

The U.S. government has many laws that protect our air, soil, and water. It's often up to environmental scientists to help make sure those laws are obeyed. These scientists are on the lookout for pollution. If they find it, they study the pollution and try to figure out ways to stop it.

You Can Do It!

Quick and Easy Project

What Is in Soil?

Materials
- soil with plants
- small shovel
- hand lens
- sheet of white paper
- pencil

Procedure

1. Dig up a small amount of soil, including plants.

2. Put the soil on the white paper. Use the pencil to break apart the soil.

3. Use the hand lens to observe the living things you find.

4. What living things did you find? What nonliving things did you find?

Draw Conclusions

How do the living things in the soil interact?

Design Your Own Investigation

Your Ecosystem

Do research on the ecosystem you live in. How much rainfall or snowfall does it get each year? What are the average temperatures in summer and winter? What kinds of animals and plants live there? Think about different ways you can observe your ecosystem. Design an observation area for observing the animals and plants in your ecosystem. Write down your observations in a journal.

Review and FCAT Preparation

Vocabulary Review

Use the terms below to complete the sentences. The page numbers tell you where to look in the chapter if you need help.

environment p. 439
ecosystem p. 440
population p. 440
community p. 440
habitat p. 441
adaptation p. 454
resource p. 463

1. A material from an ecosystem is a _____.

2. A group of living things of the same kind is a _____.

3. A living thing is surrounded by its _____.

4. A living thing gets everything it needs to survive from its _____.

5. The living and nonliving things in an environment that interact make up an _____.

6. Any physical trait or behavior that helps a living thing survive is an _____.

Check Understanding

Write the letter of the best choice.

7. Which is a nonliving part of an environment?
   A. an animal
   B. an insect
   C. a root
   D. oxygen

8. Which kind of adaptation does the animal in the picture have?
   F. camouflage
   G. instinct
   H. migration
   I. mimicry

9. In which ecosystem can only plants and animals that need very little water survive?
   A. desert
   B. forest
   C. grassland
   D. tundra

10. Which of these plants would most likely grow best in a desert?

F. cactus

H. spider plant

G. pine tree

I. sunflower

11. MAIN IDEA AND DETAILS Which is an example of an instinct?

A. a dog sitting on command

B. a raccoon getting food from a garbage can

C. a leopard's spots

D. a chipmunk eating extra food before it hibernates

12. What happens to an animal during hibernation?

F. It eats a lot.

G. It leaves its ecosystem often.

H. It is inactive.

I. It moves from one habitat to another.

13. If a bird flies south each winter, what is it doing?

A. adapting

B. camouflaging

C. hibernating

D. migrating

14. Which is an example of mimicry?

F. a white arctic hare in the snow

G. a fly with stripes like a bee's

H. a frog burrowing deep into the mud for winter

I. ducks traveling in search of food

15. Which of these includes the rest?

A. an environment

B. an ecosystem

C. a population

D. a community

16. CAUSE AND EFFECT Which can cause changes in the environment?

F. animals and plants only

G. nature only

H. people and nature

I. people only

Inquiry Skills

17. What are two living and two nonliving things you can observe in your environment?

18. Compare a desert ecosystem and a forest ecosystem.

READ/INQUIRE/EXPLAIN Read/Inquire/Explain

19. How might a blizzard change the habitats of plants and animals living in a forest ecosystem?

20. People build a new neighborhood near a tree in which a raccoon lives. How might the raccoon adapt its behavior to get food in its changed environment?

Chapter 14

Living Things Depend on One Another

Lesson 1 How Do Plants and Animals Interact?

Lesson 2 What Are Food Chains?

Lesson 3 What Are Food Webs?

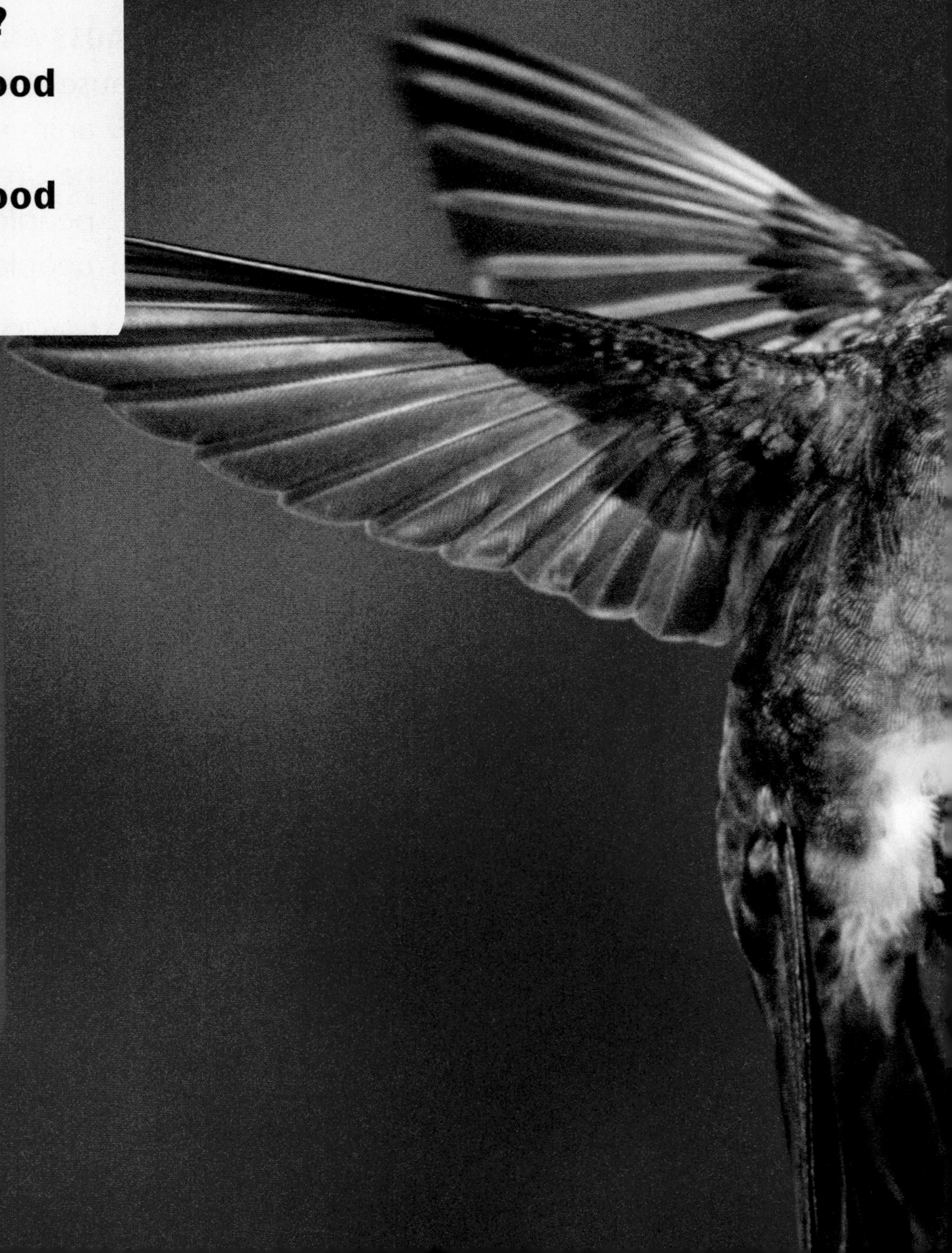

Vocabulary

FCAT-Tested

producer
consumer
decomposer
herbivore
carnivore
food chain
energy pyramid
predator
prey
food web

Other Terms

omnivore

What do YOU wonder?

Hummingbirds use their long, thin beaks to get nectar from flowers. What are some other ways that animals get their food? How do you get your food?

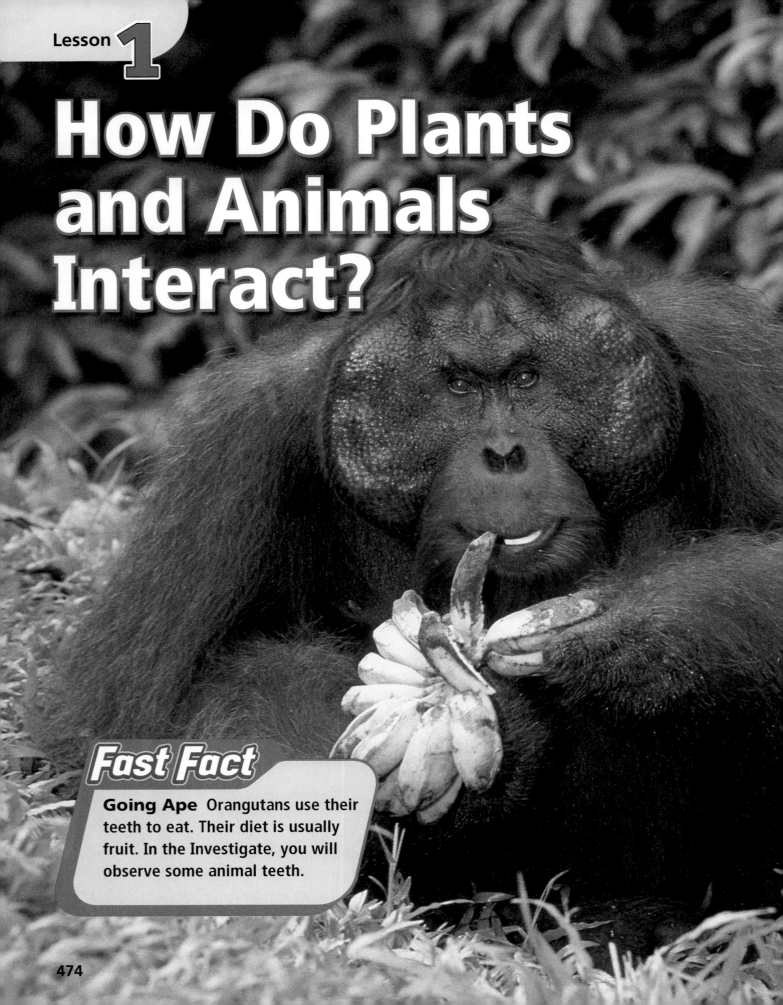

How Do Plants and Animals Interact?

Fast Fact

Going Ape Orangutans use their teeth to eat. Their diet is usually fruit. In the Investigate, you will observe some animal teeth.

Checking Teeth

Materials   • paper and pencil   • small mirror   • picture cards

Procedure

1. Copy the table onto paper.

2. **Observe** the picture cards that your teacher has provided.

3. On your table, **record** the name of an animal. Draw the shape of its teeth. It might have teeth of different shapes.

4. **Record** words that describe the teeth.

5. Read the back of the picture card. Record the foods the animal eats.

6. Repeat Steps 2–5 for four other animals.

7. Use the mirror to **observe** your own teeth. Add yourself to the table.

Draw Conclusions

1. Which of the animals in your table catch other animals for food? Which of the animals eat plants?

2. **Inquiry Skill** Scientists learn by **observing**. Then they use what they **observe** to **infer** the reasons for something. What can you **infer** about the shape of an animal's teeth and the kind of food it eats?

Teeth Table			
Kinds of Animals	Drawing of teeth	Description of teeth	Kinds of food

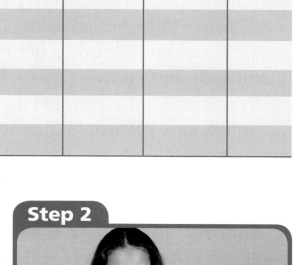
Step 2

Investigate Further

Choose another animal. Find out what it eats, and **predict** what kind of teeth it has. Then find out if you are correct.

SC.H.1.2.2.3.1 following experimental design, SC.H.1.2.5.3.1 uses diagrams, SC.H.2.2.1.3.1 makes predictions, SC.H.3.2.1.3.2 uses reference materials

Reading in Science

SC.B.2.2.1.3.1 organisms need energy, SC.F.1.2.2.3.1 animals depend on plants, SC.G.1.2.5.3.1 energy from food, SC.G.1.2.5.3.2 producers and consumers, LA.A.2.2.7 compare and contrast

VOCABULARY

producer p. 477

consumer p. 477

decomposer p. 477

herbivore p. 478

carnivore p. 479

omnivore p. 480

SCIENCE CONCEPTS

▶ how living things get energy

▶ how animals depend on plants

READING FOCUS SKILL

COMPARE AND CONTRAST

Compare how different animals get energy.

alike	different

Making and Getting Food

All living things need food. When you're hungry, your body needs food to get energy. You can make a sandwich, but can you really "make" your own food? Can you make the peanuts in your peanut butter?

Unlike you, plants are able to make their own food by using sunlight, air, and water. Plants store in their parts the extra food that they make. The food is full of energy.

Animals cannot make their own food. Some animals, such as rabbits, eat plants to get energy. The energy in the plants is taken into the rabbits' bodies. Other animals get energy by eating the rabbits.

 COMPARE AND CONTRAST How do plants and animals get food differently?

◀ The energy on Earth's surface comes from the sun. Without the sun, plants would have no energy. They could not make food and grow. Without plants, animals could not get energy and could not grow.

Producers, Consumers, and Decomposers

Plants are producers. A **producer** (pruh•DOOS•er) is a living thing that makes, or produces, its own food. Producers use this food to grow. Grass is a producer. So are trees and bushes.

Animals are consumers. A **consumer** (kuhn•SOOM•er) is a living thing that gets energy by eating other things as food. Consumers cannot make their own food. Deer, eagles, frogs, and even people are consumers.

Some kinds of living things are decomposers. A **decomposer** (dee•kuhm•POHZ•er) breaks down dead things for food. Earthworms, bacteria, and mushrooms are decomposers. Most of the decomposers are very small. You can see them only with a microscope.

COMPARE AND CONTRAST How are producers, consumers, and decomposers alike and different?

Sunflowers are producers. They store food in their seeds. The bird is a consumer. It gets energy by eating the seeds.

Earthworms eat dead plant parts and break them into tiny bits. Worms help put nutrients from the dead plants back into the soil. The nutrients will be taken in by the roots of next year's sunflowers.

Herbivores

There are three kinds of consumers: herbivores, carnivores, and omnivores. A **herbivore** (HER•buh•vawr) is a consumer that eats only plants. Tiny bees are herbivores, and so are giant pandas. People who eat only fruits and vegetables are herbivores, too.

Each herbivore has body parts that help it eat plants. A hummingbird has a long beak and tongue that help it reach nectar, a sweet liquid made by flowers. The nectar, found deep inside flowers, is the bird's food. A cow has flat teeth for chewing grass.

 COMPARE AND CONTRAST How is a herbivore different from a producer?

▲ Caterpillars are herbivores because they eat only leaves.

▲ Horses are also herbivores. When they chew grass, their lower jaws move sideways instead of up and down.

This Galápagos (guh•LAH•puh•gohs) tortoise eats only plants. Loggerhead sea turtles eat fish and crabs, so they are not herbivores. Other turtles eat both plants and animals.

▲ Wolves are carnivores. They hunt in packs and eat only meat.

Carnivores

A **carnivore** (KAHR•nuh•vawr) is a consumer that gets its food by eating other animals. Carnivores have body parts that help them hunt and eat their food.

A red-tailed hawk, for example, has sharp eyesight. It can see a rabbit a mile away! The hawk has claws to help it catch the rabbit. Its beak tears meat apart easily.

A leopard's spots hide it as it sneaks up on its next meal. Its sharp teeth and claws help it catch, kill, and eat its food.

(Focus Skill) **COMPARE AND CONTRAST** What is the same about a herbivore and a carnivore?

▲ Some carnivores are insects. The dragonfly eats mosquitoes, flies, and other insects.

Insta-Lab

Jobs for Teeth
Try eating a pretzel with just your front teeth. What happens? What does this tell you about the purposes of your front teeth and your back teeth?

Omnivores

An **omnivore** (AHM•nih•vawr) is a consumer that eats both plants and animals. Do you eat hamburgers? If you do, then you are an omnivore. The meat is from a cow. The bun is from wheat, a plant.

The chimpanzee is an omnivore. It eats mostly fruit, but it also eats ants and other insects. Sometimes it even hunts and eats small mammals.

Most omnivores have teeth that help them eat both plants and animals. Sharp teeth in the front of your mouth help you tear meat. Flat teeth in the back of your mouth help you grind plants.

COMPARE AND CONTRAST How are herbivores, carnivores, and omnivores different?

The grizzly bear is the biggest omnivore in North America. It has a good sense of smell. As the bear looks for food, it often stops to sniff the air.

◀ Although chickens don't have teeth, they eat seeds as well as insects they catch.

Raccoons eat nearly everything—duck eggs, mice, frogs, sweet corn, insects, and fruit. ▶

1. COMPARE AND CONTRAST Draw and complete this graphic organizer.

Type of Consumer	Example	What It Eats
Herbivore	Cow	Ⓐ _____
Carnivore	Ⓑ _____	Ⓒ _____
Ⓓ _____	Ⓔ _____	Ⓕ _____

2. SUMMARIZE Write a summary of this lesson by using the lesson vocabulary words in a paragraph.

3. DRAW CONCLUSIONS In what way does a wolf depend on plants for energy?

4. VOCABULARY Make a crossword puzzle from the vocabulary words.

FCAT Prep

5. Read/Inquire/Explain Which one would a carnivore eat?

A. a carrot

B. a leaf

C. a mosquito

D. a seed

Links

Writing

Expository

You have discovered a new kind of animal. Now you need to figure out if the animal is a herbivore, a carnivore, or an omnivore. Write an **explanation** of how you will do that.

Art

Consumer Mobile

Make a mobile showing the three types of consumers. Make sure to include at least two examples of each kind of consumer.

For more links and activities, go to www.hspscience.com

2
What Are Food Chains?

Lunch Time! An osprey plunges down to the water with its claws out to catch a fish. Spines on the osprey's toes keep the fish from getting away. In the Investigate, you will find out what some other animals eat.

Making a Food Chain

Materials   ● 5 index cards   ● marker   ● 4 pieces of string or yarn
● tape

Procedure

1 Number the index cards 1 through 5 in the bottom right-hand corner.

2 On Card 1, draw and label grass. Draw and label a grasshopper on Card 2. On Card 3, draw and label a mouse. Draw and label a snake on Card 4. On Card 5, draw and label a fox.

3 Put the cards in order by number. Use the yarn and the tape to connect them.

4 Lay the connected cards on a table. You have **made a model** of a food chain!

Step 2

Draw Conclusions

1. Which part of your food chain is a producer? Which parts are consumers?

2. Inquiry Skill Scientists **make a model** to study and understand a process. How does the model you made help you understand food chains?

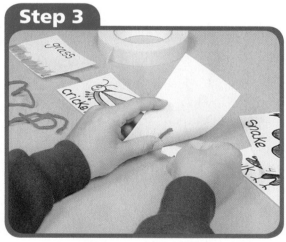

Step 3

Investigate Further

Find out what some other kinds of organisms eat. **Make a model** that shows the relationship between a producer and your consumers.

Reading in Science

 SC.B.2.2.1.3.1 organisms need energy, **SC.F.1.2.2.3.1** animals depend on plants, **SC.G.1.2.5.3.1** energy from food, **SC.G.1.2.5.3.2** producers and consumers, **LA.A.2.2.1** sequence

VOCABULARY

food chain p. 484

energy pyramid
  p. 486

predator p. 488

prey p. 488

SCIENCE CONCEPTS

▶ how energy from food is passed to living things in a food chain

READING FOCUS SKILL

(Focus Skill)

SEQUENCE Look for how energy passes through a food chain.

Food Chains

You are at the end of many food chains. A **food chain** shows the path of food from one living thing to another.

For example, one food chain begins with an apple tree that uses the energy in sunlight to help make its food. The tree stores some energy in its apples. When you eat an apple, you get the energy that was stored in the apple. That energy first came from sunlight.

A plant is the producer in this food chain. The plant uses sunlight to make its own food.

A grasshopper eats the tree's leaves. It gets energy that was stored in the leaves.

Another food chain begins with corn plants, which make their own food. Next, a chicken eats corn from the plant. Then, the chicken lays an egg, and you eat the egg. The energy in the egg that you eat started with the energy from sunlight.

A food chain always begins with a producer. Some food chains are long, and others are short. In a food chain, smaller animals are usually eaten by larger animals. When an animal or a plant dies, decomposers become part of the food chain. Decomposers break down dead plants and animals, which become part of the soil again.

 SEQUENCE What happens to the energy in a seed after a bird eats it?

A lizard eats the grasshopper. It uses the energy from the insect to live and grow.

The owl is the last consumer in this food chain. It must eat many small animals to get the energy it needs.

Energy Pyramids

A mouse gets energy by eating plants. The mouse uses some of the energy to live and grow. If a fox eats the mouse, the fox gets only the energy the mouse did not use.

An **energy pyramid** is a diagram that shows how energy is used in a food chain. The producers are the biggest group in the pyramid. Energy from the producers is passed to the herbivores that eat them. The herbivores use some of that energy. The rest of the energy is then passed to the animals that eat the herbivores.

 SEQUENCE What two kinds of consumers get energy after the herbivores?

A bobcat must catch and eat many small animals to get enough energy to live and grow. ▼

Insta-Lab

The View from the Top

Using picture cards 34–37, draw an energy pyramid on a separate piece of paper. There are fewer living things at the top of the pyramid. Make sure you draw an appropriate number of living things at each level.

Energy Pyramid

Each level in an energy pyramid has fewer living things than the level below it. The reason is that every level has less energy than the level below it.

The hawk is the top consumer in this energy pyramid.

The weasels are carnivores. They get their energy from eating the birds.

These birds are carnivores that get their energy by eating grasshoppers. Most of the energy is used to live. The rest of the energy is stored.

Grasshoppers are herbivores that get their energy by eating grass. Most of the energy is used to live. The rest of the energy is stored.

Grass, a producer, uses the energy of sunlight to make food.

For more links and activities, go to
www.hspscience.com

Predator and Prey

You've learned that some animals eat other animals. An animal that hunts another animal for food is called a **predator** (PRED•uh•ter). A wolf is a predator. So is an anteater.

An animal that is hunted for food is called **prey** (PRAY). Rabbits and mice are often prey for the wolf. Ants are the prey of the anteater.

Some animals are both predators and prey. A small bird that eats insects is a predator. If a hawk hunts the small bird, then the bird becomes the prey and the hawk is the predator.

 SEQUENCE A medium-size fish is a predator. What could happen next to make that fish become prey?

▲ The puffin can carry up to 10 fish at one time to feed its chicks.

The cheetah, a predator, can run 113 km (70 mi) an hour. It cannot run far at that speed, but that's far enough to catch most of its prey.

488

1. SEQUENCE Draw and complete this graphic organizer. Write the names of the living things in order to show a food chain sequence.

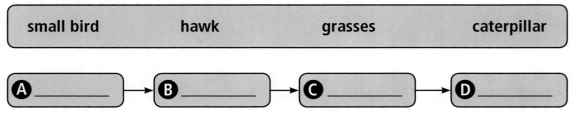

| small bird | hawk | grasses | caterpillar |

A _____ → B _____ → C _____ → D _____

2. SUMMARIZE Write a paragraph to summarize what producers, consumers, and decomposers do in a food chain.

3. DRAW CONCLUSIONS What effect would less sunlight have on an energy pyramid?

4. VOCABULARY Make up a matching quiz with this lesson's vocabulary words.

FCAT Prep

5. Read/Inquire/Explain Every night, you observe an owl catching mice. Explain how the owl gets energy that came from the sun, even though it hides in the dark shadows during the day.

Links

Writing

Expository

In 1972, a law stopped people from using DDT to kill insects. Find out how DDT affected eagles and food chains. Write a brief **report** about it.

Math

Name a Fraction

A food chain is made up of a producer, an herbivore, an omnivore, and a carnivore. What fraction of living things in this food chain eat plants?

 For more links and activities, go to **www.hspscience.com**

What Are Food Webs?

Fast Fact

Tongue Tale Anteaters catch ants with a very long, sticky tongue! Yet ants are not its only food. An anteater eats termites, too. In the Investigate, you will learn about other animals that are part of more than one food chain.

Making a Food Web

Materials
- index cards, cut into fourths
- tape or glue
- poster board
- crayons

Procedure

1 Write the name of each living thing from the table on its own card.

2 Tape or glue the cards in a circle on the poster board.

3 Use the table to make two different food chains. Record them on paper.

4 Use a crayon to draw arrows between the parts of one food chain. Use a different color to draw arrows between the parts of the other food chain.

5 Observe where the food chains overlap. You have just made a model of a food web.

Draw Conclusions

1. Why should both your food chains start with clover?

2. **Inquiry Skill** Scientists often use models, graphs, and drawings to communicate ideas. How does your model help communicate what a food web is?

Food Web Table	
Living Thing	**What It Eats**
clover	uses the sun to make its own food
grasshopper	clover
frog	grasshopper
snake	frog, mouse
owl	snake, mouse
mouse	clover

Step 4

Investigate Further

Choose an animal you like. Find out what it eats and what eats it. Then make a model of a food web that includes this animal.

Reading in Science

SC.B.2.2.1.3.1 organisms need energy, **SC.F.1.2.2.3.1** animals depend on plants, **SC.G.1.2.5.3.1** energy from food, **SC.G.1.2.5.3.2** producers and consumers, **LA.A.2.2.1** main idea and details

VOCABULARY
food web p. 492

SCIENCE CONCEPTS
▶ what food webs are and how they can change
▶ how animals stay safe

READING FOCUS SKILL
MAIN IDEA AND DETAILS Look for details about food webs.

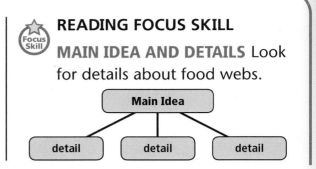

Food Web

Most animals eat many different things. You do, too. This means that you and most animals are part of many food chains. Overlapping food chains are called a **food web**.

MAIN IDEA AND DETAILS What is a food web?

This heron is a predator. It eats fish, lizards, frogs, mice, and insects. A young heron can also be an alligator's prey. ▶

▲ Every food chain and food web begins with producers. These plants provide food for animals. Some also provide shelter.

A Marsh Food Web

Alligators eat nearly anything. They're part of many food chains and are at the top of the energy pyramid. ▶

◀ Insects such as this grasshopper are an important link in many food webs.

▲ This muskrat is part of food chains both on land and in water.

In this marsh, a turtle might eat plants, fish, frogs, and insects. ▼

Some Ways Animals Defend Themselves

Mice are prey of hawks, owls, and other animals. A mouse might seem weak and helpless. Yet even small animals like mice have ways to defend themselves.

For example, the mouse's color helps it blend in with its surroundings. Mice come out mostly at night. The darkness helps to hide them. Most mice can hear, see, and smell very well. Their senses help them know if a predator is nearby.

When in danger, an opossum lies on its side with its eyes open, playing dead. Predators do not often attack dead animals. ▶

Some snakes defend themselves by biting. The poison released from their fangs may kill their prey—or their predators.

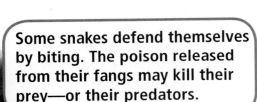

▲ Skunks spray a very smelly liquid at their predators. If you see a skunk and it raises its tail, run away fast!

▲ Wildebeests stay in herds to be safe. A wildebeest that strays from the herd may become prey to predators.

▲ When an octopus is in danger, it squirts ink into the water. The cloud of ink hides the octopus so it can escape.

▲ The anemone stings other fish but not the clownfish. This helps the clownfish stay safe from predators.

Insects can be prey, too. To hide, many insects have colors that blend in with their surroundings. Others have shapes like leaves or sticks that fool predators.

Some animals, like the gazelle, can outrun predators. A gazelle can run 80 kilometers (50 mi) an hour. Yet its main predator, the cheetah, runs even faster at 113 kilometers (70 mi) per hour. However, the gazelle runs in a zigzag pattern. That makes it harder to catch. If the cheetah does not catch the gazelle quickly, it gives up.

MAIN IDEA AND DETAILS What are three ways that animals defend themselves?

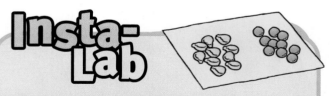

Insta-Lab

Hiding from Predators
Put ten peas and ten kernels of corn on a sheet of yellow paper. Close your eyes for a minute. Then open them and pick up the first five seeds you see. Compare your results with the rest of the class. What do you notice?

Changes in Food Webs

Many things can change a food web. An increase in plants often causes an increase in herbivores. More herbivores can lead to more carnivores and omnivores. On the other hand, fewer plants means fewer animals. A change to one part of a food web can change many other parts of the food web.

Adding a new plant or animal can also change a food web. A new plant may crowd out other plants. A new animal may eat many other animals or plants.

 MAIN IDEA AND DETAILS Name two things that can change a food web.

Math in Science
Interpret Data

The cane toad was introduced in Australia to get rid of the cane beetle. It was not known at the time that the toad would reproduce so quickly and interrupt other food webs. If the population increase of the cane toad isn't stopped, what do you think will happen in the next step of this graph?

Cane Toad Growth in Australia

Area Occupied by Toads (km²) *

300
250
200
150
100
50
0

Year Introduced | 10 Years Later | 20 Years Later | 30 Years Later

Years

* Area is estimated to the nearest 1,000 km²

1. MAIN IDEA AND DETAILS Draw and complete this graphic organizer.

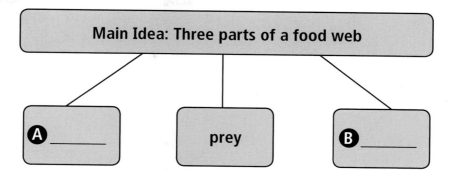

Main Idea: Three parts of a food web

Ⓐ _____

prey

Ⓑ _____

2. SUMMARIZE Write a paragraph that tells the most important information in this lesson.

3. DRAW CONCLUSIONS What is the difference between a food web and an energy pyramid?

4. VOCABULARY Write a sentence to explain to a younger student in your school what a food web is.

FCAT Prep

5. Which of these is **least** likely to get eaten in a food web?
A. herbivore
B. predator
C. prey
D. producer

Links

Writing

Persuasive

To get rid of mosquitoes in your town, some people want to bring in a bird from Brazil that eats mosquitoes. Write a **letter** to the editor of your town's newspaper telling your opinion.

Art

Paper Food Web

Make a model of a food web out of paper-chain links. Draw a plant or animal on each link. You might connect one link, such as grass, to several other links.

 For more links and activities, go to **www.hspscience.com**

SC.H.3.2.3.3.1 scientific discoveries impact humans

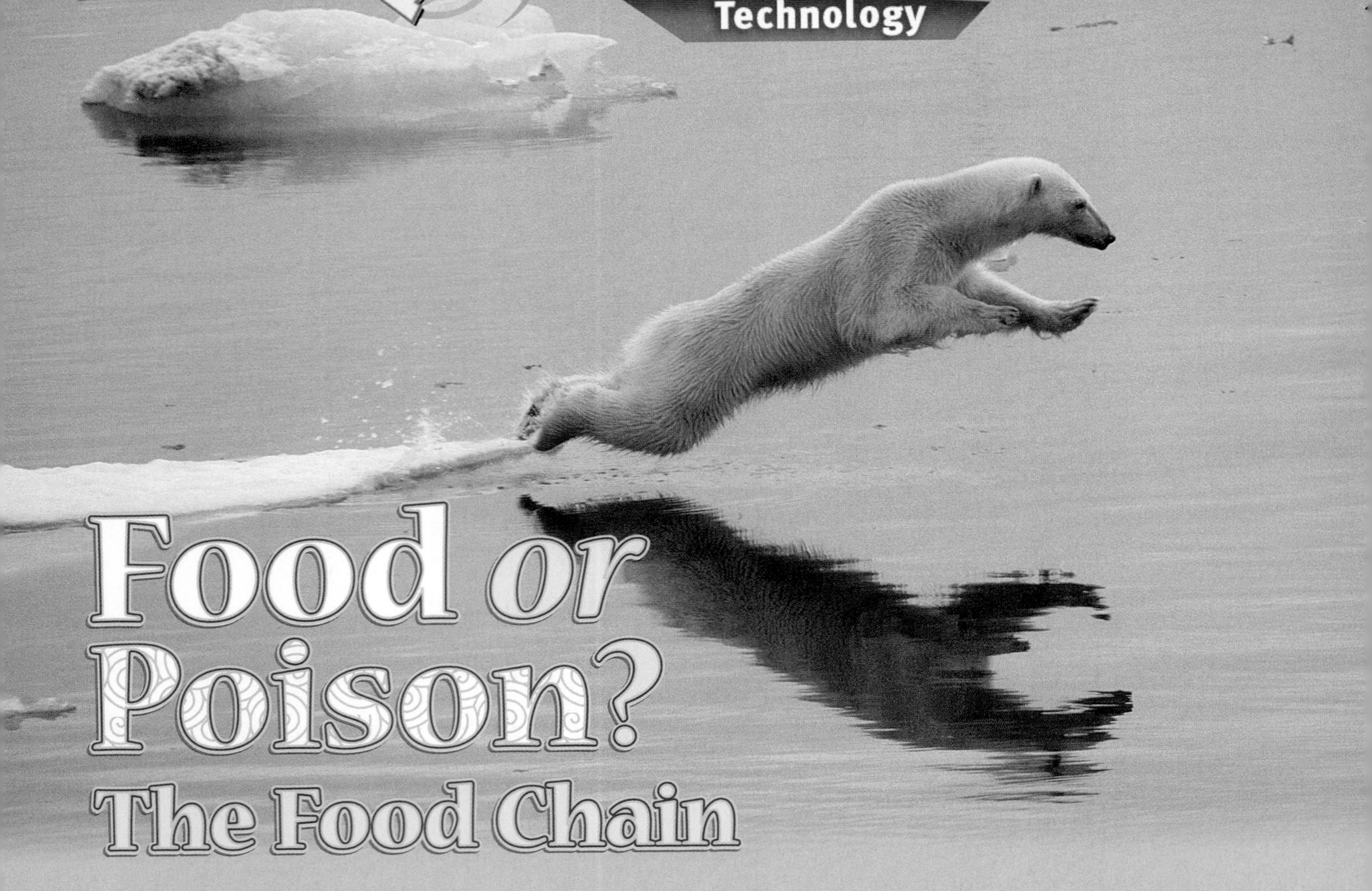

Food or Poison?

The Food Chain

A polar bear sits at the edge of a frozen lake. Nearby, a seal pops its head out of the water. Suddenly, the polar bear leaps forward and grabs the seal. But by eating the seal, the polar bear might also be eating poison.

The polar bear lives in the Arctic, the region around the North Pole. While the Arctic may seem far away, it is linked to the rest of the world by ocean and wind currents. Some scientists say that harmful chemicals are showing up in the Arctic.

Traveling by Air and Water

Most of the harmful chemicals, or pollutants, come from factories in different countries. Other pollutants are chemicals used to kill insects, weeds, and other pests. "Most of these pollutants come from outside the Arctic," said Arctic expert Samantha Smith. The pollutants are carried to the Arctic by wind and water.

Scientists study the pollutants by taking water and air samples from the Arctic. They test those samples in laboratories using microscopes and computers.

Food or Poison?

In the Arctic, the pollutants poison the food chain. A *food chain* is made up of the different plants and animals that other animals eat.

If animals eat too many pollutants, it will be difficult for them to reproduce. "Eventually, only old animals will be left, and there will be no more to replace them after they die," said one scientist.

THINK ABOUT IT

1. Where do you think a polar bear is in the Arctic food chain—at the top, in the middle, or at the bottom?
2. Other than pollutants, what else might affect the Arctic food chain?

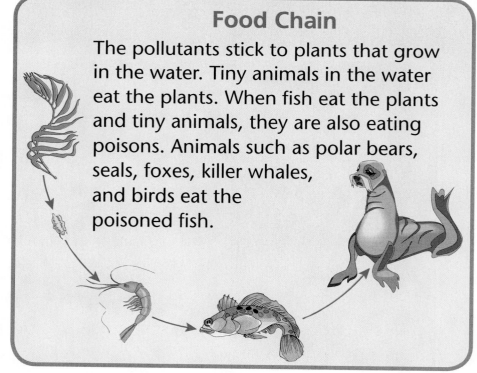

Food Chain

The pollutants stick to plants that grow in the water. Tiny animals in the water eat the plants. When fish eat the plants and tiny animals, they are also eating poisons. Animals such as polar bears, seals, foxes, killer whales, and birds eat the poisoned fish.

Find out more! Log on to **www.hspscience.com**

Protecting Food Chains

To Deshanique Williams, litter is not just ugly; it can hurt animals. That's why when she saw litter along a stream near her school in California, she decided to do something.

First, Deshanique studied the stream, the area around it, and the food chains within the stream. She noticed that animals, such as the blue heron, ate banana slugs. Deshanique was worried that animals would try to eat litter, thinking it was food. Not only could the litter make the animals sick, but it might disrupt the food chain as well.

So Deshanique organized a cleanup crew among local kids to pick up trash. She is also working on getting a law passed to protect the stream. Deshanique even wrote a book about the stream and her work.

Banana slug

Little Blue Heron

You Can Do It!

Quick and Easy Project

Your Food Chain

Procedure

1. At the top of the paper, write each food you ate for one meal.

2. Below each food, draw its source. For example, milk comes from a cow. Connect the food and source with an arrow.

3. If the source is an animal, draw the animal's food below it. Connect the animal and its food with an arrow.

Materials

- a large sheet of paper
- pencil

Draw Conclusions

In which direction should each arrow point to show how energy moves? What should be at the bottom of each food chain?

Design Your Own Investigation

Food Chains from the Sea

Do you like salmon, shrimp, or scallops? Choose your favorite fish or seafood, and predict what that animal eats. Then do some research to find out if you're correct. Make a food chain that includes that seafood and ends with you. Display your food chain on a bulletin board to share with the class.

14 Review and FCAT Preparation

Vocabulary Review

Use the terms below to complete the sentences. The page numbers tell you where to look in the chapter if you need help.

producers p. 477
consumers p. 477
decomposers p. 477
herbivore p. 478
carnivore p. 479
food chain p. 484
predator p. 488
food web p. 492

1. An animal that eats only meat is a _____.

2. Dead plants and animals are broken down by _____.

3. Food moves from one living thing to another in a path called a _____.

4. Carnivores and omnivores are both _____.

5. The overlapping paths of food are shown by a _____.

6. A cow is both a consumer and a _____.

7. A cheetah is a consumer, a carnivore, and a _____.

8. The only living things that can make their own food are _____.

Check Understanding

Write the letter of the best choice.

9. What is the source of energy for plants?
   A. food webs   **C.** producers
   B. prey   **D.** sunlight

10. **SEQUENCE** How can energy pass from a wheat plant to a wolf?
   F. through a carnivore
   G. through a herbivore
   H. through a predator
   I. through a producer

11. What can cause an increase in herbivores?
   A. an increase in predators
   B. a decrease in prey
   C. an increase in producers
   D. an increase in carnivores

12. Which group does this mushroom belong to?
   F. carnivore   **H.** herbivore
   G. decomposer **I.** prey

13. Which of these can cause a change in a food web?

   A. animals that protect themselves by running fast

   B. animals that blend in with their surroundings

   C. animals that are new to the ecosystem

   D. animals that live in herds

14. MAIN IDEA AND DETAILS What is the main purpose of this diagram?

   F. to show what eats what

   G. to outline an ecosystem

   H. to show that producers make their own food

   I. to show that the amount of energy that passes from one level to the next becomes less

15. What are most people?

   A. carnivores   **C.** omnivores

   B. herbivores   **D.** producers

16. Which of these does **not** happen?

   F. Plants become food.

   G. A predator becomes prey.

   H. An omnivore eats meat.

   I. A carnivore eats plants.

Inquiry Skills

17. How could you use index cards to make a model of a food chain?

18. A turtle is chewing on weeds growing beside a pond, and it snaps up a dragonfly that gets too close. Which group of consumers can you infer that the turtle belongs to?

Read/Inquire/Explain

19. What would happen to food webs if thick clouds from a volcanic eruption hid the sun for a year?

20. How would your life change if you were part of only one food chain?

References

Contents

Health Handbook

Reading in Science Handbook

Math in Science Handbook   R28

Your Skin

Your skin is your body's largest organ. It provides your body with a tough protective covering. It protects you from disease. It provides your sense of touch, which allows you to feel pressure, textures, temperature, and pain. Your skin also produces sweat to help control your body temperature. When you play hard or exercise, your body produces sweat, which cools you as it evaporates. The sweat from your skin also helps your body get rid of extra salt and other wastes.

▼ The skin is the body's largest organ.

Epidermis
Many layers of dead skin cells form the top of the epidermis. Cells in the lower part of the epidermis are always making new cells.

Oil Gland
Oil glands produce oil that keeps your skin soft and smooth.

Hair Follicle
Each hair follicle has a muscle that can contract and make the hair "stand on end."

Pore
These tiny holes on the surface of your skin lead to your dermis.

Sweat Gland
Sweat glands produce sweat, which contains water, salt, and various wastes.

Dermis
The dermis is much thicker than the epidermis. It is made up of tough, flexible fibers.

Fatty Tissue
This tissue layer beneath the dermis stores food, provides warmth, and attaches your skin to the bone and muscle below.

Caring for Your Skin

• To protect your skin and to keep it healthy, you should wash your body, including your hair and your nails, every day. This helps remove germs, excess oils and sweat, and dead cells from the epidermis, the outer layer of your skin. Because you touch many things during the day, you should wash your hands with soap and water frequently.

• If you get a cut or scratch, you should wash it right away and cover it with a sterile bandage to prevent infection.

• Protect your skin from cuts and scrapes by wearing proper safety equipment.

• Always protect your skin from sunburn by wearing protective clothing and sunscreen when you are outdoors.

Your Digestive System

Your digestive system is made up of connected organs. It breaks down the food you eat and disposes of the leftover wastes your body does not need.

Mouth to Stomach

Digestion begins when you chew your food. Chewing your food breaks it up and mixes it with saliva. When you swallow, the softened food travels down your esophagus to your stomach, where it is mixed with digestive juices. These are strong acids that continue the process of breaking your food down into the nutrients your body needs to stay healthy. Your stomach squeezes your food and turns it into a thick liquid.

Small Intestine and Liver

Your food leaves your stomach and goes into your small intestine. This organ is a long tube just below your stomach. Your liver is an organ that sends bile into your small intestine to continue the process of digesting fats in the food. The walls of the small intestine are lined with millions of small, finger-shaped bumps called villi. Tiny blood vessels in these bumps absorb nutrients from the food as it moves through the small intestine.

Large Intestine

When the food has traveled all the way through your small intestine, it passes into your large intestine. This last organ of your digestive system absorbs water from the food. The remaining wastes are held there until you go to the bathroom.

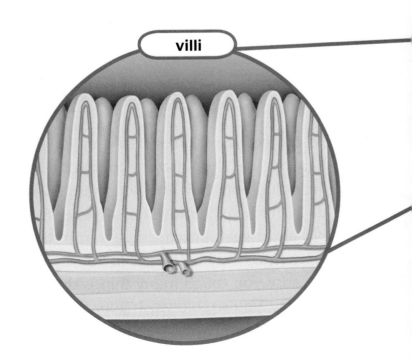

villi

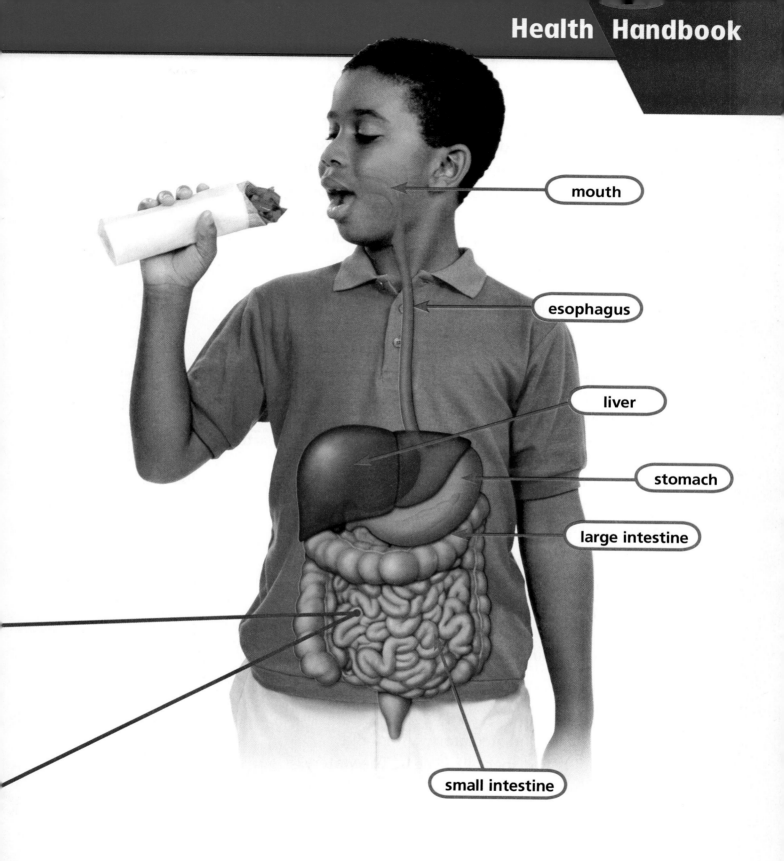

mouth

esophagus

liver

stomach

large intestine

small intestine

Your Circulatory System

Your circulatory system carries to every cell in your body the nutrients your digestive system takes from food and the oxygen your lungs take from the air you breathe. As your blood moves throughout your body, it also helps your body fight infections, control your temperature, and remove wastes from your cells.

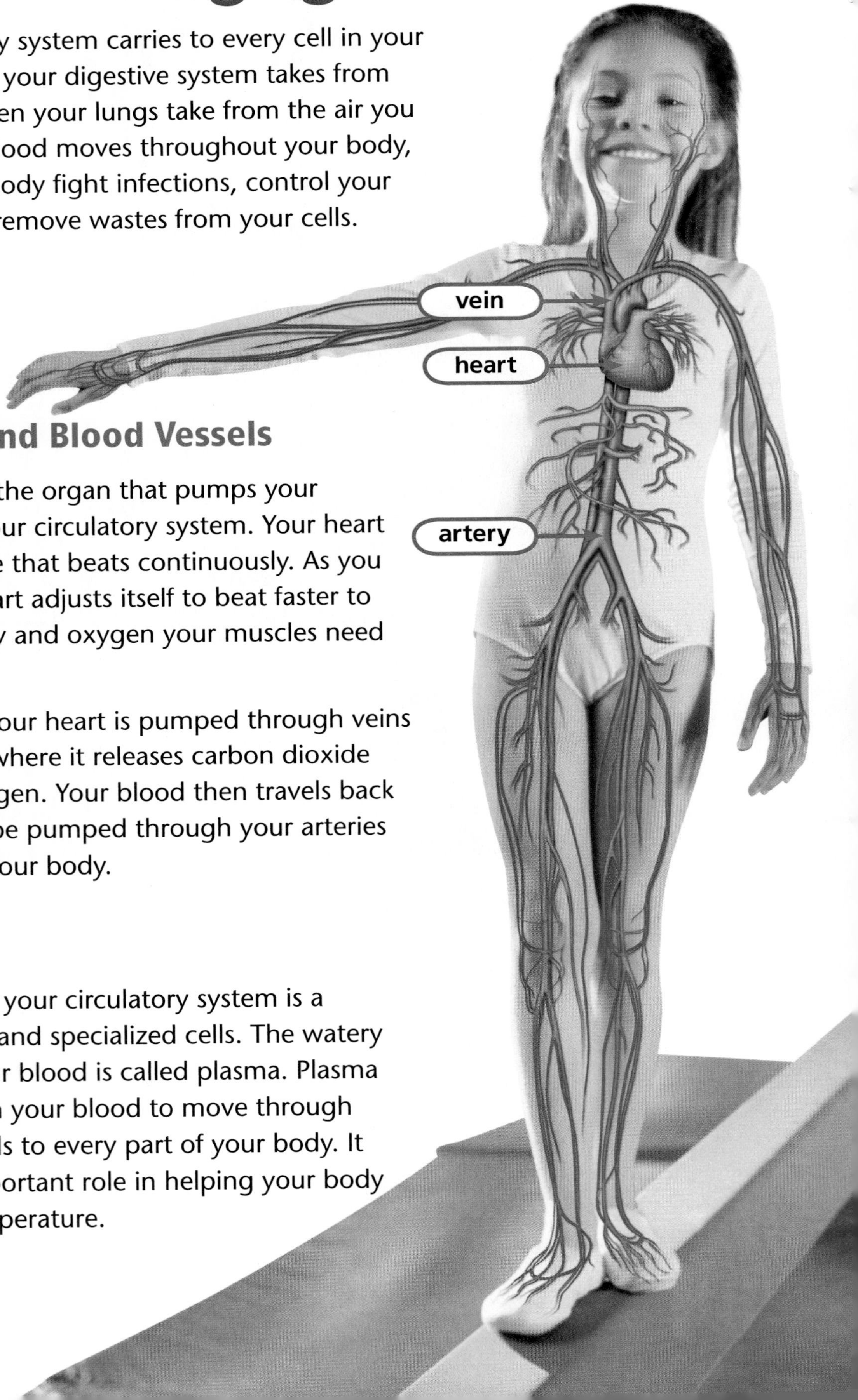

vein

heart

artery

Your Heart and Blood Vessels

Your heart is the organ that pumps your blood through your circulatory system. Your heart is a strong muscle that beats continuously. As you exercise, your heart adjusts itself to beat faster to deliver the energy and oxygen your muscles need to work harder.

Blood from your heart is pumped through veins into your lungs, where it releases carbon dioxide and picks up oxygen. Your blood then travels back to your heart to be pumped through your arteries to every part of your body.

Your Blood

The blood in your circulatory system is a mixture of fluids and specialized cells. The watery liquid part of your blood is called plasma. Plasma allows the cells in your blood to move through your blood vessels to every part of your body. It also plays an important role in helping your body control your temperature.

Blood Cells

blood cells

There are three main types of cells in your blood. Each type of cell in your circulatory system plays a special part in keeping your body healthy and fit.

Red Blood Cells are the most numerous cells in your blood. They carry oxygen from your lungs throughout your body. They also carry carbon dioxide back to your lungs from your cells, so you can breathe it out.

White Blood Cells help your body fight infections when you become ill.

Platelets help your body stop bleeding when you get a cut or other wound. Platelets clump together as soon as you start to bleed. The sticky clump of platelets traps red blood cells and forms a blood clot. The blood clot hardens to make a scab that seals the cut and lets your body begin healing the wound.

Caring for Your Circulatory System

- Eat foods that are low in fat and high in fiber. Fiber helps take away substances that can lead to fatty buildup in your blood vessels.

- Eat foods high in iron to help your red blood cells carry oxygen.

- Drink plenty of water to help your body replenish your blood.

- Avoid contact with another person's blood.

- Exercise regularly to keep your heart strong.

- Never smoke or use tobacco.

Your Skeletal System

Your skeletal system includes all of the bones in your body. These strong, hard parts of your body protect your internal organs, help you move, and allow you to sit and to stand up straight.

Your skeletal system works with your muscular system to hold your body up and to give it shape.

Your skeletal system includes more than 200 bones. These bones come in many different shapes and sizes.

Your Skull

The wide flat bones of your skull fit tightly together to protect your brain. The bones in the front of your skull give your face its shape and allow the muscles in your face to express your thoughts and feelings.

Your Spine

Your spine, or backbone, is made up of nearly two dozen small, round bones. These bones fit together and connect your head to your pelvis. Each of these bones, or vertebrae, is shaped like a doughnut, with a small round hole in the center. Your spinal cord is a bundle of nerves that carries information to and from your brain and the rest of your body. Your spinal cord runs from your brain down your back to your hips through the holes in your vertebrae. There are soft, flexible disks of cartilage between your vertebrae. This allows you to bend and twist your spine. Your spine, pelvis, and leg bones work together to allow you to stand, sit, or move.

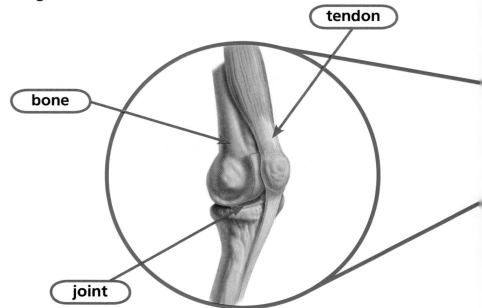

tendon

bone

joint

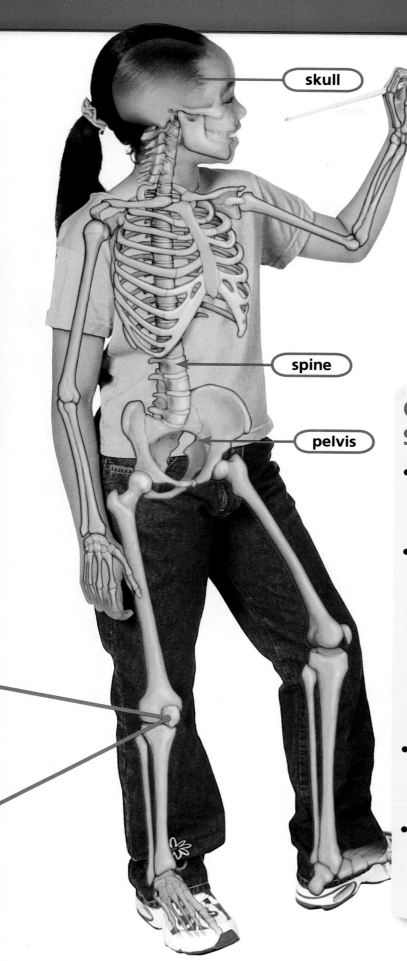

skull

spine

pelvis

Caring for Your Skeletal System

- Always wear a helmet and proper safety gear when you play sports, skate, or ride a bike or a scooter.

- Your bones are made mostly of calcium and other minerals. To keep your skeletal system strong and to help it grow, you should eat foods that are high in calcium, like milk, cheese, and yogurt. Dark green, leafy vegetables like broccoli, spinach, and collard greens are also good sources of calcium.

- Exercise to help your bones stay strong and healthy. Get plenty of rest to help your bones grow.

- Stand and sit with good posture. Sitting slumped over puts strain on your muscles and on your bones.

Your Muscular System

A muscle is a body part that produces movement by contracting and relaxing. All of the muscles in your body make up the muscular system.

Voluntary and Involuntary Muscles

Voluntary Muscles are the muscles you use to move your arms and legs, your face, head, and fingers. You can make these muscles contract or relax to control the way your body moves.

Involuntary Muscles are responsible for movements you usually don't see or control. These muscles make up your heart, your stomach and digestive system, your diaphragm, and the muscles that control your eyelids. Your heart beats and your diaphragm powers your breathing without your thinking about them. You cannot stop the action of these muscles.

How Muscles Help You Move

All muscles pull when they contract. Moving your body in more than one direction takes more than one muscle. To reach out with your arm or to pull it back, you use a pair of muscles. As one muscle contracts to extend your arm, the other relaxes and stretches. As you pull your arm back, the muscles reverse their functions.

Your muscles let you do many kinds of things. The large muscles in your legs allow you to walk and run. Tiny muscles in your face allow you to smile.

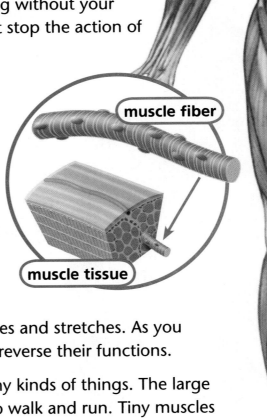

muscle fiber

muscle tissue

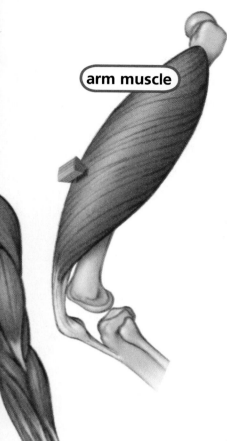

arm muscle

Your Muscles and Your Bones

The muscles that allow you to move your body work with your skeletal system. Muscles in your legs that allow you to kick a ball or ride a bicycle pull on the bones and joints of your legs and lower body. Your muscles are connected to your skeletal system by strong, cordlike tissues called tendons.

Your Achilles tendon, just above your heel connects your calf muscles to your heel bone. When you contract those muscles, the tendon pulls on the heel bone and allows you to stand on your toes, jump, or push hard on your bicycle's pedals.

Caring for Your Muscular System

- Always stretch and warmup your muscles before exercising or playing sports. Do this by jogging or walking for at least ten minutes. This brings fresh blood and oxygen into your muscles and helps prevent injury or pain.

- Eat a balanced diet of foods to be sure your muscles have the nutrients they need to grow and remain strong.

- Drink plenty of water when you exercise or play sports. This helps your blood remove wastes from your muscles and helps you build endurance.

- Always cool down after you exercise. Walk or jog slowly for five or ten minutes to let your heartbeat slow and your breathing return to normal. This helps you avoid pain and stiffness after your muscles work hard.

- Stop exercising if you feel pain in your muscles.

- Get plenty of rest before and after you work your muscles hard. They need time to repair themselves and recover from working hard.

Your Eyes and Vision

Your eyes allow you to see light reflected by the things around you. This diagram shows how an eye works. Light enters through the clear outer surface called the cornea. It passes through the pupil. The lens bends the incoming light to focus it on the retina. The retina sends nerve signals along the optic nerve. Your brain uses the signals to form an image. This is what you "see."

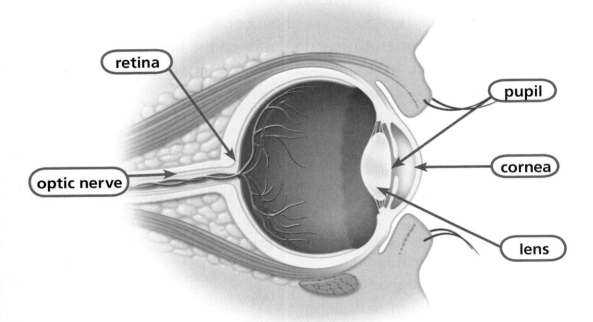

retina

pupil

optic nerve

cornea

lens

Caring for Your Eyes

- You should have a doctor check your eyesight every year. Tell your parents or your doctor if your vision becomes blurry or if you are having headaches or pain in your eyes.

- Never touch or rub your eyes.

- Protect your eyes by wearing safety goggles when you use tools or play sports.

- Wear swim goggles to protect your eyes from chlorine or other substances in the water.

- Wear sunglasses to protect your eyes from very bright light. Looking directly at bright light or at the sun can damage your eyes permanently.

Your Ears and Hearing

Sounds travel through the air in waves. When some of those waves enter your ear you hear a sound. This diagram shows the inside of your ear.

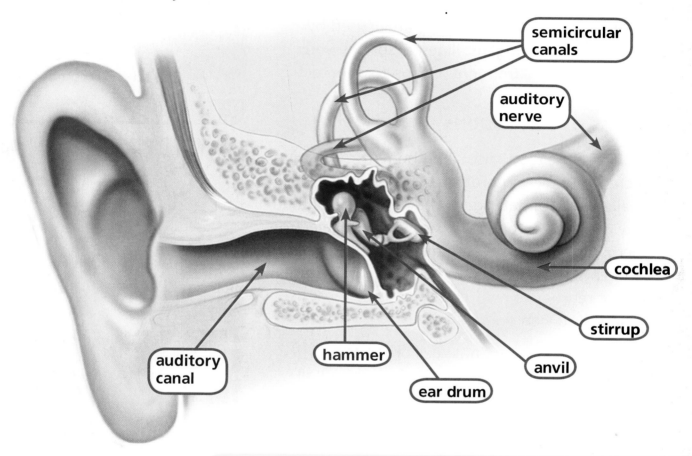

Caring for Your Ears

- Never put anything in your ears.

- Wear a helmet that covers your ears when you play sports.

- Keep your ears warm in winter.

- Avoid loud sounds and listening to loud music.

- Have your ears checked by a doctor if they hurt or leak fluid or if you have any loss of hearing.

- Wear earplugs when you swim. Water in your ears can lead to infection.

Pathogens and Illness

You may know someone who had a cold or the flu this year. These illnesses are caused by germs called pathogens. Illnesses spread when pathogens move from one person to another.

Types of Pathogens

There are four kinds of pathogens—viruses, bacteria, fungi, and protozoans. Viruses are the smallest kind of pathogen. They are so small that they can be seen only with very powerful electron microscopes. Viruses cause many types of illness, including colds, the flu, and chicken pox. Viruses cannot reproduce by themselves. They must use living cells to reproduce.

Bacteria are tiny single-cell organisms that live in water, in the soil, and on almost all surfaces. Most bacteria can be seen only with a microscope. Not all bacteria cause illness. Your body needs some types of bacteria to work well.

The most common type of fungus infection is athlete's foot. This is a burning, itchy infection of the skin between your toes. Ringworm is another skin infection caused by a fungus. It causes itchy round patches to develop on the skin.

Protozoans are the fourth type of pathogen. They are single-cell organisms that are slightly larger than bacteria. They can cause disease when they grow in food or drinking water.

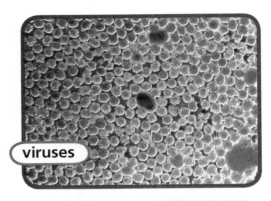
viruses

bacteria

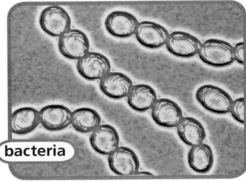
fungi

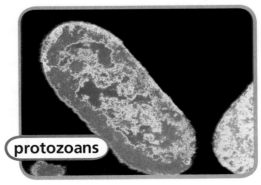
protozoans

Fighting Illness

Pathogens that can make you ill are everywhere. When you become ill, a doctor may be able to treat you. You also can practice healthful habits to protect yourself and others from the spread of pathogens and the illnesses they can cause.

The best way to avoid spreading pathogens is to wash your hands with warm water and soap. This floats germs off of your skin. You should wash your hands often. Always wash them before and after eating, after handling animals, and after using the bathroom. Avoid touching your mouth, eyes, and nose. Never share hats, combs, cups, or drinking straws. If you get a cut or scrape, pathogens can enter your body. It is important to wash cuts and scrapes carefully with soap and water. Then cover the injury with a sterile bandage.

When you are ill, you should avoid spreading pathogens to others. Cover your nose and mouth when you sneeze or cough.

Don't share anything that has touched your mouth or nose. Stay home from school until an adult or your doctor tells you that you are well enough to go back.

Even though pathogens are all around, most people become ill only once in a while because the body has systems that protect it from pathogens. These defenses keep pathogens from entering your body.

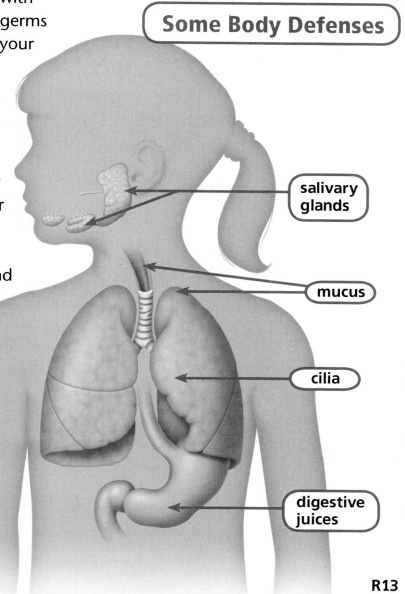

Some Body Defenses

salivary glands

mucus

cilia

digestive juices

Staying Healthy

Eat a Balanced Diet

Eating the foods that your body needs to grow and fight illness is the most important thing you can do to stay healthy. A balanced diet of healthful foods gives your body energy. Your body's systems need nutrients to function properly and work together.

Choosing unhealthful foods can cause you to gain excess weight and to lack energy. Inactivity and poor food choices can lead to you becoming ill more frequently. Unhealthful foods can also cause you to develop noncommunicable diseases. Unlike communicable diseases, which are caused by germs, these illnesses occur because your body systems are not working right.

Exercise Regularly

Exercise keeps your body healthy. Regular exercise helps your heart, lungs, and muscles stay strong. It helps your body digest food. It also helps your body fight disease. Exercising to keep your body strong also helps prevent injury when you play sports.

Exercise allows your body to rest more effectively. Getting enough sleep prepares your body for the next day. It allows your muscles and bones to grow and recover from exercise. Resting also helps keep your mind alert so you can learn and play well.

Identify the Main Idea and Details

Focus Skill

This Reading in Science Handbook provides tips for using the ⬤ Reading Focus Skills you see throughout this book. Many of the lessons in this science book are written so you can understand main ideas and the details that support them. You can use a graphic organizer like this one to show a main idea and details.

Main Idea: The most important idea of a selection

Detail: Information that tells more about the main idea

Detail: Information that tells more about the main idea

Detail: Information that tells more about the main idea

Tips for Identifying the Main Idea and Details

- To find the main idea, ask *What is this mostly about?*

- Remember that the main idea is not always stated in the first sentence.

- Look for details that answer questions such as *Who, What, Where, When, Why* and *How*. Use pictures as clues to help you figure out the main idea.

Here is an example.

Main Idea

Soil is an important resource. The plants you eat are grown in soil. Animals such as cows and chickens eat plants that grow in soil, too. The plants we use for lumber also grow in soil.

Detail

Main Idea: Soil is an important resource.

Detail: Plants you eat grow in soil.

Detail: Animals eat plants that grow in soil.

Detail: Plants used for lumber grow in soil.

More About Main Idea and Details

Sometimes the main idea of a paragraph is at the end instead of the beginning. If the main idea is not given at all, look at the details to figure it out. Look at the graphic organizer. What do you think the main idea is?

Main Idea:

Detail:
Topsoil is the top layer of soil. It is made up of humus.

Detail:
Subsoil is the next layer of soil. It is made up of small rocks.

Detail:
The bottom layer is bedrock. It is mostly solid rock.

Sometimes a paragraph's main idea might contain details of different types. In this paragraph, identify whether the details give reasons, examples, facts, steps, or descriptions.

Farmers and scientists have found a type of soil that is best for growing plants. It is soil that contains an equal mixture of sand, clay, and humus. Soil with this mixture can hold the right amount of water. It also has enough nutrients.

Skill Practice

Read the following paragraph. Use the Tips for Identifying the Main Idea and Details to answer the questions.

Soil helps all living things meet their needs. It provides a home for some animals and plants. Soil is used to grow plants for food. It is also used to grow resources such as trees for lumber and paper.

1. What is the main idea of the paragraph?

2. What supporting details give more information?

3. What details answer any of the questions *Who, What, Where, When, Why* and *How?*

Compare and Contrast

Some lessons are written to help you see how things are alike or different. You can use a graphic organizer like this one to compare and contrast.

Topic: Name the topic—the two things you are comparing and contrasting.

Alike	**Different**
List ways the things are alike.	List ways the things are different.

Tips for Comparing and Contrasting

- To compare, ask *How are things alike?*
- To contrast, ask *How are things different?*
- When you compare, look for signal words and phrases such as *similar, alike, both, the same as, too,* and *also.*
- When you contrast, look for signal words and phrases such as *unlike, different, however, yet,* and *but.*

Here is an example.

Compare

Both dogs and cats have been kept by people for thousands of years. These four-legged companions have lived in our homes and shared our food. They are different in many ways. Cats help keep small animals like mice and rats out of the house. Dogs warn us of danger. Cats like to nap, but dogs like to play.

Contrast

Here is what you could record in the graphic organizer.

Topic: Dogs and Cats

Alike	**Different**
They live with humans, have four legs, and share our foods.	Cats chase mice, dogs bark at danger. Cats nap, dogs play.

More About Compare and Contrast

You can better understand new information about things when you know how they are alike and how they are different. Use the graphic organizer from page R18 to sort the following new information about cats and dogs.

| Cats | Like fish | Afraid of dogs | Climb trees | Very independent |

| Dogs | Like meats | Bark at strange dogs | Run very fast | Will come when called |

Sometimes a paragraph compares and contrasts more than one topic. In the following paragraph, the sentence that compares things is underlined. Find the sentences that contrast things.

<u>The first boats and the first airplanes were both powered by using wooden parts.</u> People pulled wooden oars to move the first boats through water. Early airplanes were pulled through the air by wooden propellers. Wood is a strong, flexible material that is easy to shape into tools. A single oar can move a boat over water with each stroke, but a propeller must turn continuously to keep an airplane flying.

Skill Practice

Read the following paragraph. Use the Tips for Comparing and Contrasting to answer the questions.

Both boats and airplanes seem to float easily. But water is much denser than air. Boats float on top of water because their weight is spread over the bottom of the boat. Airplanes are held up by the air under their wings. Boats can float when they are not moving. However, airplanes must move forward all the time. This creates the lifting force under their wings.

1. What is one likeness that boats and airplanes share?

2. What is one difference between boats and airplanes?

3. What are two signal words that helped you identify likenesses and differences?

Cause and Effect

Focus Skill

Some of the lessons in this science book are written to help you understand why things happen. You can use a graphic organizer like this one to show cause and effect.

Cause	**Effect**
A cause is the reason, or why, something happens.	An effect is what happens.

Tips for Identifying Cause and Effect

- To find an effect, ask *What happened?*

- To find a cause, ask *Why did this happen?*

- Remember that events can have more than one cause or effect.

- Look for signal words such as *because*, *as a result*, *so*, and *therefore*.

Here is an example.

Effect

A gecko is a small lizard. It can climb up walls and walk upside down without falling. Scientists have found out how geckos stick on things so well. They have millions of tiny hairs on their feet. The hairs have flat ends that stick to almost anything. So, the gecko can walk on a ceiling without falling down.

Cause

Here is what you could record in the graphic organizer.

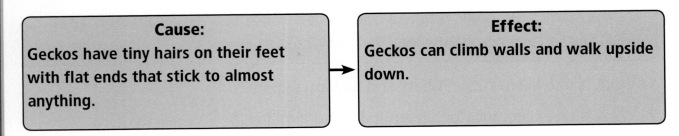

Cause:	**Effect:**
Geckos have tiny hairs on their feet with flat ends that stick to almost anything.	Geckos can climb walls and walk upside down.

More About Cause and Effect

Events can have more than one cause or effect. For example, suppose the paragraph on page R20 included a sentence that said *This helps the gecko escape from predators.* You could then identify two effects of geckos and their sticky feet.

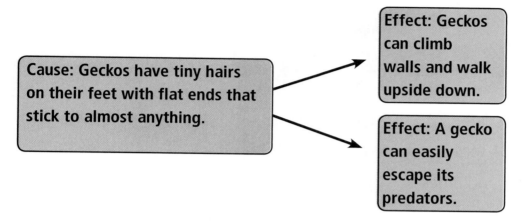

Cause: Geckos have tiny hairs on their feet with flat ends that stick to almost anything.

Effect: Geckos can climb walls and walk upside down.

Effect: A gecko can easily escape its predators.

Some paragraphs contain more than one cause and effect. In the following paragraph, one cause and its effect are underlined. Find the second cause and its effect.

Birds have a body covering of feathers. The feathers keep birds warm and dry. Feathers also give a bird's body a smooth surface over which air can easily flow. Another thing that helps birds fly is their bones. A bird's bones are filled with air pockets. As a result, the bird is very light, and this helps it fly.

Skill Practice

Read the following paragraph. Use the Tips for Identifying Cause and Effect to help you answer the questions.

The viceroy butterfly would be a tasty meal for a bird. However, the viceroy looks a lot like the monarch butterfly. Birds often mistake the viceroy for a monarch, which tastes bad to birds. Therefore, birds usually leave the viceroy alone.

1. What causes birds to not eat the viceroy butterfly?

2. What is the effect of the viceroy's looking like a monarch?

3. Name a signal word that helped you identify a cause or an effect.

Sequence

Some lessons in this science book are written to help you understand the order in which things happen. You can use a graphic organizer like this one to show sequence.

I. The first thing that happened	→	**2. The next thing that happened**	→	**3. The last thing that happened**

Tips for Understanding Sequence

- Pay attention to the order in which events happen.
- Recall dates and times to help you understand the sequence.
- Look for time-order signal words such as *first, next, then, last,* and *finally.*
- Sometimes it is helpful to add time-order words yourself as you read.

Here is an example.

> Suppose you have a mixture of rice, paper clips, and marbles. You need to separate the parts of the mixture. First, you separate the marbles with your hands. Then, you use a magnet to separate the paper clips. Finally, the rice is left.

Time-order words

Here is what you could record in the graphic organizer.

I. First, you separate the marbles by hand.	→	**2. Then, you use the magnet to separate the paper clips.**	→	**3. Finally, the rice is left.**

More About Sequence

Sometimes information is sequenced by dates. Use a graphic organizer like the following to sequence the order in which water in a pond freezes and melts.

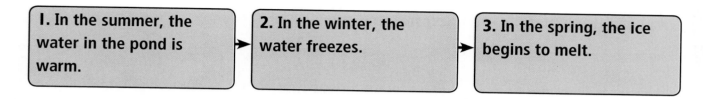

| I. In the summer, the water in the pond is warm. | → | 2. In the winter, the water freezes. | → | 3. In the spring, the ice begins to melt. |

When time-order words are not given, add your own. Look at the underlined time-order word in the paragraph below. How many more time-order words can you add to help you understand the sequence?

When you cook food, you make new kinds of matter. <u>First,</u> flour, eggs, milk, and oil are mixed to make pancake batter. The batter is poured on a stove. The batter cooks and turns into pancakes. The pancakes will never be flour, eggs, milk, and oil again.

Skill Practice

Read the following paragraph. Use the Tips for Understanding Sequence to answer the questions.

A shiny iron bolt was left outdoors. It sat in the rain and moist air. After several days, the bolt began to turn dull. After a week, it turned an orange-brown color. When it was picked up a month later, the orange-brown iron bolt was flaky and soft. The orange-brown material was rust. When a metal turns to rust, it loses some of its strength.

1. What is the first thing that happened in this sequence?

2. About how long did the process take?

3. What four signal words helped you identify the sequence in this paragraph?

Draw Conclusions

At the end of each lesson in this science book, you will be asked to draw conclusions. To draw conclusions, use information from the text you are reading and what you already know. Drawing conclusions can help you understand what you read. You can use a graphic organizer like this one.

What I Read		**What I Know**		**Conclusion:**
List facts from the text.	+	List related ideas that you already know.	=	Combine what you just read in the text with what you already know.

Tips for Drawing Conclusions

- To draw conclusions, ask *What do I need to think about from the text?*

- To draw conclusions, ask *What do I really know that could help me draw a conclusion?*

- Be sure your conclusions make sense.

Here is an example.

> When astronauts visited the moon, they left footprints. On the moon, there is no water. There is also very little air. Without air, there is no wind or weather. So the footprints that were left on the moon are still there.

Here is what you could record in the graphic organizer.

What I Read		**What I Know**		**Conclusion:**
The astronauts left footprints on the moon. The moon has no weather.	+	Footprints left on earth would be washed away by wind or rain.	=	The footprints on the moon will be there for a long time.

More About Drawing Conclusions

Text Information   Your Own Experience

What I Read		**What I Know**		**Conclusion:**
The astronauts left footprints on the moon. The moon has no weather.	+	Footprints left on earth would be washed away by wind or rain.	=	The footprints on the moon will be there for a long time.

Sometimes a paragraph might not contain enough information to draw a conclusion that makes sense. Read the paragraph below. Think of one right conclusion you could draw. Then think of a conclusion that would be wrong.

> Venus is the second planet from the sun. It is about the same size as Earth. Venus is dry and covered with thick clouds. The thick clouds trap heat and make the planet's surface very hot.

Skill Practice

Read the following paragraph. Use the Tips for Drawing Conclusions to answer the questions.

> The outer planets are Jupiter, Saturn, Uranus, Neptune, and Pluto. Four of these planets are large spheres made up mostly of gases. They are called the gas giants. Jupiter is the largest gas giant. Its atmosphere is very active.

1. What conclusion can you draw about the outer planets?

2. What information from your own experience helped you draw the conclusion?

3. What text information did you use to draw the conclusion?

Retell what you have just read. Use the main idea and only the most important details.

Tips for Summarizing

- To write a summary, ask—What is the most important idea or the main thing that happened?
- Be sure the details you include are things the reader needs to know.
- Make your summary shorter than what you have read.
- Write a summary in your own words. Be sure to put the events in order.

Here is an example.

Main Idea

Fish are a type of animal group. They live their entire lives in water. Fish have gills that they use to take in oxygen from the water. Fish have a body covering of scales. The scales are small, thin, flat plates that help protect the fish. Fish also have fins they use to move in water.

Detail

Main Idea: Fish are a type of animal group.

Detail: Fish have gills they use to take in oxygen.

Detail: They are covered with scales.

Summary: Fish are an animal group. They have gills, a body covering of scales, and fins.

> Here is what you could record in the graphic organizer.

Main Idea:		Detail:		Summary:
Fish are a type of animal group.	+	Fish have gills they use to take in oxygen. They are covered with scales	=	Fish are an animal group. They have gills, a body covering of scales, and fins.

More About Summarizing

Sometimes a paragraph has details that are not important enough to put in a summary. What if the paragraph on page R26 included a sentence about the color and size of a fish's scales? You would leave these details out of the summary. They would not be needed to understand the main idea.

Skill Practice

Read the following paragraph. Use the Tips for Summarizing to answer the questions.

Amphibians are animals that begin life in the water and move onto land as adults. Amphibians lay eggs in the water. The eggs stay there until they hatch. Young amphibians, such as tadpoles, live in the water. They breathe with gills. As they grow, they develop lungs. Once they have lungs, their gills disappear. Tadpoles also develop other body parts, such as legs. These help them live on land. Most adult amphibians live on land.

1. If a friend asked you what this paragraph is about, what information would you include? What would you leave out?

2. What is the main idea of the paragraph?

3. What two details would you include in a summary of the paragraph?

Using Tables, Charts, and Graphs

As you do investigations in science, you collect, organize, display, and interpret data. Tables, charts, and graphs are good ways to organize and display data so that others can understand and interpret your data.

The tables, charts, and graphs in this Handbook will help you read and understand data. You can also use the information to choose the best ways to display data so that you can use it to draw conclusions and make predictions.

Reading a Table

A third-grade class is studying the lengths of different sea animals. They want to find out how the lengths vary. The table shows some of the data the students have collected.

LENGTHS OF SEA ANIMALS	
Animal	**Length (in feet)**
Whale shark	60
White shark	40
Bottlenose dolphin	10
Giant squid	55
Gray whale	50

Title ← (points to LENGTHS OF SEA ANIMALS)

Header ← (points to Animal / Length header row)

Data ← (points to data rows)

How to Read a Table

1. Read the title to find out what the table is about.

2. Read the headings to find out what information is given.

3. Study the data. Look for patterns.

4. Draw conclusions. If you display the data in a graph, you might be able to see patterns easily.

By studying the table, you can see the lengths of different sea animals. However, suppose the students want to look for patterns in the data. They might choose to display the data in a different way, such as in a bar graph.

Reading a Bar Graph

The data in this bar graph is the same as in the table. A bar graph can be used to compare the data about different events or groups.

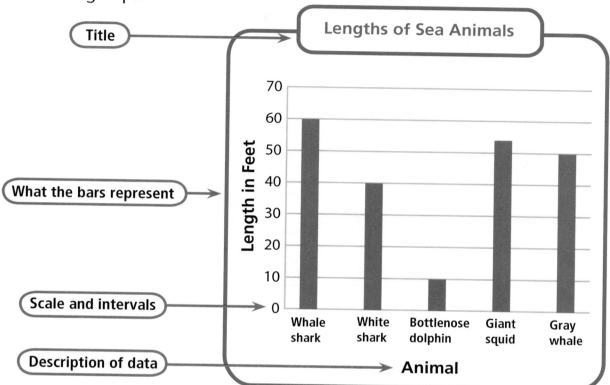

Title

What the bars represent

Scale and intervals

Description of data

Lengths of Sea Animals

Length in Feet

Whale shark | White shark | Bottlenose dolphin | Giant squid | Gray whale

Animal

How to Read a Bar Graph

1. Look at the graph to determine what kind of graph it is.

2. Read the graph. Use the labels to guide you.

3. Analyze the data. Study the bars to compare the measurements. Look for patterns.

4. Draw conclusions. Ask yourself questions like those on the right.

Skills Practice

1. How long is a gray whale?

2. How much longer is a whale shark than a white shark?

3. Which two sea animals vary in length by 40 feet?

4. Predict Which of these sea animals might you find in an aquarium at an animal park?

5. Was the bar graph a good choice for displaying this data? Explain your answer.

Using Metric Measurements

Reading a Line Graph

A scientist collected this data about temperatures in Anchorage, Alaska.

TEMPERATURES IN ANCHORAGE, ALASKA

Month	Normal Temperature in Degrees Fahrenheit
August	55
September	50
October	35
November	20
December	15

Here is the same data displayed in a line graph. A line graph is used to show changes over time.

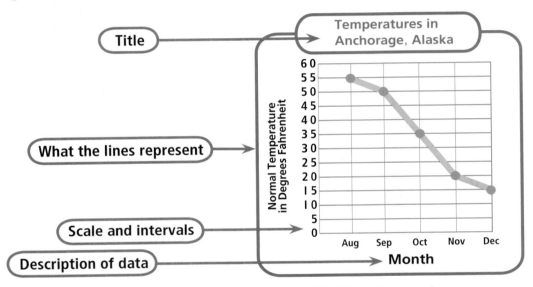

Title

What the lines represent

Scale and intervals

Description of data

How to Read a Line Graph

1. Look at the graph to determine what kind of graph it is.

2. Read the graph. Use the labels to guide you.

3. Analyze the data. Study the points along the lines. Look for patterns.

4. **Draw conclusions.** Ask yourself questions like those on the right.

Skills Practice

1. In what month is the normal temperature 35 degrees?

2. **Predict** How will the temperature change from December to August?

3. Was the line graph a good choice for displaying this data? Explain why.

Reading a Circle Graph

A family went bird watching on an island. They counted 50 birds on the island. They wanted to know which birds they saw most often. They classified the birds by making a table. Here is the data they collected.

BIRD SIGHTINGS	
Bird	Number Observed
Pelican	4
Bald Eagle	1
Osprey	10
Egret	15
Sandpiper	20

The circle graph shows the same data as the table. A circle graph can be used to show data as a whole made up of different parts.

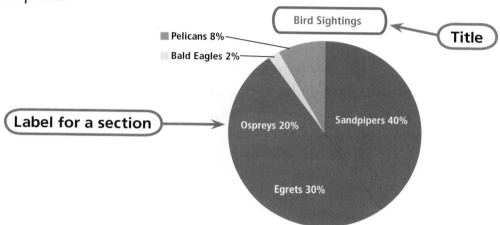

How to Read a Circle Graph

1. Look at the title of the graph to learn what kind of information is shown.

2. Read the graph. Look at the label of each section to find out what information is shown.

3. Analyze the data. Compare the sizes of the sections to determine how they are related.

4. **Draw conclusions.** Ask yourself questions like those on the right.

Skills Practice

1. Which type of bird did they see most often?

2. **Predict** If they return to the island in a month, should they expect to see a bald eagle?

3. Was the circle graph a good choice for displaying this data? Explain why.

Using Metric Measurements

A measurement is a number that represents a comparison of something being measured to a unit of measurement. Scientists use many different tools to measure objects and substances as they work. Scientists almost always use the metric system for their measurements.

Measuring Length in Metric Units

When you measure length, you find the distance between two points. The distance may be in a straight line, along a curved path, or around a circle. The table shows the metric units of length and how they are related.

Equivalent Measures

1 centimeter (cm) = 10 millimeters (mm)

1 decimeter (dm) = 10 centimeters (cm)

1 meter (m) = 1,000 millimeters

1 meter = 10 decimeters

1 kilometer (km) = 1,000 meters

You can use these comparisons to help you understand the size of each metric unit of length.

A **millimeter (mm)** is about the thickness of a dime.	A **centimeter (cm)** is about the width of your index finger.	A **decimeter (dm)** is about the width of an adult's hand.	A **meter (m)** is about the width of a door.
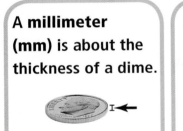		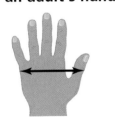	

Sometimes you may need to change units of length. The following diagram shows how to multiply and divide to change to larger and smaller units.

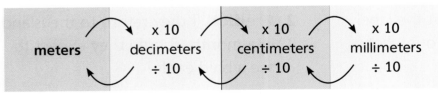

To change larger units to smaller units, you need more of the smaller units. So, multiply by 10, 100, or 1,000.

Example: 500 dm = ____ cm

Measuring Capacity in Metric Units

When you measure capacity, you find the amount a container can hold when it is filled. The table shows the metric units of capacity and how they are related.

A **milliliter (mL)** is the amount of liquid that can fill part of a dropper.

A **liter (L)** is the amount of liquid that can fill a plastic bottle.

You can use multiplication to change liters to milliliters.

You can use division to change milliliters to liters.

2 L = ___ mL

Think: There are 1,000 mL in 1 L.

2L = 2 x 1,000 = 2,000 mL

So, 2L = 2,000 mL.

4,000 mL = ____ L

Think: There are 1,000 mL in 1 L.

4,000 ÷ 1,000 = 4

So, 4,000 mL = 4 L.

Skills Practice

Complete. Tell whether you multiply or divide by 1,000.

1. 4 L = ___ mL

2. 5,000 mL = ___ L

3. 3,000 mL = ___ L

4. 6 L = ___ mL

Measuring Mass

Matter is what all objects are made of. Mass is the amount of matter that is in an object. The metric units of mass are the gram (g) and the kilogram (kg).

You can use these comparisons to help you understand the masses of some everyday objects.

A paper clip is about 1 gram (g).	A slice of wheat bread is about 20 grams.	A box of 12 crayons is about 100 grams.	A large wedge of cheese is 1 kilogram (kg).

You can use multiplication to change kilograms to grams.

You can use division to change grams to kilograms.

2 kg = ___ g
Think: There are 1,000 g in 1 kg.
2 kg = 2 x 1,000 = 2,000 g

So, 2 kg = 2,000 g.

4,000 g = ____ kg
Think: There are 1,000 g in 1 kg.
4,000 ÷ 1,000 = 4
So, 4,000 g = 4 kg.

Skills Practice

Complete. Tell whether you multiply or divide by 1,000.

1. 2,000 g = ___ kg

2. 3,000 g = ____ kg

3. 4 kg = ____ g

4. 7 kg = ____ g

Measurement Systems

SI Measures (Metric)

Temperature
Ice melts at 0 degrees Celsius (°C).
Water freezes at 0°C.
Water boils at 100°C.

Length and Distance
1000 meters (m) = 1 kilometer (km)
100 centimeters (cm) = 1 m
10 millimeters (mm) = 1 cm

Force
1 newton (N) = 1 kilogram x
   1 meter/second/second (kg-m/s^2)

Volume
1 cubic meter (m^3) = 1m x 1m x 1m
1 cubic centimeter (cm^3) =
   1 cm x 1 cm x 1 cm
1 liter (L) = 1000 millimeters (mL)
1 cm^3 = 1 mL

Area
1 square kilometer (km^2) =
             1 km x 1 km
1 hectare = 10,000 m^2

Mass
1000 grams (g) = 1 kilogram (kg)
1000 milligrams (mg) = 1 g

Rates (Metric and Customary)
kmh = kilometers per hour
m/s = meters per second
mph = miles per hour
A liter (L) is the amount of liquid that
can fill a plastic bottle.

Customary Measures

Volume of Fluids
2 cups (c) = 1 pint (pt)
2 pt = 1 quart (qt)
4 qt = 1 gallon (gal)

Temperature
Ice melts at 32 degrees Fahrenheit (°F).
Water freezes at 32°F.
Water boils at 212°F.

Length and Distance
12 inches (in.) = 1 foot (ft)
3 ft = 1 yard (yd)
5,280 ft = 1 mile (mi)

Weight
16 ounces (oz) = 1 pound (lb)
2,000 pounds (lb) = 1 ton (T)

Safety in Science

Doing investigations in science can be fun, but you need to be sure you do them safely. Here are some rules to follow.

1. **Think ahead.** Study the steps of the investigation so you know what to expect. If you have any questions, ask your teacher. Be sure you understand any caution statements or safety reminders.

2. **Be neat.** Keep your work area clean. If you have long hair, pull it back so it doesn't get in the way. Roll or push up long sleeves to keep them away from your experiment.

3. **Oops!** If you spill or break something, or if you get cut, tell your teacher right away.

4. **Watch your eyes.** Wear safety goggles anytime you are directed to do so. If you get anything in your eyes, tell your teacher right away.

5. **Yuck!** Never eat or drink anything during a science activity.

6. **Don't get shocked.** Be especially careful if an electric appliance is used. Be sure that electrical cords are in a safe place where you can't trip over them. Never pull a plug out of an outlet by pulling on the cord.

7. **Keep it clean.** Always clean up when you have finished. Put everything away and wipe your work area. Wash your hands.

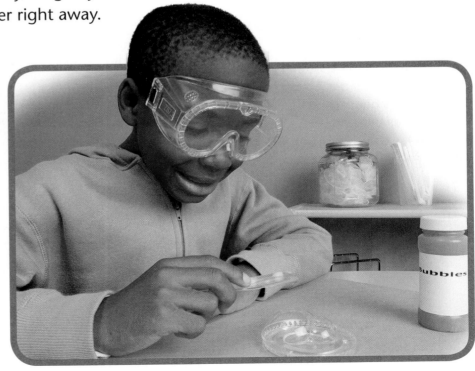

Visit the Multimedia Science Glossary to see illustrations of these words and to hear them pronounced.
www.hspscience.com

Glossary

As you read your science book, you will notice that new or unfamiliar words have been respelled to help you pronounce them. Those respellings are *phonetic respellings*. In this Glossary, you will see the same kind of respellings.

In the phonetic respellings, syllables are separated by a bullet (•). Small, uppercase letters show stressed syllables.

The boldfaced letters in the examples in the Pronunciation Key below identify the letters and combinations of letters that the respellings represent.

The page number in parentheses () at the end of a definition tells you where to find the term defined in this textbook.

Pronunciation Key

Sound	As in	Phonetic Respelling	Sound	As in	Phonetic Respelling
a	bat	(bat)	oh	over	(oh•ver)
ah	lock	(lahk)	oo	pool	(pool)
air	rare	(rair)	ow	out	(owt)
ar	argue	(ar•gyoo)	oy	foil	(foyl)
aw	law	(law)	s	cell	(sel)
ay	face	(fays)		sit	(sit)
ch	chapel	(chap•uhl)	sh	sheep	(sheep)
e	test	(test)	th	that	(that)
	metric	(meh•trik)		thin	(thin)
ee	eat	(eet)	u	pull	(pul)
	feet	(feet)	uh	medal	(med•uhl)
	ski	(skee)		talent	(tal•uhnt)
er	paper	(pay•per)		pencil	(pen•suhl)
	fern	(fern)		onion	(uhn•yuhn)
eye	idea	(eye•dee•uh)		playful	(play•fuhl)
i	bit	(bit)		dull	(duhl)
ing	going	(goh•ing)	y	yes	(yes)
k	card	(kard)		ripe	(ryp)
	kite	(kyt)	z	bags	(bagz)
ngk	bank	(bangk)	zh	treasure	(trezh•er)

adaptation [ad•uhp•TAY•shuhn] Any trait that helps a plant or animal survive. **(454)**

amphibian [am•FIB•ee•uhn] A type of vertebrate that has moist skin—and legs as an adult. **(413)**

anemometer [an•uh•MAHM•uht•er] A weather instrument that measures wind speed. **(277)**

atmosphere [AT•muhs•feer] The air around Earth. **(274)**

axis [AK•sis] A line—that you cannot see—from the top of the Earth through the center of the Earth to the bottom. **(332)**

bird [BERD] A type of vertebrate that has feathers. **(411)**

camouflage [KAM•uh•flahzh] Colors, patterns, and shapes that disguise an animal and help it hide. **(458)**

canyon [KAN•yuhn] A valley with steep sides. **(228)**

carnivore [KAHR•nuh•vawr] An animal that eats other animals. **(479)**

Celsius [SEL•see•uhs] The metric temperature scale. **(97)**

chlorophyll [KLAWR•uh•FHIL] The green substance inside leaves that helps a plant use light energy. **(387)**

clay [KLAY] Soil with very, very tiny grains of rock. **(301)**

combustion [kuhm•BUHS•chuhn] Another word for *burning*. **(77)**

community [kuh•MYOO•nuh•tee] All the populations of organisms that live in an ecosystem at the same time. **(440)**

condensation [kahn•duhn•SAY•shuhn] The process by which water vapor changes into liquid water. **(46, 268)**

conduction [kuhn•DUHK•shuhn] The movement of heat between objects that are touching each other. **(105)**

conductor [kuhn•DUHK•ter] An object that heat can move through easily. **(105)**

conservation [kahn•ser•VAY•shuhn] The saving of resources by using them wisely. **(314)**

constellation [kahn•stuh•LAY•shuhn] A group of stars that appear to form the shape of an animal, a person, or an object. **(354)**

consumer [kuhn•SOOM•er] A living thing that gets its energy by eating other living things as food. **(477)**

crest [KREST] The highest point of a wave. **(144)**

deciduous [dee•SIJ•oo•uhs] Relating to plants that lose all their leaves at the same time every year. **(379)**

decomposer [dee•kuhm•POHZ•er] A living thing that breaks down dead organisms for food. **(477)**

density [DEN•suh•tee] The mass of matter compared with its volume. **(37)**

desert [DEZ•ert] An ecosystem that is very dry. **(446)**

distance [DIS•tuhns] How far one location is from another. **(128)**

earthquake [ERTH•kwayk] The shaking of Earth's surface caused by movement in Earth's crust. **(242)**

ecosystem [EE•koh•sis•tuhm] The living and nonliving things that interact in an environment. **(440)**

energy [EN•er•jee] The ability to make something move or change. **(68)**

energy pyramid [EN•er•jee PIR•uh•mid] A diagram that shows how energy gets used in a food chain. **(486)**

environment [en•VY•ruhn•muhnt] The things, both living and nonliving, that surround a living thing. **(439)**

erosion [uh•ROH•zhuhn] The movement of weathered rock and soil. **(236)**

evaporation [ee•vap•uh•RAY•shuhn] The process by which liquid water changes into a water vapor. **(46, 269)**

evergreen [EV•er•green] A plant that stays green and makes food all year long. **(379)**

experiment [ek•SPAIR•uh•muhnt] A test done to see if a hypothesis is correct or not. **(21)**

fish [FISH] A type of vertebrate that breathes through gills and spends its life in water. **(414)**

flood [FLUHD] A large amount of water that covers normally dry land. **(246)**

food chain [FOOD CHAYN] The path of food from one living thing to another. **(484)**

food web [FOOD WEB] Food chains that overlap. **(492)**

force [FAWRS] A push or a pull. **(134)**

forceps [FAWR•seps] A tool used to pick up and hold on to objects. **(5)**

forest [FAWR•uhst] An ecosystem in which many trees grow. **(450)**

formulate [FAWR•myoo•layt] To come up with a plan for something. **(16)**

fossil [FAHS•uhl] A trace or the remains of a living thing that died a long time ago. **(210)**

fossil fuel [FAHS•uhl FYOO•uhl] A resource that comes from the remains of plants and animals that lived long ago. **(83)**

fresh water [FRESH WAWT•er] Water that has very little salt in it. **(259)**

friction [FRIK•shuhn] The force between two objects that makes it hard for the objects to move and that produces heat. **(110)**

fulcrum [FUHL•kruhm] The fixed point on a lever. **(166)**

gas [GAS] A form of matter that has no definite shape or volume. **(45)**

glacier [GLAY•sher] A huge sheet or block of moving ice. **(238, 260)**

grassland [GRAS•land] An area of land that is generally hot in the summer and cold in the winter. The main plants found in this ecosystem are grasses. **(447)**

gravity [GRAV•ih•tee] A force that pulls two objects toward each other. **(138)**

groundwater [GROWND•waw•ter] An underground supply of water. **(260)**

habitat [HAB•ih•tat] The place where a population lives in an ecosystem. **(441)**

heat [HEET] The movement of thermal energy from hotter to cooler objects. **(98)**

herbivore [HER•buh•vawr] An animal that eats only plants. **(478)**

hibernate [HY•ber•nayt] To go into a sleeplike state for the winter. **(456)**

humus [HYOO•muhs] The part of soil made up of broken-down parts of dead plants and animals. **(298)**

hypothesis [hy•PAHTH•uh•sis] A possible answer to a question that can be tested to see if it is correct. **(21)**

igneous rock [IG•nee•uhs RAHK] Rock that once melted and then cooled and hardened. **(200)**

inclined plane [in•KLYND PLAYN] A simple machine that makes moving or lifting things easier. **(174)**

infer [in•FER] To draw a conclusion about something. **(13)**

inquiry [IN•kwer•ee] A question that is asked about something, or a close study of something. **(4)**

instinct [IN•stingkt] A behavior that an animal knows without being taught. **(454)**

insulator [IN•suh•layt•er] An object that doesn't conduct heat well. **(106)**

invertebrate [in•VER•tuh•brit] An animal without a backbone. **(418)**

investigation [in•ves•tuh•GAY•shuhn] A study that a scientist does. **(20)**

kinetic energy [kih•NET•ik EN•er•jee] The energy of motion. **(70)**

landform [LAND•fawrm] A natural shape on Earth's surface. **(226)**

leaf [LEEF] The part of a plant that grows out of the stem and is where the plant makes food. **(370)**

lever [LEV•er] A simple machine made up of a bar that pivots, or turns, on a fixed point. **(166)**

liquid [LIK•wid] A form of matter that has a volume that stays the same but a shape that can change. **(44)**

loam [LOHM] Soil that is a mixture of humus, sand, silt, and clay. **(302)**

lunar cycle [LOON•er SY•kuhl] The pattern of phases of the moon. **(341)**

lunar eclipse [LOON•er ih•KLIPS] An event in which Earth blocks sunlight from reaching the moon. **(342)**

mammal [MAM•uhl] A type of vertebrate that has hair or fur and gives birth to live young. **(410)**

mass [MAS] The amount of matter in an object. **(36)**

matter [MAT•er] Anything that takes up space. **(32)**

metamorphic rock [met•uh•MAWR•fik RAHK] Rock that has been changed by heat or pressure. **(201)**

migrate [MY•grayt] To travel from one place to another and back again. **(457)**

mimicry [MIM•ik•ree] The imitating of the look of another animal. **(458)**

mineral [MIN•er•uhl] A solid object found in nature that has never been alive. **(192)**

mixture [MIKS•cher] A substance that has two or more different kinds of matter. **(52)**

moon phases [MOON FAYZ•uhz] The different shapes that the moon seems to have in the sky when it is observed from Earth. **(340)**

motion [MOH•shuhn] A change of position. **(127)**

mountain [MOWNT•uhn] A place on Earth's surface that is much higher than the land around it. **(227)**

nonrenewable resource [nahn•rih•NOO•uh•buhl REE•sawrs] A resource that, when it is used up, will not exist again during a human lifetime. **(84, 294)**

nutrients [NOO•tree•uhnts] The parts of the soil that help plants grow and stay healthy. **(370)**

omnivore [AHM•nih•vawr] A consumer that eats both plants and animals. **(480)**

orbit [AWR•bit] The path that a planet takes as it revolves around the sun. **(348)**

oxygen [AHK•sih•juhn] A gas that people need to live and that plants give off into the air. **(274, 401)**

photosynthesis [foht•oh•SIN•thuh•sis] The process that plants use to make sugar. **(386)**

physical property [FIZ•ih•kuhl PRAHP•er•tee] Anything you can observe about an object by using one or more of your senses. **(34)**

plain [PLAYN] A wide, flat area on Earth's surface. **(229)**

planet [PLAN•it] A large body of rock or gas in space. **(348)**

plateau [pla•TOH] A flat area higher than the land around it. **(230)**

pollution [puh•LOO•shuhn] Any harmful material in the environment. **(308)**

population [pahp•yuh•LAY•shuhn] A group of organisms of the same kind that live in the same place. **(440)**

potential energy [poh•TEN•shuhl EN•er•jee] Energy of position. **(70)**

precipitation [pree•sip•uh•TAY•shuhn] Rain, snow, sleet, or hail. **(270)**

predator [PRED•uh•ter] An animal that hunts another animal for food. **(488)**

prey [PRAY] An animal that is hunted by a predator. **(488)**

producer [pruh•DOOS•er] A living thing that makes its own food. **(477)**

pulley [PUL•ee] A simple machine made up of a wheel with a rope around it. **(170)**

recycle [ree•SY•kuhl] To reuse a resource by breaking it down and making a new product. **(318)**

reduce [ree•DOOS] To use less of a resource. **(316)**

renewable resource [rih•NOO•uh•buhl REE•sawrs] A resource that can be replaced quickly. **(84, 292)**

reptile [REP•tyl] A type of vertebrate that has dry skin covered with scales. **(412)**

resource [REE•sawrs] A material that is found in nature and that is used by living things. **(83, 290, 463)**

reusable resource [ree•YOOZ•uh•buhl REE•sawrs] A resource that can be used again and again. **(293)**

reuse [ree•YOOZ] To use a resource again and again. **(317)**

revolution [rev•uh•LOO•shuhn] The movement of Earth one time around the sun. **(333)**

rock [RAHK] A naturally formed solid made of one or more minerals. **(196)**

root [ROOT] The part of a plant that grows underground and takes water and nutrients from the soil. **(370)**

rotation [roh•TAY•shuhn] The spinning of Earth on its axis. **(332)**

sand [SAND] Soil with grains of rock that you can see with your eyes alone. **(301)**

scientific method [sy•uhn•TIF•ik METH•uhd] An organized plan that scientists use to conduct a study. **(20)**

screw [SKROO] A simple machine that you turn to lift an object or to hold two or more objects together. **(178)**

sedimentary rock [sed•uh•MEN•ter•ee RAHK] Rock made when materials settle into layers and get squeezed until they harden into rock. **(201)**

seed [SEED] The first stage of life for many plants. **(377)**

silt [SILT] Soil with grains of rock that are too small to see with your eyes alone. **(301)**

simple machine [SIM•puhl muh•SHEEN] A tool with few or no moving parts that helps people do work. **(165)**

solar eclipse [SOH•ler ih•KLIPS] An event in which the moon blocks sunlight from reaching Earth and the moon's shadow falls on Earth. **(344)**

solar system [SOH•ler SIS•tuhm] The sun, the planets and their moons, and the small objects that orbit the sun. **(348)**

solid [SAHL•id] A form of matter with a volume and a shape that both stay the same. **(43)**

solution [suh•LOO•shuhn] A mixture in which the different kinds of matter mix evenly. **(53)**

speed [SPEED] The distance that an object moves in a certain period of time. **(130)**

star [STAR] A hot ball of glowing gases that gives off energy. **(349)**

stem [STEM] The part of a plant that grows above ground and helps hold the plant up. **(370)**

temperature [TEM•per•uh•cher] The measure of how hot or cold something is. **(78, 96, 277)**

thermal energy [THER•muhl EN•er•jee] The form of energy that moves particles of matter. **(98)**

trough [TRAWF] The lowest point of a wave. **(144)**

valley [VAL•ee] A low area between higher lands such as mountains. **(228)**

variable [VAIR•ee•uh•buhl] The one thing that changes in a science inquiry or experiment. **(15)**

vertebrate [VER•tuh•brit] An animal with a backbone. **(409)**

volcano [vahl•KAY•noh] An opening in Earth's surface from which lava flows. **(244)**

volume [VAHL•yoom] The amount of space that matter takes up. **(37)**

water cycle [WAW•ter SY•kuhl] The movement of water from Earth's land, through rivers toward the ocean, to the air, and back to the land. **(270)**

wave [WAYV] A disturbance that travels through matter or space. **(142)**

wavelength [WAYV•length] The distance from one point of one wave to the same point on the next wave. **(144)**

weather [WETH•er] What is happening in the atmosphere at a certain place and time. **(276)**

weathering [WETH•er•ing] The breaking down of rocks into smaller pieces. **(234)**

wedge [WEJ] A simple machine that is made up of two inclined planes placed back-to-back. **(176)**

weight [WAYT] The measure of the force of gravity on an object. **(138)**

wheel-and-axle [weel•and•AK•suhl] A simple machine made up of an axle and a wheel that are connected and turn together. **(168)**

work [WERK] The use of a force to move an object. **(158)**

Index

Photo Credits

Page Placement Key: (t) top, (b) bottom, (l) left, (r) right, (c) center, (bg) background, (fg) foreground

Cover: (front) Frans Lanting/Minden Pictures; (back) (bg) Renee Lynn/Stone/Getty Images; (back) (inset) William Ervin/SPL/Photo Researchers;

Front End Sheets: Page 1 Klein/Peter Arnold; Page 2 (t) Tom Brakefield/Corbis; (b) Norbert Wu/ Minden Pictures; Page 3 (t) Frans Lanting/Minden Pictures; (b) Tom Ulrich/Stone/Getty Images; (bg for all) Tony Craddock/Photo Researchers;

Title Page: Frans Lanting/Minden Pictures;

Copyright Page: (bg) Renee Lynn/Stone/Getty Images; (inset) Frans Lanting/Minden Pictures;

Back End Sheets: Page 1 (t) Stuart Westmorland/The Image bank/Getty Images; (b) Tom Brakefield/ Corbis; Page 2 (t) Michael & Patricia Fogden/Minden Pictures; (b) Renee Lyn/Stone/Getty Images; Page 3 (t) Peter Weimann/Animals Animals/Earth Scenes; (c) & (b) Courtesy of Jerry Jennings at Emerald Forest Bird Gardens-Photography by Paul Bratescu; (bg for all) Tony Craddock/Photo Researchers;

Table of Contents:
iv-v Getty Images; vi-vii Getty Images; viii-ix George McCarthy/Corbis;

Strand A:
27 Graeme Teague; 28-29 Royalty-Free/Corbis; 32 Nancy Sheehan/Index Stock Imagery; 33 Rick Doyle/Corbis; 34 (br) Getty Images; 34 (bl) Getty Images; 35 (r) Min Roman/Masterfile; 40 Getty Images; 42 Getty Images; 43 (tr) Alamy Images; 43 (l) Getty Images; 43 (br) Joseph Sohm/ ChromoSohm Inc./Corbis; 44 (b) Dennis Degnan/Corbis; 48 Zoran Milich/Masterfile; 50 (c) Tim Wright/Corbis; 50 (b) Klaus-Peter Wolf/Animals Animals; 52 (b) Getty Images; 54 (b) Owen Franken/Corbis; 56 Corbis; 58 (t) Art resource; 58 (b) Stone/Getty; 59 (bg) Royalty-Free/Corbis;

Strand B:
63 Bill Bachmann/PhotoEdit; 66 Getty Images; 68 (l) Hubert Stadler/Corbis; 68 (c) Getty Images; 68-69 Getty Images; 69 (t) Brand X Pictures/Creatas Royalty Free Stock Resources; 69 (b) Robert Harding World Imagery/Getty Images; 72 Ed Bock/Corbis; 76-77 Lloyd Sutton/Masterfile; 77 (inset) Colin Garratt; Milepost 92 1/2 /Corbis; 78 (l) David Young-Wolff/PhotoEdit; 80 Getty Images; 82 Getty Images; 84 Bob Krist/Corbis; 86 KRT/Newscom; 88 Intel Corp/Newscom; 89 (bg) Christopher J. Morris/Corbis; 92-93 Raymond Gehman/Corbis; 96 (r) Michael Holford; 97 (t) Dennis Johnson; Papilio/Corbis; 97 (bl) Getty Images; 98 Macduff Everton/Corbis; 99 Macduff Everton/Corbis; 105 (tl) BrandXPictures/Media Bakery, LLC; 112 (br) Photodisc Green (Royalty-free)/Getty Images; 116 (t) Frederic Lewis Getty; 116 (i) Image Works; 116 (b) Index Stock; 117 (bg) SOHO/ESA/NASA/ Science Photo Library;

Strand C:
121 © Florida State Fair Authority, 2004; 122-123 Getty Images; 124 Getty Images; 126 (l) Bob Daemmrich/PhotoEdit; 128 Martin Rugner/Age Fotostock America; 129 (inset) Getty Images; 129 (t) Getty Images; 130 (l) Maryann Frazier/Photo Researchers; 130 (r) Joe McDonald/Corbis; 132 Ariel Skelley/Corbis; 134 (r) NASA; 135 McDonald Wildlife Photography/Animals Animals/Earth Scenes; 135 (inset) McDonald Wildlife Photography/Animals Animals/Earth Scenes; 137 Bill Varie/ Corbis; 138 (l) David Ball/Corbis; 138 (r) Getty Images; 140 RF/Getty Images; 144 Walter Bibikow/ Age Fotostock America; 146 AP/Wide World Photos; 148 (t) © EAA 2003; 152-153 Kevin Smith/ Alaska Stock Images/PictureQuest; 156 (l) Comstock Images; 157 (r) Royalty-Free/Corbis; 157 (inset) Royalty-Free/Corbis; 165 (inset) David Young-Wolff/Photo Edit; 169 (r) Getty Images; 170 (l) Jerry Amster/SuperStock; 170 (inset) Stephen Frisch/Stock, Boston Inc./PictureQuest; 172 Alden Pellett/The Image Works; 175 (b) Superstock; 176 (r) Index Stock Imagery, Inc.; 177 (inset) Annie Griffiths Belt/Corbis; 177 (t) Index Stock Imagery, Inc.; 180-181 © Honda Corp.; 182 Courtesy of Ann Meggitt; 183 (bg) Steven James Haggard/Mira.com;

Strand D:
187 Reuters/CORBIS; 188-189 Layne Kennedy/Corbis; 192 (t) Breck P. Kent Photography; 192 (cl) Barry Runk/Stan/Grant Heilman Photography; 192 (cr) Breck P. Kent/Smithsonian Institute; 192 (bl) Th Foto-Werbung/Science Photo Library/Photo Researchers; 192 (bc) Albert Copley/Visuals Unlimited; 192 (br) Edward R. Degginger/Bruce Coleman, Inc.; 193 (tl) Breck P. Kent Photography; 193 (tc) John James Wood/Index Stock Imagery; 193 (tr) Mark Schneider/Visuals Unlimited; 193 (bl) Jose Manuel Sanchis Calvete/Corbis; 194 (tl) Paul Silverman/Fundamental Photographs; 194 (tc) Cabisco/Visuals Unlimited; 194 (tr) Getty Images; 196 (t) Bob Daemmrich Photography; 196 (cl) Mark A. Schneider/Visuals Unlimited; 196 (c) Breck P. Kent Photography; 196 (cr) Breck P. Kent Photography; 196 (bl) Sinclair Stammers/Science Photo Library/Photo Researchers; 196 (br) Wally Eberhart/Visuals Unlimited; 198 Tom Bean/Corbis; 200 (r) Doug Sokell/Visuals Unlimited; 201 (t) Wally Eberhart/Visuals Unlimited; 201 (cl) Barry Runk/Stan/Grant Heilman Photography; 201 (cr) Barry Runk/Stan/Grant Heilman Photography; 202 Jim Sugar/Corbis; 203 (t) Grant Heilman/ Grant Heilman Photography; 203 (b) Ben S. Kwiatkowski/Fundamental Photographs; 204 Rob C. Williamson/Index Stock Imagery; 206 (t) Bob Rashid/Brand X Pictures/Alamy Images; 208 Albert Copley/Visuals Unlimited; 210 (t) Layne Kennedy/Corbis; 210 (b) Dick Roberts/Visuals Unlimited; 211 (b) Francesc Muntada/Corbis; 211 (t) Ken Lucas/Visuals Unlimited; 211 (c) Sylvester Allred/ Fundamental Photographs; 213 (t) Kevin Schafer/Corbis; 214 (b) Richard T. Nowitz/Corbis; 214 (t) Sternberg Museum of Natural History; 216 Philip James Corwin/Corbis; 217 AP/Wide World Photos; 218 (t) Courtesy the Ravin Family; 218 (b) Maurice Nimmo/Frank Lane Picture Agency/ Corbis; 222-223 David Muench/Corbis; 224 Mark Turner/Turner Photographics; 226-227 Kevin R. Morris/Corbis; 227 (inset) Jean Guichard/Corbis; 228 (inset) ArtPhoto/Diomedia/Alamy Images; 229 Photodisc Red (Royalty-free)/Getty Images; 230 Getty Images; 232 Gavriel Jecan/Corbis; 234 (b) Chris Bell/Lonely Planet Images; 234 (inset) E.R. Degginger/Color-Pic; 236 (t) Dick Roberts/Visuals Unlimited; 236 (b) Gordana Uzelac/Domedia/Alamy Images; 237 (t) Annie Griffiths Belt/Corbis; 237 (inset) Science VU/Visuals Unlimited; 238 (b) Bernhard Edmaier/Science Photo Library/Photo Researchers; 238 (inset) George Wilder/Visuals Unlimited; 240 Alfio Scigliano/Sygma/Corbis; 242 Roger Ressmeyer/Corbis; 243 Roger Ressmeyer/Corbis; 244 Amos Nachoum/Corbis; 245 (t) Michael S. Yamashita/Corbis; 245 (b) Roger Ressmeyer/Corbis; 246 (t) Bill Ross/Corbis; 246 (b) Philip Wallick/Corbis; 248 Getty; 249 AP/Wide World Photos; 250 (t) Bettman/Corbis; 250 (b) Getty; 251 (bg) Jim Sugar/Corbis; 254-255 Guy Motil/Corbis; 256 Volvox/Index Stock Imagery; 258 Francisco Erizel/Bruce Coleman, Inc./PictureQuest; 259 Ray Ellis/Photo Researchers; 260-261 Steve Vidler/Superstock; 261 (inset) Getty Images; 262 Corbis; 264 Getty Images; 266 J. David Andrews/ Masterfile; 267 Royalty-Free/Corbis; 268 (bg) J.A. Kraulis/Masterfile; 272 Jeff Greenberg/PhotoEdit; 274 Willie Holdman/Imagestate; 277 (l) Peter West/National Science Foundation; 277 (r) Simon Fraser/CGBAPS/Photo Researchers; 278 (c) 2004 www.ACCUWEATHER.com; 282 (t) International Pacific Research Ctr. Univ of Hawaii; 283 (b) Getty; 283 (bg) Larry Lee Photography/Corbis; 286-287 Jan Butchofsky-Houser/Corbis; 288 ML Sinibaldi/Corbis; 290 (inset) Fred Bavendam/Minden Pictures; 290 (b) Larry Lefever/Grant Heilman Photography; 291 (inset) Lou Jacobs, Jr./Grant Heilman Photography; 291 (r) Tom Campbell/Index Stock Imagery; 292 David Whitten/Index Stock Imagery; 293 Jean-Michel Bertrand/Index Stock Imagery; 294 (inset) Getty Images; 294 (b) Mike Dobel/Masterfile; 296 PhotoDisc Blue (Royalty-Free)/Getty; 298 Gary Braasch/Corbis; 300 (b) Getty Images; 301 Royalty-Free/Corbis; 302 Joel W. Rogers/Corbis; 304 Eunice Harris/Index Stock Imagery; 306-307 David R. Frazier Photolibrary, Inc.; 307 (inset) PhotoDisc Green(Royalty-Free)/Getty Images; 308 Getty Images; 309 (l) Chase Swift/Corbis; 309 (r) Douglas Slone/Corbis; 310 (b) Bettmann/Corbis; 310 (inset) J. Watney/Photo Researchers; 314-315 Norbert Wu/Minden Pictures; 316 (c) Getty Images; 320-321 Roy Ooms/Masterfile; 322 Bill Walter/Weekly Reader; 323 (bg) Getty Images;

Strand E:
327 NASA; 328-329 NASA-HQ-GRIN; 330 George H.H. Huey/Corbis; 336 (l) Jeff Greenberg/Index Stock Imagery; 336 (r) Thomas Craig/Index Stock Imagery; 338 David Nunuk/Photo Researchers; 341 (t) Dr. Fred Espenak/Photo Researchers; 341 (cl) Eckhard Slawik/Photo Researchers; 341 (cr) Eckhard Slawik/Photo Researchers; 341 (b) J. Sanford/Photo Researchers; 342 John Sanford/Photo Researchers; 344 Dr. Fred Espenak/Photo Researchers; 346 Geray Sweeney/Corbis; 349 NASA-JPL; 350 (t) NASA-JPL; 350 (b) USGS/Photo Researchers; 351 (b) NASA-JPL; 352 (b) NASA-JPL; 352 (t) NASA-JPL; 353 (tr) NASA-HQ-GRIN; 353 (b) NASA-JPL; 353 (tl) STSI/NASA/Photo Researchers; 356-357 NASA; 358 (t) Dr. Floyd James/North Carolina ANT State Univ.; 358 (b) D. Parker/Photo Researchers; 359 (bg) NASA/Science Photo Library;

Strand F:
363 Tammy L. Johnson/Florida Museum of Natural History; 364-365 Zoran Milich/Masterfile; 366 John McAnulty/Corbis; 372 (t) Royalty-Free/Corbis; 372 (b) David Young-Wolff/PhotoEdit/ PictureQuest; 374 Estock Photo; 376 (inset) George Harrison/Grant Heilman Photography; 376 (b) Kent Foster/Bruce Coleman, Inc.; 377 Martin Fox/Index Stock Imagery/PictureQuest; 378 (t) Martin B. Withers; Frank Lane Picture Agency/Corbis; 378 (cr) Michael P. Gadomski/Dembinsky Photo Associates; 378 (cl) Phil Degginger/Bruce Coleman, Inc.; 378 (b) Randy M. Ury/Corbis; 379 (t) Ed Kanze/Dembinsky Photo Associates; 380 (l) R-R/S/Grant Heilman Photography; 380 (c) Skip Moody/Dembinsky Photo Associates; 380 (r) C-JG/Grant Heilman Photography; 381 (l) Grant Heilman Photography; 381 (r) Bruce Coleman, Inc.; 382 (t) C-MON/Grant Heilman Photography; 382 (cl) Michael P. Gadomski/Dembinsky Photo Associates; 382 (cr) Michelle Garrett/Corbis; 382 (bl) Randall B. Henne/Dembinsky Photo Associates; 384 Royalty-Free/Corbis; 386 Patti McConville/ Dembinsky Photo Associates; 388 (b) C-TB/Grant Heilman Photography; 388 (t) Getty Images; 388 (cl) John Robinson/Peter Arnold; 388 (cr) Larry West/Bruce Coleman, Inc.; 390 USDA/ARS; 392 (tr) Courtesy Rosa Ortiz; 392 (inset) Robert Holmgren/Peter Arnold; 392 (bl) Galen Rowell/Corbis; 393 (bg) Lew Robertson/PictureArts/Corbis; 396-397 Mark J. Thomas/Dembinsky Photo Associates; 398 Getty Images; 400 (r) John Cancalosi/Nature Picture Library; 400 (l) John Giustina/Bruce Coleman, Inc.; 401 ZSSD/Minden Pictures; 402 (t) BIOS/Peter Arnold; 402 (b) Royalty-Free/Corbis; 403 Getty Images; 403 (inset) Steve Kaufman/Peter Arnold; 404 (b) Darren Bennett/Animals Animals; 404 (t) Michael & Patricia Fogden/Corbis; 406 Theo Allofs/Corbis; 408-409 (bg) Norman O. Tomalin/ Bruce Coleman, Inc.; 408 (l) Staffan Widstrand/Corbis; 408 (r) Wolfgang Kaehler/Corbis; 409 (t) Getty Images; 409 (br) Bruce Coleman, Inc.; 409 (bl) Joe McDonald/Bruce Coleman, Inc.; 410 (t) Bruce Coleman, Inc.; 410 (bl) David Fritts/Animals Animals; 410 (br) Thomas Mangelsen/Minden Pictures; 411 (tl) Thomas D. Mangelsen/Peter Arnold; 411 (tr) Tim Davis/Corbis; 411 (c) Tom Vezo/Minden Pictures; 411 (b) Diane Miller/Monsoon Images/PictureQuest; 412 (t) Zigmund Leszczynski/Animals Animals; 412 (c) Getty Images; 412 (b) George McCarthy/Corbis; 413 (r) John Burnley/Bruce Coleman, Inc.; 413 (l) T. Young/Tom Stack & Associates; 414 (t) Getty Images; 414 (c) Getty Images; 414 (b) Scott Kerrigan/Corbis; 416 Frans Lanting/Minden Pictures; 418 (t) Jesse Cancelmo/Dembinsky Photo Associates; 418 (bl) Getty Images; 418 (br) Sue Scott/Peter Arnold; 419 (t) Dwight Kuhn; 419 (bl) Douglas P. Wilson; Frank Lane Picture Agency/Corbis; 419 (br) Larry West/Bruce Coleman, Inc.; 420 (tl) Thomas Boyden/Dembinsky Photo Associates; 420 (r) CISCA CASTELIJNS/FOTO NATURA/Minden Pictures; 420 (bg) Craig Aurness/Corbis; 420 (bl) Skip Moody/Dembinsky Photo Associates; 421 (t) Donald Specker/Animals Animals; 421 (b) Larry West/Bruce Coleman, Inc.; 422 (tr) Gordon R. Williamson/Bruce Coleman, Inc.; 422 (cr) Getty Images; 422 (bl) Gail M. Shumway/Bruce Coleman, Inc.; 422 (br) Priscilla Connell/Index Stock Imagery; 423 (tr) Getty Images; 423 (cl) Fred Bavendam/Minden Pictures; 423 (bl) E. R. Degginger/Bruce Coleman, Inc.; 424 (t) ABPL/Roger De La Harpe/Animals Animals; 424 (b) David M. Dennis/Animals Animals; 426 (t) Lightwave Photography/Animal Animals; 427 (t) OSF/Bernard GI/Animals Animals; 428 Naples Daily News/Chris Suppa; 429 (bg) Ralph A. Clevenger/Corbis; 431 (l) Michael & Patricica Fogden/Minden Pictures; 431 (r) Theo Allofs/Corbis;

Unit G:
433 Arthur Morris/Visuals Unlimited; 434-435 Gail M. Shumway/Bruce Coleman, Inc.; 436 Richard T. Nowitz/Corbis; 438-439 Claudia Adams/Dembinsky Photo Associates; 438 (inset) R-GH/Grant Heilman Photography; 439 (t) John Cancalosi/Nature Picture Library; 439 (inset) Tim Fitzharris/ Minden Pictures; 442 (b) Mary Clay/Dembinsky Photo Associates; 442 (t) Royalty-Free/Corbis; 444 Stefan Meyers/Animals Animals/Earth Scenes; 446 Photodisc Green (Royalty-free)/Getty Images; 447 Jim Brandenburg/Minden Pictures; 448 Flip Nicklin/Minden Pictures; 449 Getty Images; 450 (b) Nancy Rotenberg/Animals Animals/Earth Scenes; 450 (inset) OSF/M. Hamblin/Animals Animals/Earth Scenes; 450 (t) Roger Wilmshurst; Frank Lane Picture Agency/Corbis; 452 Yva Momatiuk/John Eastcott/Minden Pictures; 454 (b) Barbara Von Hoffmann/Animals Animals/Earth Scenes; 454 (inset) Steve Kaufman/Corbis; 455 (c) Gary Braasch/Corbis; 455 (l) I-JG/Grant Heilman Photography; 455 (r) Nancy Rotenberg/Animals Animals/Earth Scenes; 456 Breck P. Kent/Animals Animals/Earth Scenes; 457 (l) Alan G. Nelson/Animals Animals/Earth Scenes; 457 (r) Stephen Dalton/Animals Animals/Earth Scenes; 458 (tl) Carl Roessler/Bruce Coleman, Inc.; 458 (tr) Anthony Bannister/Gallo Images/Corbis; 458 (bl) Martin Withers/Dembinsky Photo Associates; 458 (br) Breck P. Kent/Animals Animals/Earth Scenes; 460 Michael E. Lubiarz/Dembinsky Photo Associates; 462 (t) Gary Braasch/Corbis; 462 (b) David Muench/Corbis; 462 (inset) Dennis MacDonald/ Index Stock Imagery/PictureQuest; 463 (r) Smith Aerial Photos; 463 (l) Smith Aerial Photos; 464 (t) Getty Images; 464 (c) Raymond Gehman/Corbis; 464 (bl) Royalty-Free/Corbis; 464 (br) Dominique Braud/Animals Animals/Earth Scenes; 466 Index Stock/Picture Quest; 467 Marianna Day Massey/Corbis; 468 (t) AP/Wide World Photos/Bob Schultz; 468 (b) Royalty-Free/Corbis; 469 (bg) Getty Images; 472-473 Michael & Patricia Fogden/Minden Pictures; 474 Getty Images; 476 Ed Reschke/Peter Arnold; 478 (t) Fred Unverhau/Animals Animals; 478 (c) Yva Momatiuk/John Eastcott/Minden Pictures; 478 (b) Stephen Frink/Corbis; 479 (t) Bruce Coleman, Inc.; 479 (b) Bruce Coleman, Inc.; 480 (tl) Bruce Coleman, Inc.; 480 (inset) Getty Images; 480 (tr) Konrad Wothe/Minden Pictures; 482 Getty Images; 484 (r) C. Allan Morgan/Peter Arnold; 484-485 (bg) I-R/S/Grant Heilman Photography, Inc.; 484 (l) R-GH/Grant Heilman Photography, Inc.; 485 (r) Bruce Coleman, Inc.; 485 (l) John Cancalosi/Peter Arnold; 486 Kevin Schafer/Peter Arnold; 488 (t) Frans Lanting/Minden Pictures; 488 (b) Gerard Lacz/Animals Animals; 490 Tom Brakefield/Corbis; 494-495 (t) Kennan Ward/Corbis; 494 (c) Joe McDonald/Corbis; 494 (bl) Pete Oxford/Nature Picture Library; 494 (br) Tom Brakefield/Corbis; 495 (tr) Fred Bavendam/Peter Arnold; 495 (b) Sea Images, Inc./Animals Animals; 496 Getty Images; 498 Hinrich Baesemann/UCEP/Peter Arnold Inc.; 500 (t) Courtesy Stephanie Larsen; 500 (bl) Shmeul Thaler/Index Stock; 500 (br) Index Stock; 501 (bg) Sylvain Saustier/Corbis;

Health Handbook
R5 Dennis Kunkel/Phototake; R12 (t) CNRI/Science Photo Library/Photo Researchers; R12 (tc) A. Pasieka/Photo Researchers; R12 (bc) CNRI/Science Photo Library/Photo Researchers; R12 (b) Custom Medical Stock Photo; R15 (inset) David Young-Wolff/PhotoEdit; R15 (b) Bill O'Connor/ Peter Arnold, Inc.;

All other photos © Harcourt School Publishers. Harcourt Photos provided by the Harcourt Index, Harcourt IPR, and Harcourt photographers; Weronica Ankarorn, Victoria Bowen, Eric Camden, Doug Dukane, Ken Kinzie, April Riehm, and Steve Williams.

CHARACTERISTICS A toucan's beak is made of a protein called keratin, just like your fingernails.

BEHAVIOR Most toucans are very social. Often 6 to 12 adults will roost in the same tree.

Habitat A toucan builds its nest in a hole in a tree.

Movement The beak of a toucan is hollow. A solid beak would make a toucan too heavy to fly.

Women and the AIDS Crisis

Diane Richardson is a social psychologist and a feminist who researches and writes on women and sexuality. She is joint author of *The Theory and Practice of Homosexuality* (RKP 1981) and her book about feminism, motherhood and childrearing will be published, also by RKP, later in 1987. Recently she was Visiting Professor at the Centre for Education and Research in Sexuality at San Francisco State University. She currently teaches in the Department of Sociological Studies at Sheffield University.